About th

C000174777

B orn in Ludlow in 1978 ̶ ̶ ̶ ̶ ̶ ̶ ̶ University in 2000, Bath-based author Jem Roberts has a publishing heritage which goes back over 20 years, with extensive magazine experience – as well as being a performer, with shows all round the United Kingdom.

Although he has made himself the biographer of choice for comedy's elite – the official, authorised historian for *I'm Sorry I Haven't a Clue*, *Blackadder*, Douglas Adams and *The Hitchhiker's Guide to the Galaxy* and now Stephen Fry and Hugh Laurie, in *Soupy Twists* – Jem has been a committed children's writer for a lot longer.

As a journalist, he edited titles including *Pokémon World*, *Disney & Me* and *Disney's Puzzle Land*, and has been a contributor as storyteller for *Muffin the Mule*, *Disney Girl*, *Winnie the Pooh* and many other publications. His short story 'Little Wee' (about a very annoying baby llama) was published as part of charity fairytale collection *Homespun Threads* in 2012, and he continues to write his own tales as well as adapting traditional ones.

JEMROBERTS.COM
TALESOFBRITAIN.COM

Tales of Britain

TALES OF BRITAIN

By Brother Bernard

As told to Jem Roberts

This edition first published in 2018

Unbound

6th Floor Mutual House, 70 Conduit Street, London W1S 2GF

www.unbound.com

© Jem Roberts, 2018

ISBN (eBook): 978-1-912618-45-3

ISBN (Paperback): 978-1-912618-44-6

Design by Mecob

Printed in Great Britain by Clays Ltd, Elcograf S.p.A.

MIX
Paper from
responsible sources
FSC® C018072

For Terry Jones

'Sit by the fire, and I shall make soup from your stories,

And we'll have our hopes for bread.'

Other books by Jem Roberts

The Clue Bible: The Fully Authorised History of 'I'm Sorry, I Haven't a Clue'

The True History of The Black Adder

The Frood: The Authorised and Very Official History of Douglas Adams

Soupy Twists: The Official Fry & Laurie Story

Contents

Dear Reader,

The book you are holding came about in a rather different way to most others. It was funded directly by readers through a new website: Unbound.

Unbound is the creation of three writers. We started the company because we believed there had to be a better deal for both writers and readers. On the Unbound website, authors share the ideas for the books they want to write directly with readers. If enough of you support the book by pledging for it in advance, we produce a beautifully bound special subscribers' edition and distribute a regular edition and e-book wherever books are sold, in shops and online.

This new way of publishing is actually a very old idea (Samuel Johnson funded his dictionary this way). We're just using the internet to build each writer a network of patrons. Here, at the back of this book, you'll find the names of all the people who made it happen.

Publishing in this way means readers are no longer just passive consumers of the books they buy, and authors are free to write the books they really want. They get a much fairer return too – half the profits their books generate, rather than a tiny percentage of the cover price.

If you're not yet a subscriber, we hope that you'll want to join our publishing revolution and have your name listed in one of our books in the future. To get you started, here is a £5 discount on your first pledge. Just visit unbound.com, make your pledge and type BERNARD18 in the promo code box when you check out.

Thank you for your support,

Dan, Justin and John
Founders, Unbound

xii

Super Patrons

Teresa Ankin
Joshua Arnett
Grace Bagshaw
Paula Clarke Bain
Elizabeth-Jane Baldry
Jem Barnard
Emma Bayliss
Joshua Bergenroth
Jurek Bijak
Julian Birch
C Blanche
Alan Bonnyman
Tom Boon
David Bowyer
Tracy Boyle (Bailey)
The Braakenburg Family
Beatrice Brailey
John Brassey
BrotherRock
Jon Buckeridge
Colin Callan
Elizabeth Childs
Karen Christley
Freyalyn Close-Hainsworth
Rosie Corlett
Stephen Cox
Julia Croyden
Ian Cummings
David
Ashley Davies
Andy Davis
John de Jong
John Dexter
Emma Dixon
Gemma Donald
Cormac Dullaghan

Laura Đurinec
Valerie Duskin
Christopher Easterbrook
Barnaby Eaton-Jones
Brian Edwards
Karl Egerton
Mark Everden
Peter Faulkner
Stuart E. Fewtrell
Paul Fillery
Terence Flanagan
John Fulton
Steve Gall
Antonia Galloway
Tim Gee
Mark Gethings
Matthew Gilbert
Tony Gill
Marcus Gipps
The unholy sprites at Godchecker.com
Susan Godfrey
Paul Godfrey
Caroline Goldsmith
Amy Gore
Mike Griffiths
Mark Griffiths
David Haddock
Dorothy Halfhide
Nick Hamil
Samantha Handebo
Kate Harbour
H Hargate
Dianne Harmata
Perry Harris
Tilly & Lucy Harris
Christine Harris Fosdal
Jane Hayward
Mark Hewlett
Sheila Higgins
Steve Higgins
Jacquelyn Higgins

Tanya Hinton
Robert Hoare
Anne Hobson
Stephen Hoppe
Violet Horne
Gareth Hughes
Laura Humphrey
Neil Innes
Joseph and Adam Jackson
John Jencks
Amanda Jennings
Tristan John
Davey Jones
Julie Jones
Jan Keeling
Michael Kelly
Rik Kershaw-Moore
Philip King
Taylor Lankford
Nick Lansbury
Rick Le Coyte
Kim Le Patourel
David Learner
Alan Lee
Mike Lewis
Helen Lewis
John & Christine Lomax
Kari Long
Robert Lukins
Dave Lusby
James Lydon
Dirk Maggs
Jane Malcolm
Peter Maloy
Larry Mandt
Alasdair Mathieson
Carol McCollough
Anna McDuff
Ian McGill
Lucy McGrath
Kt Mehers

Oliver Mernagh
Jonny Mohun
Rowan Molyneux
Ross Montgomery
K. Murray-Brooks.
Chris Newman
Clare Norris
Gabriel & Stella O'Connor
Elizabeth O'Hara
Lev Parikian
Matthew Pellett
Justin Pollard
Beki Pope
Glenn Prangnell
Janet Pretty
Arthur Prior
Francis Pryor
Jameson Rainha
Colette Reap
Carlos Rehaag
Helen Reid
Nick Roberts
George Roberts
Tony Robinson
Stian Rødland
Paul Rose
Sam Ross
Emma Samuel
Jenny Schwarz
Jonathan Seamons
Dale Shaw
Andrew Shead
Josephine Sherwood
Rachel Simon
David Simpkin
SisterRainbow
Helen Smith
MTA Smith
Simon Smith
Richard Soundy
Henriette B. Stavis

Kelly Stevens
Jim Stevens
Jason, Lisa & Joseph Stevens
Arielle Sumits
Scott Sundberg
Steven Sutton
Ewan Tant
Rob Taylor
Helen Thompson
Adam Tinworth
Pete Waller
Julie Warren
Olivia Watchman
Paul Watson
Tim Weaver
Paul West
Nick White
Alex Wilcock
Simon Williams
Thom Willis
Sarah Wilson
Pip Winstone
Howard Wix
Jo Worsfold
Alex Wright
Lou Yates
Tara Young

MAP

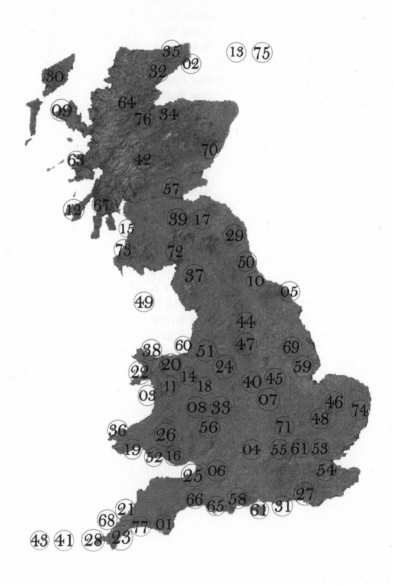

TALE KEY

MONSTROUS Features horrible monsters or weird creatures

SUPERNATURAL May have ghosts, or some kind of spooky magic

RUDE BITS Adult elements, and some sexy bits

LANGUAGE Will include at least one rather rude word

BLOODY Packed with violence and blood! (This is common)

TRAGIC May make you cry, with no happy endings

SICK! Best not read while enjoying a meal

WEIRD Just totally daft one way or another

A QUICK HELLO
FROM BROTHER
BERNARD

Hello!

Now, 'Native Britons' – who are you? Do you call yourself British, or English, or Scottish, or Welsh? Or Manx? If English, don't you want to apologise to the Welsh folk for pushing them out into the (admittedly very pretty) western hills? If Scottish, are you a 'Pict' or a 'Celt', or are you one of the millions of Irish, Gaelic folk who took up residence centuries ago, while many Scots swapped over to Ireland? Even the name 'Scot' comes from Ireland, the story going that the Scoti were a people descended from an exiled Egyptian Princess in the time of Moses, who came here via the Emerald Isle. All these lands are relatively new concepts, the creations of men scribbling on maps – but united, as Britain, it's a different story.

So how do you rate your claim to this island? Do you really think the colour of your skin has anything whatsoever to do with it? Are you pink, or as dark-skinned as the Cheddar Man who roamed these hills 10,000 years ago? Or do you think you can trace your family back to the giants who, it was once said, roamed this island of Albion and called it their own?

Every country on planet Earth has its own origin story – Britain's most famous and ancient can be found in our first tale – but many years of digging and clever pointing at maps have given us the popular knowledge that hairy humans were scratching out a living on this land hundreds of thousands of years ago, before the final Ice Age. The low lands around these hills became flooded only 8,000 years ago, creating the British Isles, suddenly alone in a chilly ocean out on the western fringe of Europe. And from that time onwards, wave after wave of humanity has washed up on these craggy shores, looking to find themselves a home – and to create their own tales.

Any hardy nomads who were there to greet the first visitors (or probably to ask for a fight, knowing that lot) would have a great deal of budging up to do in the millennia to follow. With the land warming up nicely, the swarthy Iberian Beaker people are said to have tramped up from Africa, through Spain, and were eventually pushed out of the way by a bunch many call Celts, from somewhere sort of Swiss. Soon these newbies were rooting out Britain's precious metals, sowing the fertile fields and calling themselves British, in their own small ways – small ways which they would defend to the death with the big sharp bits of metal they'd dug out of the ground. We tend to call the further waves 'Celtic' to save time, because frankly the Bronze and Iron Ages were anyone's game, with boat after boat bursting with hopeful folk joining up for a plunge into the British soup. This lot tended to really like stones. Big stones.

Then just before and after 'Year Zero' came the Romans of course, spoiling all the fun, and slaughtering all those poor loopy druids. This is where your average 'History of Britain' starts; but you see, by this point folk had been living and loving and regularly going to the toilet, right here, for several long millennia (in fact, the oldest toilets in the world can be found in the Stone Age village of Skara Brae, in the Orkneys). Each wave of what we'll call invasion (because by now there really was little greeting involved when more tribes washed up on the shore) brought fresh ideas and goods to the people of the island that adopted them, and they called this stuff British, be it tea, or decent shoes, or central heating, or DNA.

Once the Romans had given up, on came the Saxons, the Angles (they soon teamed up and decided to call themselves the Anglo-Saxons; you might know them as 'English'), and all those frankly rude Vikings and Danes. Slaves. Normans. French Huguenots fleeing religious persecution. German aristocrats keeping Britain Protestant. Colonial immigrants from the British Empire and beyond. Asylum seekers trying to find a safe place to make their own stories. All have made their home on this little green island, and decided to be British.

Where does Britannia herself come into this, you might wonder? Was she a giant, that fine, fork-brandishing helmeted Warrior Queen of this island people? It seems, alas, that Britannia was probably invented as a sort of mascot by the Romans, a noble woman to be crushed under their heel. But centuries later, the mysterious lady arose again, shining and proud.

That's rather what we hope can be said of the 77 stories we have gathered for you to share and enjoy. Many old wives' tales bear few retellings – ask around your town; there will be shaggy dog tales of big black ghost dogs, and maybe the odd holy well where some saint had their head chopped off in the Dark Ages (which, incidentally, had much the same ratio of light and dark as today). But sometimes, every generation or so, all the very best tales of heroes, villains, weird creatures, tragic love, bloody battles and magic riddles, as recorded by the endless muddle of folk who rub shoulders from Land's End to John O'Groats, do benefit from being brought together, buffed up nicely, and shown in a new light, shining and proud.

It's impossible to please everyone with a vast treasury of such breadth and strangeness, and with 77 tales to choose from, some will always be somebody's favourite – and least favourite. Most of these retellings are suitable for all ages, but a few folktales have an indelibly rude flavour, or are steeped in buckets of blood (check our Tale Key for warning signs). It's also best to be prepared that not every one of these stories completely adds up – that's part of the charm: what on earth were the original storytellers getting at? Maybe two thousand years ago the druid, bard or teacher who was entertaining the crowd was offered a cup of warm mead at just the wrong time, and suddenly a crucial detail was left out of a plot. Why does the Welsh legend of Queen Rhiannon seem to passionately explode out of nowhere in *The Mabinogion*? *What* was the person who first told the very silly 'King of Cats' *on*? Was Robin Hood swinging through Sherwood in the 12th century or the 14th? Do eagles even have ears? And so on. As far as possible, these retellings do straighten things out a little, but sometimes that would be unfair on the sheer mysterious whimsy of the tale as it has come down to us.

So if any of the following myths and stories leave you confused, or perhaps even freaked out, relax – that's what they have been doing to people for centuries! If you want complete narrative clarity, there's always soap opera. But if you are intrigued enough to investigate further, and find your own answers to any of the mysteries contained within, then: mission accomplished. All of these stories are here to be retold, again and again.

Hopefully you will find your own favourites among this treasury of oddities – because, whether they are exciting, terrifying, saucy, perplexing, spooky, heartbreaking or just very very daft, the 'British' folk have left these tales here, for you.

There are some who claim that Britain is the greatest country on Earth. This is, of course, utter poppy-nonsense. Every region on our planet has tales to tell, and people being people, wherever they come from, very interesting yarns they are too. But Britain is our home, and the home of these tales, and we should be proud to share them with the whole wide world.

1. BRUTUS: LAND AHOY!

Totnes, Devon

Any country which can confidently claim to know how it came to be must be a very young country indeed – the youthful states of North America, for instance, or the positively newborn country of Australia, where natives had lived for thousands of years before the invaders arrived. You can be sure that the origin stories of most nations begin with invasion, and murder, and theft.

Dear old Britain has been around and filled with proud Britons for a very generous amount of centuries, so it's impossible to say for sure how such a land – call it the United Kingdom, Britain, Albion or what you like – really first came to be.

There is, however, the whoppingly ancient tale of Brutus, the great Trojan Prince who gave Britain its very name... so some say.

Perhaps you have never heard of the Trojan War? It was very famous, once upon a time. Many hundreds upon hundreds upon even more hundreds of eons ago, out towards the hot dusty lands of Turkey, war broke out between the early civilizations of Troy and Greece – reportedly due to a naughty Trojan Prince called Paris, who stole away with Helen, the wife of the Grecian King. Ever after, it was said that Helen's beauty was somehow enough to launch a thousand ships, as soldiers amassed from all over the civilised tribes to settle the dispute at Troy itself.

Many tales are told of this war and its aftermath. One Greek

1. BRUTUS: LAND AHOY!

general, Odysseus (the clever dick who thought up the Trojan Horse ruse), had lots of unlikely adventures on his sails away from victory at Troy. But while Odysseus headed one way for his own mad journey, another Trojan Prince, Aeneas, was sailing off in the opposite direction.

'Good luck, Aeneas!' Odysseus whooped as his ship's sails caught the wind eastwards.

'Have fun, Odysseus!' Aeneas waved back, 'See you at the next World War perhaps!'

Aeneas' troops of friends wandered throughout Europe for years, and his children had children. Prince Brutus, however, is the grandson who interests us in this story. Brutus was a wiry little warrior, wily and sharp, a born leader of people. Great wizards predicted exciting things for little Brutus when he was still potty-training.

The young lad got into a spot of bother one day by accidentally shooting his father with an arrow during one truly awful beach holiday in Italy. However, Brutus' natural leadership was to come in very handy, because he was exiled – with his own gang of brave young Trojans to follow him.

'But where am I supposed to go?' young Brutus whined, 'All my stuff is here!'

'Never you mind, my lad,' said the coastguard. 'Hooligans like you aren't wanted on the Continent. Here's a boat, you find a home, just like your Grandad did.'

'Fine then, I will!' answered back Brutus, 'Come on, gang!'

This band of friends sailed up around Spain and found themselves in Gaul (the place people now call 'France'), where a bit more trouble was caused – this time, by Brutus' best mate, Corin. Corin was another Trojan Prince, but gigantic where Brutus was compact and nippy. He stood the height of any self-respecting tree, and impossibly bulging muscles rippled under the mass of his huge arms and belly. Corin's favourite thing was food. It was just like Corin to eat all of the boars in the King of Aquitaine's forests, and spark a war which spilled gallons and gallons of blood before the Gauls begged Corin to 'Just leave us alone and go away!'

'But we only just got here!' Brutus complained.

'Well, we already live here, find another home!' the Gaulish King stormed back. 'Here, have a boat, anything, but get off my land!'

The daughter of this King of Gaul was called Ignoge – and yes, it was pronounced just like 'eggnog'. Ignoge had taken a fancy to brave young Brutus, and announced that she was going wherever he was.

And so without a glance back, Brutus, his young wife, and all his Trojan friends set sail away from the continent of Europe for the last time, to see what was 'out there'.

Unfortunately, what was 'out there' was wind, and rain, and horrifying storms that bashed and buffeted Brutus' boat up, down, under and over a thousand times, the whole crew churning their guts up into the remorseless waves, day after day – and only maggoty biscuits to eat. Nobody on board had ever thought to ask if anyone knew how to sail a ship. But they sailed on, and on. The life on the ocean wave, it turned out, stank.

It was with great relief that this half-wreck of a ship all but smashed itself into pieces on a scraggy little island somewhere out north-west-ish. Annoyingly, there was nothing on this chalky outcrop but an old half-ruined temple, devoted to the Greek goddess Artemis.

'Oh dear, everyone, I'm afraid we're not quite as saved as we thought we were,' admitted Brutus.

'Artemis!' gasped Ignoge. 'The goddess of the moon, and of hunting!' Artemis was absolutely her favourite god of the many gods people had to choose from back then.

'Grrr, not so much as a nesting gannet to roast for supper, or the odd strange root to suck on!' grumped Corin, and Ignoge hugged one of his enormous arms.

The exhausted crew fell on their knees and prayed to Artemis for a sign. And oddly, because this sort of thing still happened in those days, she gave them one.

A clear, crystal voice broke out from the temple, and sang on the winds:

'Brutus! There lies beyond the Gallic bounds
An island which the western sea surrounds,
By giants once possessed, now few remain,
To bar thy entrance, or obstruct thy reign.
To reach that happy shore thy sails employ
There fate decrees to raise a second Troy
And found an empire in thy royal line,
Which time shall ne'er destroy, nor bounds confine!'

'Did that lady just say I was going to be King of somewhere?' asked Brutus.

1. BRUTUS: LAND AHOY!

'Something like that,' grumped Corin. 'But anyway, let's get what's left of this ship lashed together and set off north, I'm starving. I don't even mind rowing if it gets me something for my supper.'

'Back on the ship, everyone!' Brutus called, and off they went again. However, at Ignoge's suggestion, they took with them a spare stone from the rubble around the magical temple, to remind them of Artemis's promise.

With Corin whirling his mighty oars through the grey waves, the rest of their journey was much swifter – and before they knew it...

'LAND AHOY!' cried Brutus with a grin.

White cliffs stretched up for what seemed like miles, and the sun shone above on the greenest fields any of them had ever seen. There, peeping over from the top of the cliffs, they saw sheep, deer, boars, and huge cows called aurochs – who all ran away at the sight of the ship, to the shelter of trees weighed down with deep shining fruit of all kinds.

Ignoge's smile was bedazzling. 'This land is a vision of home I have never imagined before. A fruity place of mysteries and comforts. Brutus – are we home at last?'

Brutus was the first to set his foot ashore. 'Here I stand and here I rest. And this town shall be called Totnes!' he announced, and everyone whooped and cheered and poured down onto the dry land, and set about finding gorgeous things to eat, building fires, erecting shelters and thanking Artemis for their safe arrival in this land, newly-named 'Brutus land', or perhaps 'Britain'...

Britain? Safe? The giants who romped around this green and pleasant land took issue with both of these words. This place, you see, was Albion, a playground for the giant children of an even more ancient Greek Princess called Albina and her sisters – and these cheeky little strangers were not at all welcome.

Brutus awoke the next morning to smouldering campfires and, as he looked up, wiping the sleep from his eyes... there were a whole host of slavering mountain-sized giants bearing down on them all, roaring righteous bloodlust!

'HUMANS HUMANS HUMANS! OUT! OUT! OUT!' they bellowed, and the ground shook as they drew near.

The battles were many and frankly upsetting. You wouldn't want to hear about upsetting things like battles between dumb giants and sword-wielding humans, would you? All the biffing, and splatting, and nibbling of ears and so on... it was all very messy. It's enough to say that Brutus and his army had Corin on their side, and soon there was only one giant left of this attacking party. His name was Gogmagog, and he was the hugest of all the huge giants of Albion – as big as two giants in one!

'Come here then, big fella,' Corin laughed, 'then it's time for breakfast!'

Corin and Gogmagog wrestled and struggled all along the south coast. Sometimes Corin had the upper hand, both fists up Gogmagog's nostrils in a special killer move he'd developed, called 'The Bogey Basher'. Sometimes Gogmagog forced himself back into power position, swinging Corin around like a particularly beefy rag doll.

Eventually the wrestlers arrived atop a monstrously tall cliff in an area now known as Plymouth Hoe – and there, a particularly timely poke in the eye from Corin toppled the mighty Gogmagog over the side. He crashed all the way down with such a big splat, the locals put two chalk outlines there to mark the body for generations to come, and called them 'Gog' and 'Magog'.

Brutus was so glad his best friend was alive, he gave him the whole wodge of land he stood on, and it became known as Cornwall. Brutus and Ignoge themselves rode out east trying to find the perfect spot to call home.

'To found an empire in our royal line!' Ignoge reminded him.

'Well yes, dearest, but just somewhere cosy and relatively safe from giants would be good,' replied Brutus. Eventually they both agreed on an unspoiled hillside on the banks of the river Thames, and built their home there, calling it 'New Troy' – so it really was home from home. The cosy settlement of 'Troia Nova' became known to the Romans as Trinovantum – and only many eons later by its other name, 'London'.

In this city Brutus and Ignoge built a new temple to Artemis, and ruled happily together for 25 years. They had three sons – Locrinus, Albanactus and Kamber – to rule in the east, the north and the west when their time was done. But the couple never wandered far from their new home ever again.

THE END

1. BRUTUS: LAND AHOY!

TOTNES, DEVON

The London Stone, said to have been a piece of Trojan temple brought to
the capital by Brutus, is held in a not-very-secret corner of England's
capital city, on Cannon Street, and very nearby is the Guildhall, guarded
by statues of Gog and Magog. But London is so entirely packed with
tourist spots, Totnes is a better place to let the record of Brutus' life ring
out. It also has its own Brutus Stone, allegedly the exact spot where the
brave adventurer first set foot on this island. Filled with more listed
buildings than almost any other British town of its size, the not-quite-
coastal beauties of Totnes, perched on the River Dart, are a world away
from the dirty metropolis for which Brutus claimed the credit. There is a
castle to please any visitor who has only seen one in a book before, and
all manner of maritime pursuits to look into if you make the journey
south-west.

totnesinformation.co.uk

2. THE THREE
BEARS

Keiss, Highlands

You may think you know this story – the one about the Three Bears and their unwelcome visitor. But that naughty little blonde called Goldilocks was entirely made up! This is the real story of what happened to those poor Three Bears many centuries ago, when wild bears were still to be found in the forests of Britain – in this case, the wild brown bears of northern Scotland.

These Three Bears lived very happily together in their own broch – which was a sort of dry stone castle – up on a little hill, in a clearing of a huge, luscious forest which stretched for hundreds of miles around. There was one Big Bear, and one Little Bear, and a third who was neither big nor little, but just the size that they were.

These Three Bears were wild, of course, but very civilised for all that. Every morning, they would arise from their cosy beds, bid each other 'A very, very good morning!' and then pad down to the kitchen to enjoy a piping hot bowl of porridge together to start the day.

One day, however, all three found that their porridge was just too hot.

'I have had a momentous idea!' announced the Middle Bear.

'Oh good, I do love it when you have your ideas,' replied the Big Bear. 'Go you on ahead.'

'It's a truly splendid day, why don't we take a stroll around the forest while our breakfast cools?'

'I declare it to be the idea of the year!' cried the Little Bear, often

11

2. THE THREE BEARS

the decider of all decisions for the trio. The wee fluffball set down their little spoon and said, 'Let's go, chums!'

And the Three Bears trooped out into the morning sun, with a 'tra-la-lee' on their lips. They did not even pause to put the broch's door on the latch. That's just the kind of trusting, idealistic, possibly naive young bears they were.

Because, no matter how far away from the madding crowd you may be, there may well be a rotter somewhere in the vicinity. It was all well and lovely that the Three Bears wished no harm to anyone, but in the shadows of that forest lurked many a scamp, not to mention numerous scoundrels, cads and the odd miscreant. That morning, a miscreant stepped into the sunshine, and sniffed the air excitedly.

'Milky milk! And mmm, cinnamon! Porridge!' The loud sound of a tummy rumble filled the clearing where the Three Bears' broch stood.

This was one of the wily fox brethren – sly and usually clever animals known to some storytellers, from Scotland to France, as 'Reynard' – but this particular fox's name was Scrapefoot. And what a hungry fox he was!

Scrapefoot tiptoed up to the broch's door, the heavy porridge aroma drawing him in, and he spied through a chink in the door to case the joint. 'Abandoned, and fair game, and I am game for that!' he whispered to himself, and stealthily let himself into the Bears' home.

Porridge was the only thing on Scrapefoot's mind as he crept over to the kitchen's broad oak table. He scampered up onto the biggest chair, picked up a spoon, licked his drooling lips and tucked in. But then he stopped, and pulled a face. 'This porridge,' Scrapefoot said, 'is far too lumpy!'

And so he shifted over to the next chair, and sampled the contents of the next bowl. He pulled a worse face. 'This porridge,' he announced to himself, 'is far too runny!'

One more time, he moved over onto the next chair, and picked up the smallest spoon. One big gulp. 'Mmm, this porridge is just right,' said Scrapefoot, and even though he was a fox, he wolfed down the whole lot.

Then Scrapefoot felt like a nice sit down, after his long prowl through the forest, and so he looked around and saw a huge chair. He scampered up onto it, but soon his bottom was hurting, and he pulled a face. 'This chair is too hard!' he said.

And so he clambered up onto the next chair, which was covered in cushions and covers and antimacassars galore. He circled around and tried to get comfy, but his back hurt. He pulled yet another face. 'This chair is too soft and squidgy!' he said, but he had already seen the third chair.

Well, this chair could have been made for him, he thought, with its nice velvet seat and armrests. 'This chair is just right!' he announced, as he began squeezing his big foxy behind onto it. But then – KER-RACK! – his bottom fell right through the bottom, and he landed on his bottom! Scrapefoot dusted himself down, and snarled at the chair, which was a write-off.

'Silly cheap chairs,' he growled, and gave a deep yawn.

All this eating and sitting had tired Scrapefoot right out, and so he slunk upstairs to the bedroom. The first bed he tried was the largest, and it was just a huge log with a thin sheet over it. 'This bed is too hard!' said Scrapefoot, after much fidgeting.

He pounced on the next bed, which was so festooned with cushions and cosies it looked like a huge marshmallow. When Scrapefoot leapt onto it, the mattress springs sprung him right up to the ceiling, and he hit his head! He tried to cuddle up in the eiderdown, but it was no good. 'This bed is too soft and springy!' he wailed.

But, of course, the Little Bear's bed felt like a dream come true. 'This bed is just right!' he yawned, and was soon snoring away with a big dopey grin on his porridge-smeared muzzle…

The Three Bears could only have been gone less than ten minutes, and they all happily plodded through the front door without any worries weighing on them. But then the Big Bear saw a spoon sticking up out of their own thick lumpy porridge. 'Someone has been eating my porridge!' the Big Bear growled.

The Middle Bear also found their porridge half splattered across the table. 'Someone has been eating MY porridge too!'

The Little Bear examined the last bowl, and found it empty. 'Someone has been eating my porridge,' the wee fluffball squeaked, 'and they've eaten it all up!'

2. THE THREE BEARS

Then the trio came across their disrupted sitting room area. 'Someone has been sitting on my chair!' grumbled the Big Bear.

'Someone has been sitting on MY chair too!' added the Middle Bear, tutting, 'The antimacassars are all over the place!'

The Little Bear gave an even bigger squeak when they saw the splintered remains of the last chair. 'Someone has been sitting on my chair, and they've broken it all up!' The poor Little Bear didn't know whether to growl or cry, but the Bears all cuddled and promised to mend everything, and the Middle Bear had one of their great ideas.

'Today has really not worked out for us, has it?' they said. 'Let's just go back to bed.'

And so they all trooped sullenly upstairs, and saw that even their bedroom had been burgled!

'Someone has been sleeping in my bed!' the Big Bear fumed.

'Someone has been sleeping in MY bed!' added the Middle Bear, 'and bouncing up and down on it!'

The Little Bear had padded over to their own bed, and let out a jubilant little growl. 'Aha! Someone has been sleeping in my bed,' they announced, 'And he's STILL IN IT!'

At this cry, Scrapefoot let out a colossal snore and became wide awake! But his wiliness was no use to him. He had no time to scarper before the Big Bear had grasped him by the tail and was holding him in the air as he scrabbled for freedom.

'Hi there, Bear friends!' Scrapefoot beamed, desperately. 'Thank goodness you're here, I heard this sound and I thought, "There's a burglary in progress here!" So I was trying to investigate, as a good neighbourly fox, of course, and...'

'Can it, Reynard!' the Little Bear snarled, as they opened the window. 'Okay, pals, Middle Bear, you take his left paws, Big Bear you take his right, and let's give him a good swing!'

And so the bigger Bears began to swing the giddy, sickly Scrapefoot backwards and forwards, counting '1 – 2 – 3' as they did so, and the Little Bear took a big run-up and booted the naughty fox right in his big fox rear end! BOOF!

'Nnnyaarrrgh!' cried Scrapefoot as he sailed out of the broch's window and through the air, landing with a crash in a thistle patch. The Three Bears shook their paws at him through the window, and promised each other to be more careful in the future!

But it took more than a few thistles to keep Scrapefoot down. He pulled the worst of the prickles out of his bottom, was pleased to note that no bones were broken, and then he turned back to the broch, waggled his claws in front of his nose and blew a great big raspberry back at the angry Bears.

'Thanks for the porridge, teddies!' the cheeky fox hooted, and pelted back into the darkness of the forest to scam his way through another day.

The Three Bears made some more porridge. It was delicious. And they also bought a big padlock for their front door.

THE END

KEISS, CAITHNESS

Claiming a historical site for the Three Bears' legendary home would be impossible to do with a straight face, but this is indeed a very ancient tale from Britain somewhere, and once upon a time, the island was home to many real wild bears. The retelling of this tale which originally caught the public imagination was by Bristolian poet Robert Southey, who preferred an interfering old woman rather than a fox, and in turn she became more famous as a little blonde housebreaker called Goldilocks. But we've set the tale at the Keiss Broch up in the Highlands, at the very tip of Britain, because it's the oldest site where archaeological study has found evidence of British bears — a huge fang of an *ursus arctos* was discovered there (though there was no reported evidence of porridge).

caithness.org

---

3. THE LOST LAND

Ceredigion Bay

Welsh words can be tricky to get your tongue around at times. On the page, 'Cantre'r Gwaelod' looks like an uncomfortable mouthful, but just try it now – 'Can-Trer G-why-lod' – see, it's not really that hard! Lots of people panic when faced with the language of the Welsh, with all its extra Y's and phlegmy crunchy sounds. But in this case, you needn't worry too much about how to say the name – as Cantre'r Gwaelod doesn't exist any more.

This wonderful land once stretched twenty miles out west into the Irish Sea, halfway down the coast of Wales, in the area now known as Cardigan Bay. Aberystwyth is a famous seaside town, but once it was the entrance to the happy kingdom of Cantre'r Gwaelod. A low-lying land of ripe and sun-kissed meadows, for as long as anyone could remember, the country here had been prized. Every acre of Cantre'r Gwaelod was worth four acres anywhere else, due to the rich fertility of the soil and natural beauty. King Gwyddno, lord of all the land, so revelled in those times of peace that every day was a holiday for all, with feasting and drinking and merrymaking galore.

However, Gwyddno's beautiful Kingdom only existed because of a very clever and ancient system of dykes and dams that held back the raging sea. There were two main sluice gates that were key to the safety of the realm, each one guarded by a Prince. Both of these princely brothers liked a laugh and a drink and a dance. However, the elder of the pair, Seithenin, liked nothing else! He was known as one of the greatest party animals in all Welsh history, and he liked to live up to his reputation. His little brother Teithryn, on the other hand, couldn't help but feel that fun was so much more, well, FUN, once all the chores of the day were done.

Every so often these two brothers, Seithenin and Teithryn, had the duty of checking on the main sluice gates, opening the safety valves and ensuring that everything was safe. This was their one and only job, and like many of the folk of Cantre'r Gwaelod, they were then free to spend the rest of their time carousing, drinking the fine wines grown from Gwyddno's rich vineyards, and generally having a blast. This idle life suited Seithenin down to the ground. The elder brother was very popular, a great dancer, loved by the ladies, and never without a foaming flagon of booze in his hand. Teithryn was more of a worrier – as a Prince, he felt he had to earn his cushy life.

One windy winter, Teithryn took a sniff of the cold, whistling weather, and became worried. In fact, he became so worried he had to face his boozy brother, and tell him the truth. 'Now we all like a drink and a dance, Seithenin,' he began, 'but aren't you beginning to worry a bit about the sea defences, brother? They're getting so old and rusty, every time I check them I fear they may crumble, and then where would we all be?'

'Oh, you moaning minnie,' Seithenin laughed at his brother, 'Those sluice gates are older than you or I, Teithryn, and they can look after themselves perfectly well. Why worry? Have a drink, bach.'

But Teithryn was unconvinced, and he bravely announced to everyone who would listen that unless the defences were strengthened right away, it was quite probable that the land of Cantre'r Gwaelod would be in big trouble! 'We shall be flooded by the raging sea! The sluice gates need to be looked to, look you!'

Seithenin happily mocked his fretting brother in front of the whole royal court. 'This mighty Kingdom of Gwyddno?' he slurred as he knocked back another goblet of wine, 'It's been standing for centuries, and shall stand dry for centuries... BLEHHH!' – he let out a resounding belch – 'Centuries more to come! Now, who fancies a bit of a dance, eh?'

How they all laughed at the idea that Cantre'r Gwaelod could ever be in any danger! What a wet-pants Teithryn was! And that's what they all sang at him: 'Wet-pants Teithryn!' 'Go and put on your swimming costume, wet-pants! Hahaha!'

3. THE LOST LAND

With a face like thunder, the clever Prince left the party, and went off to do his daily duty by checking on his sluice gates, beyond the north wing of the castle. This was Seithenin's usual cue to go and do the traditional checks on his own half of the water defences on the opposite wing. At first, it seemed that he was going to do exactly that, as he headed out to the coastal area where those sea defences stood. However, the lazy Prince then merrily staggered off to a secret cave for a tryst with a special friend.

'Where's that mermaid Mererid, then?' the drunken Prince sang. 'Where's my little fishy friend, eh?'

'Is that my British Prince, is it?' came a tinkling reply, and an undeniably saucy young maiden was seen curled on a rock, combing her long blonde hair. 'You're early tonight, cariad,' Mererid smiled. 'I thought you had to go and do all your sea defence business you were telling me about. You must be so brave, keeping the sea at bay like that, you big chunk of muscle, you.'

Seithenin hiccupped, and laughed. 'Nooo, chestnuts to all that, darlin', I've come to see you instead, brought you some wine and everything, I have.'

'But I thought your brother said...'

'Never mind what that little cissy Teithryn says, love,' Seithenin replied, 'Don't worry, everything's gonna be all right, now come here and give me a great big cwtch where it counts.'

'I was only asking anyway,' Mererid said as soon as her lips were free to do so. 'I'm part mermaid, obviously, so it's not my problem if everyone drowns.' At that, Seithenin simply laughed a big boozy laugh, and belched again. Neither of them would have given up their cosy cove to be out in the storm, battling the wind and the rain to check on the silly old sluice gates!

If ever there was an evening that this was a mistake, it was that wintry night. Teithryn arrived at his post and could see at once that the sea defences were mere moments away from collapsing! The poor Prince barely had time to shout a warning to all the partying folk who had been laughing at him, but still he rang an ancient bell, and called as loud as he could over the storm: 'BEWARE THE SEA! RUN, FOLK OF CANTRE'R GWAELOD, AND NEVER LOOK BACK!'

Before he had even finished speaking, the mighty dam which secured the land from flooding began to crumble dramatically, and –

'WHOOOOSH!' – in one almighty tidal wave, the sea crashed in on the land, flooding every field, every garden, every house!

Teithryn raced the wave on his speeding horse, and eventually joined the few survivors who managed to reach the safety of the mountains – or rather, now, the coast. They looked out across the waves as the moon shone down upon them. It was as if Cantre'r Gwaelod had never existed. King Gwyddno was fine – his castle was further north in Meirionnydd – but Seithenin and all those crazy, boozy, ignorant party animals were somewhere deep under the waves now.

Prince Teithryn was not the kind to gloat and say 'I told you so' – and besides, nearly everyone he had told was now far beneath the waves, never to be seen again. He shed a tear for his foolish brother, and told himself that he had done everything he could.

Although the land of which he was a Prince was lost forever, Teithryn spent the rest of his life telling his tale to all who would listen, and urging everybody never to take their safety for granted. Those who did listen were lucky to learn an important lesson: fun and games are usually more enjoyable after the day's important business is taken care of, and not before – and certainly not instead of it! But this lesson, unfortunately, never made Teithryn very popular at parties.

THE END

CARDIGAN BAY

There's no way of buying a return ticket to the land of Cantre'r Gwaelod — if it ever really existed, it's far beneath the cold Irish Sea. Marine archaeologists have tried to explore this submerged area to turn up solid evidence of the lost kingdom of King Gwyddno, but although some evidence of pre-Roman habitation has been seen, and signs of a prehistoric forest over 3,000 years old have been found off the coast of Borth, the land remains a legend. Ceredigion, or Cardigan Bay itself, is still blessed with the usual seaside pleasures, including donkey rides along the beach at Aberystwyth every summer, but in or out of the summer season, visitors can gaze out onto the grey waves of the Irish Sea, and imagine what it might once have looked like in the days of Teithryn and his boozy brother.

visitcardigan.com

4. WAYLAND AND FLIBBERTIGIBBET

Ashbury, Oxfordshire

First, of course, we had the Stone Age. (Well, okay, the dinosaurs came before that, but stay with me for now.) Then one day, some brainbox of a cave-person dug around and found a funny-looking rock, then went further, and found that when they buried that rock deep within a really really hot version of one of those new-fangled fire things, shiny liquid began to leak out, which then set harder than the rock it emerged from!

And so, with the invention of this amazing new technology, the first ever blacksmith was created, and the Bronze Age was underway. Before long – only a couple of paltry millennia later – the Iron Age took over, and by that time, the blacksmith was seen as one of the most important people in any village, right up there with the chief, the warriors, and the shaman. These brawny, sweaty metal-forgers could make you a sword out of a puddle of glowing liquid! Now, that was real magic!

And no blacksmith was better known than Wayland.

According to the Saxons, Wayland the Smith was friends with Thor, Odin and all those other Norse gods we've all heard so much about. Wayland was the best blacksmith in the known galaxy, and could make you almost anything you wanted in any metal he could get hold of. From Thor's helmet to Loki's braces, all metallic objects in Asgard and Valhalla originated in Wayland's smithy.

Wayland had a bit of bother at one time, when a greedy human

4. WAYLAND AND FLIBBERTIGIBBET

King tricked him into becoming his own personal blacksmith and slave on a distant island. Thankfully, he escaped imprisonment by crafting his own metal wings, killing the King and all his family, and then flying far, far away. The message was clear – you don't mess with Wayland!

Eventually the beefcake metal-magician touched down in the far west of the British county of Oxfordshire, and decided from then on to keep his head down, set up a new smithy, and pose as a normal blacksmith for the people of the area. There was plenty of work for one, as horses were all the rage and needed shoes – someone had even drawn a huge chalk horse on the hill near Wayland's smithy!

The good folk of Ashbury and Faringdon were very pleased with Wayland's work, and soon he was obliged to hire an apprentice to keep up with demand. His contacts at Asgard sent along young Flibbertigibbet, a cheeky wee immortal who had caused so much mischief at home, it was felt that Wayland should teach the pest a decent trade. Flibbertigibbet moaned and whined – 'Awww, metal's boring! I didn't ask to be born immortal!' – but he didn't dare argue with Wayland.

Still, the moody Flibbertigibbet was not happy in the hot, sweaty forge, and was soon just getting under Wayland's feet, whistling his annoying Norse tunes and wiping bogeys all over the shiny new swords. He fitted in very well with all the local lads and naughty gangs, and would go missing for whole days as they roamed the hills getting up to mischief, stealing bird's eggs, playing football with random heads and so on.

'This just won't do, young fellow, me demi-god!' insisted Wayland one busy morning, when he had an order to shoe a whole cavalry's worth of horses for an imminent tribal battle. 'I'll tell you what, you can be of some use to me at last – I don't have time to make a hundred nails with all these shoes to forge, so pop down to the shops in Farringdon and get me a big bag. Here's a gold coin that should cover it. And be sure to be back by noon – these horses have to be ready to roll into battle at three!'

'Bah, okay, if I have to,' griped Flibbertigibbet, pocketing the gold and slinking out of the smithy towards the town.

However, if you've ever heard his name before, you will know that 'flibbertigibbet' has become another word for a flighty figure, someone who cannot be depended on – and so, our Flibbertigibbet soon forgot the task Wayland had sent him to do. He spent the gold on honey candy, and wandered around the countryside throwing stones at great big aurochs, cartwheeling across fields and climbing trees to pick conkers.

Soon, the midday hour had long been struck, and still Wayland was waiting for his nails. Being an Asgardian, however, he could soon find out what the matter was. He took to the skies with his metal wings, and used his super-sight to scope out the countryside for his wayward apprentice. There he saw Flibbertigibbet, not that far from the smithy, picking his belly button and eating sweets, which Wayland knew could only have been bought with the gold he had given him for the nails.

It does not do to annoy a mighty Norse god like Wayland. The angry smith swooped down to the ground and picked up a huge menhir – a stone very like the ones in Stonehenge, which would take twenty humans to lift. With one almighty lunge, Wayland threw the stone right down to the street corner where Flibbertigibbet was idling, and it landed with a horrendous 'KER-BLAMMO!' right on the lazy apprentice's foot! It was a good job that Flibbertigibbet was immortal, as no human could have survived that bombardment! As it was, the young truant was pinned to the spot, bawling fit to burst at his predicament – 'Waaaah! I want my Mum!' and so on – until Wayland came along, picked him up by his ears and dragged him home, muttering about teenagers. To this day, the spot where the stone struck is still called Snivelling Corner, after the crestfallen Flibbertigibbet.

Nobody knows what happened to the pair after that. Perhaps Flibbertigibbet was sent home, or left to wander the human world being irresponsible forever more. Or perhaps he changed his ways and became an excellent blacksmith just like Wayland?

Certainly, either Wayland or the both of them were believed to have remained in that smithy for a long time after – if not up until the present day. If you visit Wayland's Smithy in Oxfordshire, there's a long-held tradition that any horse rider in need of a new shoe for their steed can tie the horse up at the smithy with a single silver coin. When they return in the morning, the horse's shoes will be good as new! Perhaps if you try this, and it doesn't work, but the silver coin is gone… it's quite possible that Flibbertigibbet took it to go and buy himself some sweets.

4. WAYLAND AND FLIBBERTIGIBBET

THE END

ASHBURY, OXFORDSHIRE

Some five thousand years ago, just south of where the modern day village of Ashbury stands (the nearest town being Faringdon), some people built a curious burial structure. How the ancient monument came eventually to be linked to the old Saxon character of Wayland the Smith is anyone's guess, but at least you can still go and visit it today. Sadly, that can't be said of many of the other prehistoric markers which used to be here, like a sarsen stone at Snivellings Corner or Beahilda's Barrow — these crucial pagan sites have long been lost forever due to the ploughs of ignorant farmers. It's a good job the Smithy itself is still worth the visit, and is only a stroll from the famous prehistoric Uffington White Horse. And of course, you can still leave your horse and a shilling there, and see what happens...

faringdon.org

5. WADE AND BELL

Whitby, N. Yorks

You may all be thinking by now that giants – those colossal original inhabitants of Britain – were interested in nothing but fighting, stealing and eating people like us. But that's just not fair at all. Only somewhere in the region of 99 percent of giants were actually like that! Some giants were nice as especially nice pie. A few giants. Not many giants. But some of the decent ones are at least remembered with affection.

Two of these huge good apples were known as Wade and Bell – a very pleasant gigantic couple, who lived on the north-east coast of the island, round about the modern town of Whitby. Well, you could say they lived in the Whitby area, but it would be more accurate to say that they made a lot of it with their own bare hands. Like many giants, they were big enough to lift whole hills and throw them around – and that they did, and more.

Each morning, up Bell would rise, and roar, 'COME ON, WADE, WAKE UP YOU LAZY WHALEFACE! THERE'S THINGS TO BUILD!' while the strong but silent Wade only gave her a wink and, both grinning as if it was their first ever job, the two of them would stomp off for a day's mighty landscaping.

The castles of Mulgrave and Pickering, for instance, were each personal projects of Wade and Bell. The couple only had one hammer between them, so when one needed to use it, the other would hurl it across the countryside. Sometimes they actually managed to catch it! But these days this would be considered an extremely unsafe work environment.

And then there's the ancient road known as Wade's Wife's

5. WADE AND BELL

Causeway – it's not called that for nothing! People who like to consider themselves experts on this kind of thing insist that the Romans built it, but they actually only smartened it up when they came across it two thousand years ago – the road itself was thousands of years older than that!

You see, poor old Bell had to travel that way to take her giant cow, Sycamore, onto the moors for milking. This big beautiful heifer stood at least fifty storeys tall, and the milk from her colossal swinging udders made cheese, yoghurt and cream for hundreds of villagers for miles around. Bell believed in being friendly to the locals, rather than eating them, and she and Wade were beloved in return.

This milking journey, however, was a pain, even for a milkmaid with legs as long as Bell's. 'OOH, WADE, I FEEL LIKE I'VE TRAIPSED TO THE SUN AND BACK!' she would often complain when she got home, sinking her gigantic hot feet into a lake to cool them.

And so she and Wade built the shortcut specially. Wade went on ahead, scooping up all the earth he could to build a raised walkway in a straight line for several miles. This is how the great bowl known as the Hole of Horcum came to be. When he'd finished, he dropped all the extra earth in a spot which is now known as Blakey Topping.

While Wade was doing this, his wife was busy following behind with her apron full of mighty rocks to pave the road. Sometimes her apron split under the weight of the stones, and the jumbles that fell became stone circles all around the area.

But eventually the work was done, the road was built, and all the villagers came out to applaud the clever giants, and a special cream tea was laid on to celebrate the road's opening, with cream buns and cheese sandwiches courtesy of dear old Sycamore herself.

Nobody knows what became of Wade and Bell, though hopefully they weren't murdered by Jack, or one of his fans. And now, as you travel around North Yorkshire, the apparently natural beauty you see all around you is a lasting testament to their wondrous building craft – and so they will always be remembered, with fondness, and cream.

THE END

WHITBY, N. YORKS

Whitby itself is already a hotbed of tourism activity, with its links to the Dracula legend and pirates in the bay. But as if you needed any extra reason to enjoy the natural landscape of the area, you can follow in the gigantic footsteps of Wade and Bell in a number of places. What remains of the causeway (which is also known as Wade's Causeway, or Old Wife's Way) can be found linking the towns of Malton and Eskdale, and in the area you can also find the Hole of Horcum. The hill created by Wade is disputed, but it's either Blakey Topping, Roseberry Topping or Freebrough Hill, or maybe all three. Cream teas are also quite possibly available.

visitwhitby.com

6. BLADUD AND THE PIGS

Bath

ARE YOU SPOTTY? This rude issue has vexed mankind since the dawn of time, and it can't have escaped your keen and clever observation that Britain's history began a long, long time ago. Most people only know how to tell the story of Britain by starting with the Romans two thousand years ago, but that's only because those conquerors from Italy brought writing with them. Their words and pens and ink and scrolls were as much of a shock to the people of Britain as the swords and fire with which the alien invaders laid waste to the tribal towns they found here.

But humans have been living, and loving, and fighting, and picking their belly buttons here for a lot longer than Rome itself ever existed. The only method Ancient Britons had of recording their lives and adventures was to repeat gossip around the fire until it solidified into a story with a beginning, a middle and an end. But the stories were all true, once upon a time.

The name 'Bath' conjures up images of hot soapy bubbles, which is why it's fitting that the south-western city of that name is built on top of steaming bubbly springs. Many people presume that this was the Romans' idea, but the city of Bath is also famous for being very, very old, and has been home to Britons for many millennia. So if we remember that fireside gossip, there must be some truth in the story of how the place first came to be built, by Prince Bladud, centuries before any Roman had even heard of Britain.

28

Bladud was the son of King Rud Hud, who ruled from the city of New Troy, which they've since renamed 'London'. King Rud Hud was a horribly snooty chieftain, who had very little time for his son.

When he was only small, Bladud was sent away to the Greek colleges of Athens, to learn how to spell and how to think and how to cure a wound by squeezing a pigeon's bum onto it, and everything else Princes were supposed to know in those days.

A clever lad, Bladud sailed home to Britain after passing his exams, and rode jubilantly up to the gates of New Troy, expecting a warm princely welcome... But the gates were locked shut! And when Bladud impatiently hammered for assistance, it was the King himself who grumblingly unlocked the gate and stuck his head out.

'What do you want, spotty?'

'Father! It is I, Bladud, I have come home! Won't you let me in?'

'You're not Bladud. Bladud was never covered in spots like that. You're not coming in, Spotty-spot-face.'

This confused Bladud. But when he lifted his sword to see his reflection, he could see what King Rud Hud was getting at. Since leaving Athens, he had somehow picked up a very nasty case of bright red spots all over his face and body, and he could already hear the villagers inside the gates screaming: 'SPOTS! Spotty man at the door! Everyone run and hide, or we'll all be catching the spots and the whole city will be a spotty mess!' Poor Bladud pounded on the solid wooden gates, but there was no way they were letting him in.

'I don't care who you are, you can get far away from here!' King Rud Hud yelled. 'Go and live your life how you will, but you are no son of mine, spotty!'

And so, with a heavy heart and a spotty face, Bladud drifted away, feeling lost and not sure what to do.

He rode out far west until his poor spotty horse could take no more, and from there he continued on foot, begging at the roadside but forever being spurned for his spottiness.

One day, many miles out, at the base of the busy settlement on Solsbury Hill, Bladud saw a farmer. This farmer kept his distance from the spotty stranger, but he still had some pity for his plight. 'I'll tell ye what, young lad, if ye want to earn a living how about ye look after me pigs for me?' he offered, kindly. 'You might be a bit of a

6. BLADUD AND THE PIGS

horror to look at, but they're not fussy and I can't have 'em running round wild. You can live in the sty an' eat what they leaves behind. How's that sound?'

Well, it was not a life the educated Prince had ever imagined for himself, but it was the best offer he had. And so Bladud took to collecting acorns, which he fed to the pigs to make them follow him, and he wandered the fields as contented as he could be – which was not very much.

Sometimes he would try and teach the pigs things he'd learned in Athens as they travelled, but they were simply not interested in multiples of seven, types of triangles or the boiling point of treacle, no matter how often he banged on about it all. Still, he began to get used to his new life in the sty, and before long the pigs were as spotty as he was.

The spotty student was not exactly cut out to be a swineherd, however, and one day he awoke to find that all of his piggy friends had disappeared! Then he heard a splash, and a happy 'OINK!' Bladud headed downhill to where the River Avon snaked through the valley, following the sound of splashy, honking glee, and soon discovered his porky gang.

The pigs had happened upon the biggest, messiest mud bath that ever there was. It was hot and gloopy, steaming in the morning air, and every last one of them was rolling in the dark warm wet dirt, with pure ecstasy written all over their piggy little faces. Bladud was not impressed. Here he was trying to teach them important things, and all they were interested in was mud! He angrily ordered them out, but it was no good – it took a double dose of tasty acorns to lure them back onto dry land, where he had to clean them all off like the naughty pigs they were.

But when he began to scrape off the thick mud, he was astonished to see that the pigs were no longer spotty! The jolly porkers had given themselves the first ever mud bath beauty treatment in history, and they had never looked better.

All that education was not wasted on young Bladud. As a man of science, he guessed that it had to be the bubbly mud that had cleared away their spots. And so without a second thought, the Prince sped off to test his theory.

'SPLASH! KER-SPLAT!' went Bladud, as he jumped into the steaming, squelchy mud bath. He had to admit that the hot black goo felt wonderful slopping and slurping around his unmentionables, and as he basked in the bubbly bath the pigs eyed him with unmistakable disgust. It was clearly one rule for pigs, and another for annoying know-it-all Princes.

Bladud had been right, though – it was the hot springs that bubbled up around that western valley which cured his spottiness. As he cleaned himself up and saw his reflection in a still, clear pond, he could see that he was back to full health, and himself again.

Not only that, but when he and his piggy friends marched back to the capital at New Troy, he found that his snooty father King Rud Hud had popped his clogs. So Bladud was given a hero's welcome, crowned as the clever new King of the Britons along with his pretty pink pigs, and was cheered to the rafters. He was finally home! HOORAY!

King Bladud did many great things as an inventor and wise man, but the first thing he decreed was that anybody found calling spotty people 'spotty' would be pelted with rotten parsnips. His second decree was that he and the pigs would return to the hot springs out in the western valley, and build a brand new city where everyone could enjoy the beautifying benefits of a roll in the mud, and the city would be called, quite simply, 'Bath'. And folk still enjoy the bubbles there to this day.

THE END

BATH

There are many tall tales told about Bladud — he is said to be the father of Leir, and died Icarus-style attempting to invent a flying machine — but Bath is his home. Legend tells us that the very site where Bladud discovered his pigs rolling in the mud was the tiny village of Swainswick, a couple of miles north of Bath city centre, not far from Solsbury Hill. There's very little to see there, however, so it's a good job that the city of Bath itself is one of the busiest, prettiest World Heritage sites on the planet. Famed for its architectural beauty, with iconic Georgian sandstone streets set against views of the Avon valley, Bath is also festooned with museums for everything from fashion to Chinese art. The

6. BLADUD AND THE PIGS

Roman Baths — where a statue of wise King Bladud still sits high above the bubbling spa — are not open for public bathing any more, so the closest you can get to experiencing the pig's bath is by going over the road to the Millennium Spa, where hot water is pumped up to a top floor pool, allowing you to bathe in the warm as you enjoy the view for miles around.

visitbath.co.uk

7. KING LEIR

Leicester

People talk about 'Ancient Rome', but the city was only founded about 2,800 years ago – not that different to two minutes, when you sit down and have a think about it. They say that Rome was founded by two brothers, Romulus and Remus, who were suckled by wolves when they were babies. But then they say lots of silly things in Rome.

At just the time that the first Roman walls were going up, however, Britain already had its own King. His name was Leir, and it's said that he was the son of Bladud, the spotty swineherd. Whether that's true or not, this King Leir made his home in the city which now almost bears his name: Leicester.

This warrior chieftain had ruled the land for many years, and been a mighty soldier to boot, but as he grew older and richer King Leir grew cold and grand, ruling from his fine castle with an army of rowdy knights at his bidding.

After sixty years of rule, Leir grew tired of the responsibilities of being King. He had no son, but three daughters to rule after him: Goneril, Regan and the youngest, Cordelia.

One day King Leir called the whole Kingdom before him, with all the golden pageantry and ceremony he so adored. With much fanfare, he announced that he would split Britain into three lumps – 'And the biggest lump,' he boomed, 'will go to the daughter who can show the whole world… who LOVES ME the most!' Everybody knew that this was a crazy way to divide a Kingdom, but they had to obey – he was the King!

Goneril, tall and grinning in a flowing blue dress, arose and loudly proclaimed, 'Most Royal Leir, I love you more than anything in all the world!' And when the cheers died down, the King gave her hand in marriage to the Duke of Cornwall, and one third of the Kingdom.

Then came Regan, a vision in a red dress, beaming a special smile for her father as she cried, 'I love you more than Goneril, because I hate everything in the world except you!' Once again, there were cheers as Regan was promised to the Duke of Albany in the North, and granted her very fertile section of the Kingdom to rule over.

Lastly came Cordelia's turn, youngest as she was, and plainly dressed in a white robe. When Leir commanded her to speak, she had nothing to say.

'Nothing?' Leir boomed. 'Nothing will come of nothing!'

Cordelia knew how foolish her father's plan was, but she eventually spoke: 'Can't you see that this is madness? Father, I do love you, but as any child should, and I will not make false promises, or make a show of my love to earn a part of the Kingdom. One day I will marry, for love, and if I love my husband, how can I promise that I love you more than the world?'

In his old age King Leir had a quick temper, and lost no time in cursing Cordelia: 'If you are so cold, then out into the cold you will go, and take nothing with you! Goneril and Regan can rule half of Britain each, and take it in turns to look after me, and my army of one hundred knights. But you must be gone, for by all the Gods, you are no daughter of mine!'

Cordelia wept freely as she fled the country. But thankfully, a King of Gaul heard of the wisdom of the fair Princess, sought Cordelia out, and asked her to be his Queen.

Leir thought he would be happy in his retirement, staying with Goneril, but despite all her promises of love, she soon tired of the old man and his rowdy knights filling up her palace. She told her father that he was only allowed fifty knights at most, and would need to send half of his followers away.

Only one person in the land was allowed to speak their mind to the King – his Fool, a funny little fellow who told jokes as he sat on Leir's knee, and this time he laughed, 'When you split your crown in two, you did your third daughter a blessing, nuncle!'

Leir ignored his Fool, and turned on Goneril – he was not used to being told what he could or could not have! 'How sharper than a serpent's tooth it is to have an ungrateful child!' Leir yelled, and went on to curse Goneril twice as fiercely as he had cursed Cordelia, and rode out with his army to Regan's palace. His cry carried on the wind: 'I know where I'm wanted!'

But he was wrong – Regan was even less happy to put up with her old father than Goneril had been, and told him that she would only allow twenty-five knights – or maybe ten. 'How could you need any more?' she snarled.

'What do you know about NEED?' the old King wailed. Leir could see how wrong he had been to mistake Goneril and Regan's flattery for real love. In the greatest passion and with a voice of thunder, he cursed Regan worst of all. 'Strike her young bones, ye gods!' he cried, and roared off into a mighty catastrophe of a storm that was brewing ominously across the land, Fool following in his wake.

Wind, hail, rain, thunder, lightning – it was no night to be out.

'BLOW, WINDS, AND CRACK YOUR CHEEKS!' Leir howled in the storm as he trekked his way across blasted heaths. The cruel gales blew his crown away, the cold rain soaked his fine clothes, and he was left as nothing but the poor, weak old man that he really was.

By now the Fool was Leir's last remaining servant, still mocking the old man's foolishness: 'Who is the King and who is the Fool?' he sang against the noise of the storm, 'This old man's not fit to rule!'

The wild storm made Leir truly mad as he raged at the elements – but if the wild weather showed him anything, it was that underneath his crown and all his fine clothes he was just a human being like everyone else. 'I have taken too little care of this!' the old man screamed, 'I thought I was everything, but I am just a poor bare creature!'

The Fool left the frail old man to make his way down to Dover, ready to sail for Gaul and beg forgiveness of poor wise Cordelia, who had been the most loving of his daughters after all.

But as he travelled, Leir realised just how kind people could be. When folk saw the broken old man limping along, they gave him food, and drink, and showed him the way. They were being kind not because he was a King, but because he was a fellow human being who needed help.

Leir and Cordelia were happily reunited, and the old man kneeled before his daughter in sorrow, begging her, 'Forgive and forget – I am a foolish, fond old man.' Together, Leir and Cordelia sailed back to Britain and triumphed over the cruel sisters Goneril and Regan in battle.

Once again, the old man was made King of Britain, from coast to coast. But this time, for his remaining years, he ruled with kindness, and valued honesty above all. When King Leir eventually died, clever Queen Cordelia ruled in the very same way. With tears for the father she always loved, she laid Leir to rest in a special temple beneath the River Soar, which flows through the city that almost bears his name to this very day.

THE END

LEICESTER

Open-minded historians place Leir's reign at circa 800 BC, although most insist that no such man ever existed, and that he was probably confused with an ancient pagan water god. But if there really ever was a Celtic chieftain of that name, a warrior with three daughters who caused strife by the way he divided his kingdom, and if this historical King was buried, as alleged, in a temple under the River Soar, the most likely spot would have been in the region of Leicester's Jewry Wall, a Roman ruin that makes for a fascinating trip to this day. Once there was a temple here dedicated by the Romans to their God Janus, but it would only have been built to displace an existing pre-Roman temple — and who would have been buried at Caer Leir but Leir himself? You can even complete a Shakespearean day out by visiting the nearby resting place of that other infamous King, Richard III.

goleicestershire.com

36

8. THE STOKESAY
KEY

South Shropshire

Once upon a time at least, there were two brothers. One was called Nordy, and the other has gone down in legend as Slop. They were very rich brothers, on account of the amount of jewels and gold doubloons they had punched out of unsuspecting travellers over the years and hidden away.

Nordy and Slop, you see, weren't normal brothers – THEY WERE REALLY UNPLEASANT GIANTS! Hundreds and hundreds of years ago, giants were becoming rare in Britain, but were still annoying – some of them were as big as eleven houses placed on top of each other, for no good reason. Nordy was over fifty feet high, and his little brother Slop was nearly sixty feet high. They lived on hills many miles apart in the county of Shropshire, halfway down the right-hand side of the Welsh border, and bellowed out to each other over the valleys, long into the night, neither wanting to let the other brother have the last word. Kings and peasants alike found it almost impossible to get much sleep when all this was going on.

'WHERE'S MY FAVOURITE JUMPER?' Slop would boom from his fort perched high on Titterstone Clee Hill.

'I USED IT TO WASH THE COWS!' Nordy would bellow from his home out on Norton Camp.

'WHAT, THE ONE WITH THE BUMBLEBEES ON IT?' the reply would echo, for miles around.

'YEAH. IT'S COVERED IN MUCK,' Nordy's offhand admission would reverberate through forest and valley.

8. THE STOKESAY KEY

'YOU DUNG-GOBBLER!' Slop would yell, and so on, and so forth. For years on end.

But nobody would dare ever ask these noisy giants to keep their din down, or the poor protestor would certainly be biffed, splotted and squished in a second by whichever brother fancied biffing, splotting and squishing them. Once squished, every penny the poor victim had to their name would be stolen away by the brothers, and safely stored in their enormous oaken treasure chest, hidden in the bowels of Stokesay Castle.

Whenever Nordy or Slop wanted to count their ill-gotten loot (or just to bask in their precious gold, as if the chest was a cold, hard, uncomfortable bath), they would get hold of the one and only silver key that would open the chest and stomp over to Stokesay. Then they would lift the entire Castle high up in the air, revealing the mighty treasure chest, and marvel at the riches inside. They never did any good with all their stolen gold – they only hoarded it up and fought over it.

That was until one day, roughly twenty-two-hundred-and-thirty-eight-years-four-months-and-a-week ago. Nordy had walloped an impressive sack of pearls and emeralds out of a terrified Earl of some kind, and wanted to add it to the Stokesay booty.

Slop had the key, so Nordy cupped his hands to his big slavering mouth and bawled out across the hills:

'OI, SLOP! I'VE GOT SOME NICE LOOT HERE, BOY, CHUCK US THE KEY OR I'LL CHEW YER EYES OFF!'

'ALL RIGHT,' came the reply, eventually. 'BUT JUST YOU WATCH OUT, I COUNTED EVERY LAST DOUBLOON ONLY LAST WEEK!'

You see, these lumbering, plug-ugly brothers did not trust each other one tiny bit. But, they had sworn an oath on their mother's very feet to share the treasure, so Slop removed the ornate silver key from a grubby bronze locket around his neck, took a running jump, and hurled it far off over the Shropshire hills.

The silver key twisted and glinted as it whistled through the air, turning and rolling high over the River Onny, to where Nordy stood, expectantly, by Stokesay Castle, and –

'SPLA-LOOSH!'

There was a deafening pause.

'WHERE'D THAT GO, THEN?' Nordy wondered to himself, ever so loudly.

'WHAT?'

'THE KEY, THE BLIDDY KEY, BOY, I DIDN'T CATCH IT!'

'GRRRAH! YOU COMPOST-HEADED EXCUSE FOR A GIANT,' returned Slop, and sprinted over to Stokesay to have a good look.

Nordy and Slop stomped around the county looking for the precious key, uprooting trees and terrifying villagers, but all to no avail whatsoever. They sent their pet Raven, Derek, out to search high and low, but not even his ever-beady eye could turn up the goods.

This was the point when Slop's patience reached its lowest ebb, and his suspicions were at their highest. He leaned over to his tired brother and whispered, so quietly that no one any further away than Dudley could hear:

'THAT'S FUNNY, THAT IS.'

'WHAT?'

'ALL THESE YEARS WE'VE BEEN HURLING THAT KEY BETWEEN US, AND NOT ONCE HAS IT BEEN LOST.'

'YEAH. FUNNY.'

'YOU'VE POCKETED IT, HAVEN'T YOU?'

'DO WHAT?'

'YOU'VE DECIDED TO KEEP THE KEY TO YOURSELF, SO YOU DON'T HAVE TO SHARE THE GOLD AND JEWELS AND SHINY THINGS.'

'SHUT YOUR GOB, YOU! YOU CHEEKY LITTLE PIG-SNOGGER! REMEMBER, WE SWORE AN OATH ON OUR MOTHER'S FEET!'

'YES WE DID, AND YOU'VE BROKEN IT!'

And that was when the argument got really nasty.

So where was this silver key? Well, it had landed with the previously mentioned 'SPLA-LOOSH!' right into the Stokesay Castle moat, where it sank down past the marestails and watersnails, right into the parlour of the home of a pair of newts, known as Newton and Newtoo.

'I say, what's this?' asked Newton, aloud.

'What's what, old brother of mine?' asked Newtoo in return, from the kitchen where he was rustling up a tasty marestail risotto for them both.

'This big shiny ornate thing. It looks like a sword, or perhaps a sceptre or something.'

Newtoo came into the parlour and marvelled at the lovely silver key his brother was brandishing.

'Gosh, yes, pretty, isn't it?'

'Yes it is, do you want it?'

'Well, you found it matey!'

'I know, we'll share it!' said Newton. And that's precisely what they did. The Stokesay Key was placed above their mantelpiece, and the friendly newts often took it in turns to take it down and play with it, with never a cross word.

Meanwhile, above the moat, things turned from ugly to positively hideous. 'FIRST YOU COVER MY FAVOURITE JUMPER IN COW MUCK, AND NOW THIS!' yelled Slop, loud enough to wake the King of Siam even after an especially exhausting day's being the King of Siam.

'DON'T YOU DARE, POO-NECK!' Nordy roared back – but the angry Slop did dare. He raised his knotty club high above his stupid head and brought it crashing down on Nordy's. The stunned elder brother staggered slightly as a big lump appeared on his head. Then he smashed his own mighty club into his brother's belly with a crack.

And that was just the beginning. The two angry giant brutes stayed on that spot, bashing and biffing and bludgeoning each other for weeks on end, until finally Nordy flopped to the ground... and didn't get up.

However, Slop was in no better shape, and sank to his knees next to his brother. Before he passed out, he put Stokesay Castle back over the chest, and with his last breath, commanded the shrewd Derek to keep a watch over the treasure, until such time as the key should show up. Then he lay down with Nordy, and the two silly brothers never arose ever again.

A forest of fir trees grew up over them, and both Nordy and Slop were soon forgotten. Everyone in the county of Shropshire breathed a sigh of relief that, at last, they could get a good night's sleep.

Stokesay Castle is very different nowadays – a man called Laurence of Ludlow bought it as a fixer-upper, and Time has added a half-timbered gatehouse and posh panelled chambers, not to mention a shop where you can buy ice-lollies and cuddly dragons.

But do watch out if you ever go to Stokesay in search of Nordy and Slop's treasure, because somewhere, Derek the Raven will be keeping his ever-beady eye on you, determined that the giants' riches will never be found. And you'd be wasting your time anyway because, although the moat at Stokesay Castle is now bone dry, you can be sure that somewhere, the descendants of those two polite newts still share that lovely key, fifty-fifty. Because that's how brothers should be.

THE END

SOUTH SHROPSHIRE

Stokesay is six miles north of Ludlow, and although not an ideal place to try and reach on foot, you can take a train to Craven Arms only a mile or so away and head south, which provides a wonderful walk on a sunny afternoon. The castle itself, taken care of by English Heritage, is open for weekend visits all year round, and is open daily throughout the summer. The timbered 13th-century building may be of more interest to adults than children, but as the setting for pretend sword fights, you could do no better. Besides, the hills surrounding the castle provide 360 degrees of breathtaking views. So Nordy and Slop were good for something, after all.

shropshiretourism.co.uk

---

9. THE BROWN BEAR OF THE GREEN GLEN

The Western Isles

T he following tale of the chilly north was originally loudly told to me in a snug corner of Inveraray, in the Western Highlands. To tell the truth, however, a sweet smell hung thickly in the air, and empty jars of Scotch whisky clanked around the feet of the giggling tinker as he unveiled the story to me. You will just have to make of it what you will.

It seems that there was once an old, poorly, mangled King who had three sons. The twin elders, Angus and Donald, were vain and selfish, but as they would snort, 'At least we're not stuuuupid, like Graeme!'

Prince Graeme was the youngest, and though he suffered uncomplainingly under the name of 'Stupid Graeme', he was far from it. He was, however, quite terribly shy and quiet.

One grey day this elderly King brought his three sons together and croaked, 'Boys, I am knackered. No, do not interrupt lads, the doctors say I'm done for. My eyes are crossed, my back is bent and even my beard stings a bit. Quacks tell me that nothing can be done – well, short of one thing…' Prince Graeme leaned forward to hear what it was – his two elder brothers weren't really interested, but they pretended to show some concern just in case. 'I must eat the fruit of The Tree Of Feeling A Lot Better! Nobody has plucked goodies from that tree for many a century, if indeed it still exists. It's somewhere on the Green Isle, and the

Green Isle itself is always hidden by fog and mist and hard to reach. So you see, I'm not long for this world.'

On hearing this, Graeme had already vowed to do all he could to bring that fruit to his father. Angus, however, had his own idea, and not being shy, he was the first to speak up: 'Father, we shall go forth and find that fruit for you, and heal you so that you can rule over us all for years to come.'

'And years!' Donald added.

'I said years!' Angus snapped back.

'M-me too!' Graeme whispered, but they all ignored him, as they always had done.

And so, early the next day the three Princes set off to find the magical healing fruit, Angus and Donald galloping off on their fine steeds, and Graeme clip-clopping out from the castle on his faithful donkey, Martin.

Arriving at the first town westwards, Graeme was not at all surprised to find his two brothers guzzling at the bar of the inn, bragging to all and sundry about their quest.

'… And once we've done that, of course, I shall be a cert for King!' Angus brayed.

'No, that will be me who's King, brother,' Donald interrupted.

'No no, I'm the elder by a full five minutes!'

'But I'm taller by a whole quarter-inch, and that's how we decide things in the Western Isles!'

'Since when?'

Graeme coughed.

'Oh, it's you,' Angus sneered. 'I don't know why you bothered to set off at all, little Graeme, you're too stupid to find your own toes, let alone The Tree Of Feeling A Lot Better. Why don't you run back home for a nice warm cup of milk and have an early night?'

'Don't you worry, boys,' Graeme stammered. 'I won't be holding you up, you just go ahead and I'm sure you'll both find the Tree before me.'

And with that, he left them – but he knew they had no intention of really finding the Tree. All they wanted was for their father to die so they could fight over the crown themselves. Graeme, on the other hand, was on a mission.

9. THE BROWN BEAR OF THE GREEN GLEN

Eventually Graeme and the tired Martin found themselves in a knotty and deserted wood, and it was time to give up travelling for the day. Martin was happy to rest and chew on the odd tasty thistle, but Graeme knew he had to be more careful, and so he climbed up into a tree to make his bed.

However, he hadn't so much as closed his eyes when he felt the trunk of the tree quake, and there below him he saw a big brown Bear, pawing at the bark.

'Come on down, Prince, I won't hurt you!' the Bear growled.

Graeme may have been shy, but of course, as he shouted down to the Bear, 'I'm not stupid! You'll eat me!'

'No I won't, Graeme, I have better taste than that!' the Bear returned. 'Come down here or I'll climb up there!'

'You're too big to climb up here, you big teddy!' Graeme laughed, with unusual bravery for him. But as the Bear decided to show him what's what, and the tree began to sway from side to side, he changed his mind. 'Okay, okay, I'm coming down! You'd better be as good as your word, Bear!'

Luckily, the Bear was. In fact, having discovered that the shivering Prince had not even had any tea, the Bear caught and cooked a salmon to share over a roaring campfire. And when they were both full, he invited Graeme to lie down in his furry warm embrace, the safest place in the forest.

'You'll have no fear of hunger or cold while we are friends!' the Bear told Graeme, and so the Prince happily drifted off to sleep.

In the morning, the bossy but wise Brown Bear already had Graeme's mission mapped out for him. First he gave Graeme a warm bowl of porridge for his breakfast, then he kindly sent Martin back to the castle with an extra carrot, and finally he said to the shy Prince, 'Get on my back, and let's go, we have crazy miles to travel.'

Graeme had already learned that the Brown Bear was not to be argued with, so on he got, and with just a few mighty leaps, from isle to isle, the miles flew past.

Eventually the Bear dropped Graeme off at the house of a vicious Ogre, telling him, 'If this Ogre gives you any trouble at all, just tell him that The Brown Bear of the Green Glen dropped you off here.' And with that, in a single bound Graeme's fuzzy saviour was gone.

Banishing every single drop of shyness which had held him back for so long, Prince Graeme knocked at the mighty oak door of the Ogre's house, and just about managed to keep his heart from bursting with fear when a huge slavering beast stood in the doorway, clearly ready to bite him in two and spit out the halves.

'WHAT DO YOU WANT, YOU LITTLE PINK PRINCE?' the Ogre bellowed. 'GET OUT OF HERE BEFORE I SQUISH YOU.'

'Well it was the Brown Bear of the Green Glen who dropped me off here,' Graeme replied, 'And the Bear said it would not go well with you if you were impolite to me.'

'Well why didn't ye say so?' Instantly, the Ogre's manner was completely changed. With a hearty laugh, he welcomed Graeme in and gave him dinner and a fine feather bed.

In the morning, the Ogre sent Graeme out of the door, telling him, 'Just wait two minutes and an Eagle will swoop down before you to eat the nuts off my hazel tree, there. Take a knife and cut a wart off her ear, and you will...'

'Whoa whoa whoa!' Graeme, shy no more, had had enough of this. 'Cut a wart off an Eagle's ear? What is this daftness? Eagles don't even have ears!'

'IF YOU WEREN'T FRIENDS WITH THE BROWN BEAR OF THE GREEN GLEN, I'D REALLY ENJOY STAMPING ON YOUR HEAD. JUST DO AS I SAY.' With that parting shot, the Ogre slammed the door and went back to his knitting.

No sooner had he gone than an enormous Eagle swooped down just as predicted. Graeme had to admit he had been wrong – there, bulging on one side of her head was an enormous wart, which he sliced off with one swipe.

'Ohhh, that's so much better!' the Eagle sighed. 'Now, get on, Prince Graeme, and let's get going.'

Graeme was long past wondering why every mythical creature seemed to know all about who he was and what he was up to, and mounted the Eagle without question, grabbing handfuls of feathers to steady himself as the gigantic bird swooped off into the clouds.

The Green Isle was every bit as green as its name suggested, once the pair of them had flown through the mists and landed safely on the mystical scrag of land. There, Graeme found The

9. THE BROWN BEAR OF THE GREEN GLEN

Tree Of Feeling A Lot Better and filled his pockets with the precious fruit, which hung in great profusion, shining and golden. Not only that, he found a jar of whisky that would never run dry, and a wheel of cheese that never went off, and above all, he found the Princess of the Green Isle, and in a completely unrealistically short space of time, the two fell insanely in love with one another.

Before long, however, Graeme had to return home to save his poor father, and the Eagle was impatient to leave. Prince Graeme promised to return for his Princess, and with one final kiss, he was whisked all the way back to the castle.

There, however, having said his goodbyes to the Eagle and asked her to pass on his thanks to the Brown Bear, Graeme met his cruel older brothers. They had long ago given up on their quests and were just hanging around waiting for their father to die – and arguing about who would be first in line when he did.

When they saw how clever their so-called stupid brother had been, Angus and Donald did not flinch. They bashed poor Graeme on the top of his head, stole his fruit and threw him into the blacksmith's trash-pile, where the poor lad was scraped and scratched with the rusty metal, leaving him blind, deaf, dumb, bald and completely unrecognisable!

With snorts and sniggers, the frankly horrible Angus and Donald set off to claim Graeme's rewards for themselves.

Finally fully fortified by the golden fruit, it was not too long before the King appeared grinning before all his happy subjects to announce to the world who would be the next in line to the throne. 'I am so sad that my poor shy little lad Graeme could not be here as well,' the King said, 'But then he always did seem a wee bit dim...'

'Not at all, your Kingness!' cried a voice from the crowd. As the King goggled, the crowds parted to reveal the Brown Bear of the Green Glen, and sitting on his back, the Princess of the Green Isle, with a remarkable chaffinch sitting on her head. 'It was Prince Graeme who found the golden fruits that saved your life, majesty!' said the Bear. 'The poor Prince also found that whisky and cheese your two elder sons seem to be enjoying. I,

The Brown Bear of the Green Glen, know this well, and Princess Morag here can prove it. Princess?'

The angry Princess stood on the Bear's back and roared, 'This chaffinch belongs to me, Morag, the Princess of the Green Isle! And it will only fly to the man that I love! To the Prince who truly deserves your throne! Fly away, Sharon!'

And Sharon the chaffinch flittered around the crowds, over the heads of Angus and Donald (being sure to enjoy a nice relaxing poo on them as she went), and alighted on the head of a very sad looking poor blind, dumb, deaf, bald figure who was slumped outside the Blacksmith's forge.

'GRAEME!' chirped the lovesick Princess Morag, and ran to his side, covering his poor scratched face with healing kisses.

As happiness was now assured for everyone but the ill-deserving elder brothers, there remains little to tell you. The Brown Bear of the Green Glen hugged Prince Graeme, and in a flash all his ailments disappeared. He then hugged Princess Morag, gave Sharon a wink, and leapt off into the wide grey yonder once again, crying, 'If ever you need a huge brown magic Bear, you kids know where to find me!'

The foul Princes Angus and Donald were flown by the Eagle directly to have tea with the Ogre, and were never heard of again, and the King ruled for several more years. But there to follow him on the throne was the jubilant, not at all shy or bald Prince Graeme, and his love, Princess Morag of the Green Isle.

They were married, and the wedding party was awash with never-ending jars of whisky and wheels of tasty cheese, and the celebrations went on for seven days and seven years. That sounds like a long time for a party, but the guest of honour was The Brown Bear of the Green Glen, and with him around, the party never stopped.

THE END

THE WESTERN ISLES

Nobody really knows where the Green Glen was, but although the famed folklorist Joseph Campbell did learn this very silly old saga from a tinker in Inveraray, a town on the shore of Loch Fyne, the Brown Bear's leaping

9. THE BROWN BEAR OF THE GREEN GLEN

from isle to isle may as well include the whole range of islands which fan out from Scotland's west coast, as messy and magical a cluster of lands as the tale itself. Which isle will you choose to land on first?

explore-western-isles.com

10. THE HEDLEY KOW

Hedley on the Hill, Northumberland

L ife has always been very difficult for the poorest people in our society, since the very day money was invented. It's not as if money is the secret to happiness, not by a long chalk, but when a crust of bread is hard to find, it will always be a challenge for most people to find a smile for the neighbours.

But one poor woman of the Northumberland village of Hedley-on-the-Hill was always known for her warm smile, despite being by far the poorest person for many miles around. She only scraped a mouthful of food every day by running errands for the local farmers' wives, and collected firewood from the wayside as she travelled.

Some of the less kind farmers' wives put her smiling down to sheer stupidity, but the poor woman was not one bit dumber or smarter than the best of them – what the snooty wives did not realise, with their posh houses with no holes in the roof and all the food they could eat, was what really matters in life, and how easily happiness can be found if you look in the right places.

Some folk believe that fortune has a habit of rewarding the poor and virtuous, and this seemed to be the case when one day this lady was on her way back from scrubbing one farmer's doorsteps until they shone (for which she was only given a slice of cheese and an apple). As twilight began to fall on the road up to her home, the poor woman tripped over some kind of boulder in the road. That doesn't sound

49

like good fortune, but when she picked herself up and examined the boulder, she saw it was an old pot brimful of...

'GOLD!' The woman gasped. 'That's what that yellowy shiny stuff is, I have no doubt, though I've never seen it before. I thought it would be a nice pot to put a flower in, but blow me! Well, I suppose this means that all my worries and hardships are over at last. Stroke of luck, really.'

She looked about her to see if anyone had dropped the pot, because she could never happily just take such a golden treasure as her right, but there was nobody to be seen. She knew it would not be easy for her to carry the huge pot of gold up to her humble hovel, strong though she was, but she tied her shawl to a corner of it, and turned up the road to begin dragging it slowly homewards, wondering what on earth she would do with all her new riches.

'Well I do be feeling rich and grand!' she said to herself, occasionally looking back to check that the pot wasn't leaking its riches all over the road. 'With all this yellow stuff, I shall be able to live like a Queen. One of the posher Queens, indeed! How very grand! Or maybe I could bury it in the garden and just use it when I need to. Or maybe...'

She puzzled away to herself, until it was time to stop for a rest and have another look at her pot of gold. But when she pulled it in with her shawl, she saw it was no longer a pot, but a big round silver ball! How had she been so mistaken?

'What a daft girl I must be to mistake a round silver ball for a pot of gold! But nevertheless, this is all to the good for me really. Gold attracts thieves after all, and there was far too much for me to cope with. This pretty ball will be much safer, and is still well worth having! How very grand!'

And with that, she continued on her way, the ball rolling along behind her – which also made it easier for her to get up the hill. She was very content.

Until, that is, she felt the going hard once again, and after a mighty tug, she looked behind to find that her silver ball had been turned into...

'A lump of iron? Now that is the very best of good fortune!' she smiled – iron was worth quite a bit of money in those days. 'This will be so much easier to sell and harder to steal. I'd never have got a wink of sleep with all that gold or silver clogging up my house. This will get me plenty of pennies and far less trouble, for all that it's a little heavier. Aye, I do feel rich and grand.'

The poor woman was nearly home by this time, so she merrily returned to dragging her iron lump towards her hovel, whistling a happy tune as she went.

Coming into her own neighbourhood, she took another look behind her, just to be sure that the iron was still there, as she told herself. But this time there was no iron. She saw nothing but a rather ordinary-looking rock, dawdling along behind her on her stretched and ragged shawl.

This caused her to pause for a moment. And scratch her head. Finally, she said, 'Now that is JUST what I have been looking for to keep the front door open on the hot summer days! It couldn't be better for me! Now that is grand.'

And with that, she picked up the rock to hurry to her home and see how it looked propping open her door. But no sooner had she stepped through her broken old gate than the rock in her arms let out an almighty giggle, and wriggled out of her grasp.

In the murkiness of her front yard she stood agape as the rock unfurled itself, first two long straggly legs poking out, then two more, then a long neck like a giraffe, but with a giant horse's head atop, and shining eyes blazing out at her, and finally a long, luxurious tail. This tail twitched in the twilight as the Hedley Kow laughed fit to burst at the poor poor woman.

'Hohoho! You stupid poor woman, you thought you had found all the riches of your dreams, but you have been fooled by none other than THE HEDLEY KOW! And now I shall laugh at you for a very long time!'

The poor woman stared in astonishment at the magical shape-shifter as it whinnied and chortled, and pointed at her with a foreleg. Finally, she spoke.

'Well, blow me down, back up, and then blow me away!' she smiled. 'This really is the luckiest day I ever did see. Who would have thought that I would ever get to see the Hedley Kow with my own eyes! I shall dine out on this for the rest of my life. Oh, I do feel so GRAND.'

And with that, she went into her hovel to sit by the fire and think about her good luck. The door slammed in the Hedley Kow's face, and very silly indeed he felt.

From that day forward, the pesky Hedley Kow learned never to play such silly tricks on honest folk. And the poor woman remained poor, and remained happy, and she smiled. Only stupid people thought that this made her stupid.

THE END

HEDLEY-ON-THE-HILL

As the poor woman's happy surprise shows, you would have a very hard time if you went to her village expecting to find the Hedley Kow just like that. After all, it could look like anything, from a tree to a traffic warden! But that's no reason not to give it a try, not least when the quaint village of Hedley on the Hill has so much to offer, being right in the middle of Hadrian's Wall country, a World Heritage site way up in the very north of England. It's a singular village, strangely untouched by the disasters and wars which kept its neighbours moving with the times, being a place of peace through all the battles on the borders. And if the gorgeous views of the Tyne valley are not enough to tempt you to make the journey up, why not pay a visit on a bank holiday, when the Great Hedley Barrel Race has been staged for eons? Villagers compete in a race up the hill while carrying a nine-gallon beer barrel to the finish line... Nobody has yet reported any barrels transforming into the Hedley Kow. But nobody has ruled it out either.

visitnorthumberland.com

11. VENGEANCE WILL COME

Lake Bala, Snowdonia

The folk of Wales seem to have a thing for 'lost lands' – which perhaps makes sense when you consider that they've had more than enough land stolen from them in Britain's history. Telling two tales about Welsh palaces flooded into legend may seem over-generous, but this yarn does have a certain flavour all of its own, and it was originally told by the very clever Taliesin the Bard, so should be worth remembering...

As Taliesin told the tale, this must have happened many thousands of years ago, but once there was an old town called Bala, in what is now Snowdonia, in North Wales. Don't go looking for it, you won't find a single slate of that ancient Bala, just a rebuilt new town of the same name – near where Taliesin himself lived as a young boy. This modern town is on the shores of Lake Bala, a vast, deep pool, said to be the only place you will meet the endangered gwyniad fish, no less.

Down in the hollow where that lake now lies, there was once a fine slate-roofed settlement, overshadowed by the opulent palace of Llyn Tegid. This was where the wicked Tegid Foel was King. His name means 'Bald Tegid', but while he was King, everyone told him it meant 'Brilliant Tegid', because if this miserable old ruler ever realised that everyone knew full well that his big blonde mop of hair was a wig, and made fun of his shiny slaphead behind his back, he would have ordered the entire town to be put to the sword, axe, and whatever sharp thing was generally to hand.

11. VENGEANCE WILL COME

That might sound like a bit of an overreaction, but King Tegid prided himself on his evil. From the moment he opened his beady eyes to the last bogey he flicked at his servants before bedtime, everything he did was unpleasant, immoral, selfish, spiteful or just plain wrong.

One day, the horrid old King was told that his daughter had given birth to a son, and he was a grandfather at last, with a male heir to rule Bala when he died. Not that his daughter couldn't have done a much better job as ruler than him anyway, but he'd decided that only men could take the throne because, quote: 'Girls are only good for having male babies.'

King Tegid the nasty wig-head announced to the people of Bala: 'As we are now a grandfather, we have decided to throw a HUGE PARTY. It will be a grandfather party, all for me. It's gonna be the best, everyone, just the best party there's ever been. We'll have the best food, the best booze and the best music. We're gonna have no squealing babies, oh no, absolutely no girls, and I will only invite all of my most evil and villainous colleagues! None of you dirtbags are invited, it's just the best for the best of the best. It's gonna be the best.'

And so that was what happened. Invites went out to the evil Wizard Growlmouth, Horrible King Larry of Ruislip, the witch Grotbogies, the positively stinking warrior Dumbum the Stranger-To-Soap, and a few other cruel characters from neighbouring kingdoms. On a rainy Saturday night, these bad eggs all travelled out to Bala's palace to find a feasting room packed with wild boar, suckling calves and fat chickens, all cooked so rare they weren't just dripping blood, some of them were still blinking. There was a huge extravagant bath filled with strong wine, into which the guests dipped the skulls of their enemies or close family members and drank deep. Soon this bad lot were carousing evil songs like 'I Love Hurting Puppies' and the chilling ballad, 'That Girl From Rhyl (Who I Ate For Supper)'.

These songs were requested with blood-dripping roars from the drunken mob. And, like it or not (and the answer was definitely not!) the poor musician just had to play along.

There was only the one musician – Ilid the Harpist – and she was also the only woman allowed at the party, besides Grotbogies, who barely counted as human. In fact, the noise was so bad from the howling guests that most of the folk of Bala had all gone away for the weekend, so she was one of the only women left in the whole town. Ilid the Harpist was, as her name suggests, a wonderful player of that most Welsh of musical instruments, the tinkling Welsh harp. Not that any of her skilled plucking could be heard above the din of the drunken baddies, but at least while they were bawling ballads they weren't shouting abusive threats her way, calling her 'babes' or 'toots', or making unforgivably rude suggestions.

For poor Ilid, it was a gig, anyway. And she knew that if she'd said no to the King, he would only have killed her family, so she was just trying to make the best of a bad night. However, Ilid was not exactly playing at her best that evening, partly because of the hideous party guests, but mainly because she kept getting distracted by a strange green bird who was flapping about the rafters, singing something.

'Hey! Somebody shoot that nasty little bird!' roared King Tegid, and his despicable guests twanged off a few arrows, but were so sodden with wine they missed by a mile. They couldn't even hit the bird when it flew down onto the feasting table, looked King Tegid right in the ugly mush, and sang:

'Vengeance will come!'

'Someone squash the warbling little tit!' roared the King.

'Did it say something?' one of the drunken guests said.

'Course it didn't SAY anything, you chuntering old bucket of pus!' spat back the King, 'It's a gods-damned bird!'

But somehow Ilid couldn't stop herself: 'It said, "Vengeance will come", I'm sure!' she piped up. She was bedazzled by the little green bird's song and beautiful glistening plumage, and had quite forgotten her place, and the dangerous company she was keeping.

'Keep your slattern gob shut, you harpist harpy!' fired back King Tegid. He felt quite pleased with that one.

'Vengeance will come!' sang the bird again, and flew back up to the rafters.

'There it goes again,' Ilid said, 'Vengeance will come!'

The King spluttered, his wig slipping on his shiny bonce. 'It was just a warble! I'm not paying you to use your imagination, am I?'

'You're not paying me at all, you just said you'd set fire to my parents if I didn't show up!' she replied.

'Yeah, well, I still might, especially if you don't stop making stuff up and keep your fat trap shut. I never got to be King by using my imagination.'

'Vengeance will come!' trilled the green bird once again.

11. VENGEANCE WILL COME

'Now I hired you to play the harp, and play the harp you will. Let's have a chorus or four of "I'd Like To Rip Open The World's Guts!" Huh, what d'ya say, guys? Hyah-hyahaha!'

It was one of Ilid's least favourite songs, but once the boozy gathering had begun yelling a few lines so off-key they were inventing new keys, it was clear that nobody was really listening to her harp playing anyway. Yet she could still hear one more 'Vengeance will come!' trilling from the wondrous green bird as she spied it flying out of a top window. Ilid never knew why, but she just had to follow that little songbird. She stood up, slipped out of the great hall and dashed into the welcome fresh cool night air.

'Vengeance will come!' she heard, whistled from the courtyard, and saw the bird fly along the drawbridge, beyond the town of Bala, and uphill. When Ilid arrived at the brow of the banks surrounding Bala, the green bird stopped, and flapped down onto her shoulder. This time it did not say 'Vengeance will come', but sang the most enchanting melody in her ear. It was a rare treat for Ilid to have music played for her rather than the other way around, and this gentle trilling soon sent her into a deep sleep in the thick warm wet grass...

When Ilid the Harpist awoke the next morning, she was astounded to find herself lying on the banks of a large lake, lapping at the shore, with no sign of Bala at all! The only thing she did see was her Welsh harp, which floated on the water and came within easy distance for her to pull out of the lake. With one tinkling strum – brrring! – she could tell it was unharmed.

Soon she ran into a large gaggle of discombobulated Bala townsfolk, and learned what had happened – as all the despicable party guests got drunker and drunker, the ancient well in the castle courtyard suddenly began to gush with water like never before, and simply never stopped until the whole town of Bala was drowned, right up to the tips of the chimney pots! Thankfully everyone who wasn't on holiday or passed-out drunk at King Tegid's party had managed to scramble up into the hills, and the good people of Bala were all accounted for.

The survivors decided that they would all join together to build a new town, free from the cruelty of King Tegid – and so they did. And while they worked away, hammering, sawing and laying slate with light hearts, they were entertained by the beautiful music of Ilid the Harpist.

When they listened very carefully, they could also hear a small high voice singing along – 'Vengeance has come! Vengeance has come!'

THE END

LAKE BALA

This area of North Wales is just so rich in beauty, in mythology and indeed in exciting action holiday options, you could pick almost any spot to set up camp and explore the region, its stories and legends. Bala Lake alone has given us two stories for our collection — see Taliesin the Bard! This tale comes from the Mabinogi, of course, and is also told of the drowned town of Kenfig in Glamorganshire, to the south. But there are more recent drowned towns in Wales as well — Capel Celyn in Gwynedd, for instance, was turned into a reservoir to serve Liverpool only fifty years ago. Bala is actually a natural lake, the largest in Wales, but when visiting it is tempting to listen out for the cry 'Vengeance will come!' Legend says that if you shout back, 'When?' the reply will come, 'In the third generation!' What that actually means is anybody's guess.

bala.org.uk

57

12. MOLLY WHUPPIE

Isle of Islay

I n the Western Isles, many people still remember the name of brave young Molly Whuppie, even though there have been more years since her time than there are twigs in the forest of Gearach. So many tall tales are told of Molly's bravery; some involve her leaping over mighty rivers, some fighting giants, but whatever the tale, nobody ever doubted her wit, wiles, kindness, and valour.

Molly was the youngest of three sisters who lived with their poor mother in a cottage on the isle of Islay, one of the biggest blobs of land in the Hebrides, which float off the west coast of Scotland. She was the smallest of the girls, and was regularly told she was not the prettiest; but although she tended to be ignored alongside her louder, bossier sisters, what she lacked in size she more than made up for in heart and brain.

At the end of one cruel winter the girls' mother had to solemnly announce that they were now so poor she could no longer feed them all, and it was time for the three sisters to go out and make their own way in the world. 'Once upon a time,' she told them, 'we Whuppies were rather rich, but all our precious family trinkets were stolen long ago by a horrible old pair of deeply nasty bogles, and hoarded away at the bottom of the old well at Trudernish. I'm too frail to attempt such a journey now, and so you, Polly, must be the first to set out to try and recover the family fortune.'

Molly's eldest sister was not happy – she'd rather have been combing her long hair or trimming her long toenails, but there was nothing to do but agree.

'I'll go and get our trinkets, Mother!' Molly Whuppie insisted, but nobody took any notice.

Before Polly set off, Mother Whuppie gave her a round, flat hunk of bread, rather like a scone, which was called a bannock. 'Now, Polly, my pretty,' said Mother Whuppie, 'You may take this whole bannock, or only half of it, along with my special blessing. Which is it to be?'

Polly was no fool – as she was often heard telling everybody! – and so she insisted on the whole bannock, and set off down the road in a huff.

Halfway to Trudernish, a trio of friendly crows flapped down onto Polly's shoulder.

'Now that there is a tasty-looking bannock, young lady!' they chorused, 'May we sample a few crumbs?'

'Away and plummet, crows!' scoffed Polly, 'This is my bannock – MINE, you hear? Go and peck at someone else's ears.'

With crowing laughter, the black birds flapped away, and Polly continued on to the well with her empty basket.

But when she arrived at Trudernish, she found that the well was padlocked and guarded by a very weird and worried-looking roly-poly lady, who lived in a hovel close by.

'I would love to let you help yourself to the well, my dear, but it's my husband!' the lady cried. 'Why oh why did I marry a bogle?'

'What actually is a bogle?'

'Sort of a troll, dear. A twisted and warty old git of a man,' returned the old wife, 'Covered in hair and stinking of kippers!'

'Well… yes, why did you marry him, then?'

'Oh, he caught me off guard with a compliment about my shoes, and the next thing I knew, we were wed and I was trapped! He jumped right down into my well and has been living there ever since, only coming out at night to find something innocent to eat for his supper! If you really need to have a nosy down in the well, you had better take this.' She gave Polly a big twisted wooden bat with a nail sticking through it. 'My old man's as short-sighted as a senile mole in a steam room. He pops out of the well at twelve midnight sharp, all you have to do is give him a bang on the head and help yourself!'

'Why don't you do it?' asked Polly with a sneer.

'Well he is my husband, hen,' returned the old wife. 'I did promise to honour him and all that, but there's nothing to stop you giving him a real old what-for!'

And with that, she bolted back inside her hovel and closed the shutters.

Gloomy Polly sat down by the well to wait, and gobbled up the whole expanse of her tasty bannock. It was a lot for such a youngster to eat, but finish it she did, and she soon felt full and very sleepy...

Back home the next morning, the Whuppie girls' poor Mother felt more unhappy than ever when she saw that her eldest, prettiest daughter had not come home laden with gold. She was quite an impatient lady.

'I will go and look for her, Mother!' piped up little Molly, but if anyone heard her, they did not bother to reply. In fact, her mother decided that Holly, her second daughter, would have to be the one to go out and find Polly, and manage what her big sister had failed to do. Holly was a ruddy-faced, sporty, outdoors type who would rather have been off hunting hares or kicking hamsters – but she knew there was no point in arguing. If anyone could find the riches, she hooted, it would be her. She took the enormous bannock rather than the special blessing, just like Polly before her, and set off down the path to Trudernish...

But the next morning, once again, there was no sign of Holly, or Polly.

'I told you, I'll be the one to restore the Whuppie fortune, Mother!' announced Molly. And so, it was with sheer desperation that poor old Mother Whuppie made one more bannock, and sent her smallest daughter off to the well at Trudernish.

There was one difference this time, though – little Molly told her mother that she would take only half the bannock, and her special blessing. Mother Whuppie was quite taken aback, and so pleased she gave Molly the whole bannock anyway, and kissed her at the door, her face awash with tears.

'Poor little Molly,' the frail lady sniffed as she watched her youngest girl stride off in the weak spring sunshine. She felt sure that the Whuppie family would never be together again.

A long way down the road, Molly Whuppie was visited by the three friendly crows, who perched on her shoulders and head, and exclaimed as one: 'You do look blessed! That there is a tasty-looking bannock, young lady! May we sample a few crumbs?'

'Well it is far too big for me alone,' reasoned Molly. 'Of course, help yourselves, my crow friends!' And she smiled as the hungry murder of crows took a slice (or scone) of the bannock out of Molly's hands, and gratefully gobbled down an equal piece each.

After such kindness, the crows did not fly away, but chatted and sang to young Molly as she made her way to the well. Once again, the silly old Bogle's wife accosted her visitor, and once again she explained about her villainous husband, and handed over the twisted old wooden bat, before disappearing back into her hovel.

'What a confused old joker!' thought Molly to herself with a smile, and sat down to eat her bannock by the well. Of course, she shared what she had with the crows once again, but despite this, once the bannock was all gone, she too felt full and sleepy...

In fact, if it hadn't been for the crows chatting with her, and occasionally playfully nipping at her ears, she may well have fallen asleep right there and then... and missed the BOGLE! As promised, on the stroke of twelve, the well covering blasted open and out jumped a huge, hairy, slimy, bogey-green monster with an evil leer on his chops. His eyes were like frogspawn, his teeth were like thorns, and his smell was... beyond any description. He STANK so fishily!

'WHERE'S ME SUPPER, MORAG?' the Bogle bellowed, and looked around for his usual midnight treat. But he wasn't quick enough to see young Molly Whuppie bring down the wooden bat with a THUNK on his ugly bonce! BOP-KER-SPLAT!

The Bogle didn't reel or stagger, he simply BURST with a cascade of rotten-kipper-and-poo-smelling gunk, which poured and slopped down into the well. And he was never seen again.

Luckily, the precious Whuppie trinkets were not spoiled by the Bogle's nasty slime, as Polly and Holly were still being kept prisoner down below, and they took the brunt of the smelly explosion. They were not exactly happy when young Molly wound them up to freedom in the bucket. The Bogle had also ravenously eaten their shoes, and they were so completely covered in stinky green slime that neither sister ever quite smelled right again.

Nonetheless, Molly filled Polly's basket with all the family heirlooms, coins, jewels and whatnots, and the three set off for home and their frail old mother.

12. MOLLY WHUPPIE

A little further along the road, the Whuppies were hailed by a very tall and goofy-looking posh Laird, accompanied by a couple of even goofier youths, all of them wearing rather silly kilts. The Laird had already heard of the Bogle's defeat, and wanted to hire Molly Whuppie for a special mission of his own.

'I am the Laird of all you see here, and these are my very aristocratic sons Ross and Gyles. I know they look rather goofy, but Ross is heir to all of this, and Gyles is very good at sport, you know – tossing cabers and suchlike, wrestling elks. I will give you your choice of either as husband if you can only defeat a bogle for me.'

'But I just defeated the Bogle!' Molly beamed, brandishing her bat and giving them a grin.

'No, this is that Bogle's third cousin thrice removed! He's no nicer or less smelly than the one you offed so impressively! This bounder has stolen my golden teapot, my golden eggcup and – if you'll excuse me mentioning it – my golden potty, and I want them back, blast it!'

The road to this Other Bogle seemed clear, and so all three Whuppie girls set off until they came upon an old tumbledown, or at least crumbledown, cottage.

'Is this the home of the Other Bogle?' Molly asked the frightened-looking scrawny old woman who answered the door.

'Aye, that'll be my husband!' Mrs. Bogle replied. 'Look, don't you judge me, girls. My sister married a bogle and I always just wanted whatever she had. Of course, I regret it noo…'

Despite such silliness, the old lady was kind-hearted, and could see how tired Molly, Holly and Polly were. She invited them in for the night, and they were given a bowl of porridge each.

The girls were also introduced to this strange Bogle couple's three 'daughters'. These weren't strictly speaking 'daughters', but big old dry and dirty lumps of muck roughly shaped into dolly form, with long shaggy wigs stapled onto the top of each one. They made a sorry sight.

'Well,' explained Mrs. Bogle, 'between my shyness, and my husband's, you know, total and utter hideousness, this was the best we could do to have children. Aren't they pretty?'

The Whuppie girls did not dare do anything but agree wholeheartedly, and soon all six 'young ladies' were put to bed, and the Whuppie sisters were snoring. However, Molly slept only softly, so she heard every word when the Other Bogle finally came home and began berating his wife for lending their bed to nasty little humans.

'Ah'm oot all day, killin' people in degrading ways an' stealing all their goodies, an I come home to this! Look what ah got for oor girls!' The Other Bogle produced three fine amber necklaces which Molly saw glinting in the candlelight through one squinted eye, and she formed a plan.

As swiftly as she dared, without making a sound, Molly rolled Polly and Holly over to the other side of the bed, swapping places with the mucky dolly daughters, and pushing her hair and that of her sisters up over the pillows so it looked just as if the Other Bogle's 'daughters' were lying right there. Bogles have terrible eyesight anyway, so Molly's plan worked a dream when the foolish old monster came along. He placed an amber necklace on each of the silent Whuppie sisters, and then grabbed the shaggy hair of the other three apparently sleeping figures in one of his huge gnarled fists.

'This is what ah think o' your hospitality, woman!' snarled the Other Bogle, and with a mighty swing he hurled his three dolly daughters out of the window and flying off to the moon, leaving him holding three rather filthy wigs. The dollies crashed to earth, and crumbled into dust.

'WHAT HAVE YOU DONE TO OUR GIRLS?' demanded the old lady, frail no more, but so suddenly wrought with rage that she took up Molly's own gnarled bat, and brought it down on her husband's head as hard as she could – BOP! Brown slime splurged out of his nose and all over the bed, but this Bogle didn't quite burst – he simply roared!

'OOOW! Whit did ye do THAT for, ya silly woman?'

'You just flung our daughters out the window! That's it, I want a trial separation! And I'm going to get one using this big twisted club with a nail through it!'

BOP! SPLAT! Once again, it was Polly and Holly who had to take the brunt of the splurge of smelly Bogle juice, and they were not very happy when they woke up. Or at least, they were not happy until they found the amber necklaces! Then they saw the Laird's other golden objects, the golden teapot, eggcup and potty, which Molly had found under the bed and wrapped in the bed sheet.

'Whisht!' Molly whispered as the Bogle couple argued, 'We need to get out of here – double quick, girls!' And the Whuppie sisters ran out into the night as hard as they could, with the fuming mad Bogle

12. MOLLY WHUPPIE

thundering out after them, and not too far behind him his angry wife, brandishing the big club with a nail through it.

'COME BACK WI' MA LOOT, YA LITTLE COOS!' he roared.

'COME BACK AND LET ME BURST YOU, YOU ROTTEN HUSBAND!' she yelled.

And they all ran, ran, ran, ran, ran! Soon the Whuppie sisters came upon a bridge, which started out strong and wide, but tapered down into a single hair's breadth! 'Keep running, as fast as you can!' cried Molly Whuppie, pushing her sisters ahead and violently hurling the bed sheet full of golden goodies with them before arriving at the perilous hair's breadth section of the bridge herself... and skipping over to the other side with one graceful leap!

'AW NOOO, BRING BACK MA GOLDEN POTTY!' roared the Other Bogle in hot pursuit, but of course he only got halfway along the bridge before his colossal weight snapped it right where he stood, sending him plummeting far below, landing in the valley with a final 'BANG-SPLAT!' that signalled he had finally burst once and for all.

His wife gazed over the edge of the broken bridge with a look of satisfaction and ran away into the night, yelling 'Agnes, what fools we were! Let's marry bogles no more!'

The Laird was ecstatic to have his golden riches returned, and Polly and Holly were also quite pleased when Molly explained to him: 'It's very kind of you to offer me a hand in marriage, Laird, but personally I would rather marry a bogle than either of your daft sons.' When Molly smiled, as she did at that point, it was hard to feel too offended by anything she said. 'But I'll tell you what, Polly and Holly here are clearly ideal matches for them both. They do smell just a wee bit kipper-ish, but...'

'WE LOVE KIPPERS!' chorused Ross and Gyles as one, and they all quickly fell in love without any fuss at all.

Once the marriages were agreed upon, everyone headed back to the Whuppie cottage and Molly's poor old mother at last. 'Home' had a lovely sound to it, but Molly, she was sure, had many other adventures lying ahead of her.

Later that evening, all the Whuppie women, the happy Laird and his daft sons sat down to tea with the biggest, tastiest bannock any of them had ever seen.

Of course, from then on the sisters made sure to share all their crumbs with the three friendly crows, who had helped kind, clever little Molly Whuppie live to see another day – and have many more adventures ahead of her, not all of them involving bursting bogles. As the crows flew off after supper, they promised to spread Molly's name and tall tales of her kindness far and wide throughout the Isles.

This story was their idea.

THE END

THE ISLE OF ISLAY

Molly's story is Celtic in origin, and as 'Maol a Chliobain', it was first recorded in John Francis Campbell's *Popular Tales of the West Highlands*. Although the fairytale isn't specifically tied to any one place, at least one version has been told by the folk of Islay for generations. It may not be that easy to pop out to the Hebrides for the afternoon, even if you live in Scotland, but for a holiday soaked in folklore, it is well worth making the pilgrimage one day. With thousands of years of history, Islay was once the seat of power for western Scotland. Known as 'the Lord of the Isles', it's a good place to base your holiday. Many people go to Islay and nearby Jura to visit one of the many famed whisky distilleries; and Scotland may have a reputation for the cold, but the Gulf Stream gives the surrounding islands a warm (for Britain!) climate all of its own.

islayinfo.com

---

13. THE SILKIE

Shetland Isles

The British Isles stretch so far out into the cold North Sea, bits of it are often surprised to find themselves being British at all. Way beyond Scotland are the distant isles of Shetland, and Orkney, caught between the icy waves of Britain and Scandinavia.

Oh, but the nights are cold and wet up there – it's no place to be alone. This is certainly what one lonely fisherman repeated to himself, day after day, as he landed his usual catch and returned to his lonely cottage on the northernmost isle of Unst every night.

This poor loner – some call him Herman, so let's go with that – was not exactly an ogre. He was quite young, tall, fit, and prided himself on a very well kept beard, by fisherman standards. But there was no denying he was very, very lonely.

One grey drizzly Friday Herman had landed his quota of cod and was about to set off home for another quiet weekend of rereading his book on kippers (the only book he owned), when he almost slipped on a grey glossy swimsuit which seemed to have been left on the craggy shore. Had somebody swum out to sea in this weather? He slipped the sealskin material into his bag and gazed out at the frothing waves.

Herman didn't think of himself as the bravest of men, but he was just preparing to strip off and try and find the poor mad swimmer when something highly unusual caught his eye – over on a small shingly beach were two totally nude people, dancing around and waving their legs, oblivious to the biting cold.

Not being primed to have the best manners, there was nothing Herman could do but goggle at this sight; but in no time at all the dancers had seen they were being watched, and to Herman's astonishment, one of them jumped into their own sealskin suit and flopped off into the sea in the shape of a seal, honking at their friend to join them as it dived beneath the waves.

Herman had heard old tales about so-called Selkie people, or as they were known in Shetland, 'The Silkie' – a happy tribe of part mer-person, part seal folk – but he never expected to see such a thing with his own eyes. His jaw dropped even lower when the other naked person swam over to where he was standing, and shiveringly asked him: 'Excuse me, Mr. Nice-Beard, but have you seen, um, a sealskin anywhere?'

This mermaid was without question the single most beautiful person Herman had ever seen. The fact is, if she had been presented at court hundreds of miles south in London, she would still have been considered a beauty above anyone else. But to a lonely fisherman like Herman, who only ever saw any other people once or twice a fortnight, and then they tended to be hairy, grizzled fishermen... Well, it will save a lot of time to admit that Herman instantly fell head over heels, then under heels, then over once again, in love.

He lied to the poor shivering girl at once, of course – his heart would not let him do anything else. After all these years, his dreams had come true! The strange naked lady – whose name turned out to be Eek! – accepted his warm coat and the two of them searched for the sealskin in vain, but as the poor confused young stranger wept streams of salty tears, Herman announced there was nothing for them to do as the light failed, but return to his cottage, where it was at least warm and he had plenty of kippers, and they would continue to search in the morning.

Except, to his shame, Herman hid that sealskin under a rock in his back garden, and nursed the poor distraught Eek back to health, forever knowing he was stopping her from returning to her own home. Love can make people do very bad things indeed, but, he reassured himself, at least it seemed that this mysterious woman was also falling for him – what else could she do? She had often wondered what life on the dry land was like, and now it seemed her lot to be marooned there forever more.

So Eek and Herman were married, and lived together in the cottage

13. THE SILKIE

for several surprisingly happy years. In time, two children, a boy and girl, were born – and didn't seem to have any visible flippers or anything like that – and so the strange courtship of the couple was almost forgotten…

Until one sunny day, when their young daughter, Yella, was playing in the back garden and… yes, you've already guessed – she innocently turned over a stone and found what seemed to be a wrinkled old grey skin of some kind.

'Mummy, what do you think this is?'

Tears had already begun to fall from Eek's sparkling eyes as she at last saw her precious Silkie skin, and knew that the time had come for her to return home. Silkies are not like us full-time humans, they have little room for emotion when the call of their home is hammering in their ears. But Eek did just have time to call her children to her, and give them one long, tight loving squeeze, saying, 'Your mother must return home, but I will never stop loving you.' Then she ran down to the craggy coast as fast as her human legs could carry her.

Poor old Herman was just in time to see his Silkie wife slip into her skin, and flop into the grey North Sea, where he could also just make out another honking seal on the horizon, waving for Eek to join them.

'EEEEEEEK!' yelled the heartbroken fisherman as the two seals swam off together, never to be seen again. But he was just too late.

Back at his cottage, he found a simple note, reading: 'Dearest Herman, I know now with what lies you kept me here as your wife, but I cannot say I was always unhappy here with you. Now the time has come to be myself again. Love our children well, and make them understand, as must you, that I am a Silkie, and Silkies belong in the sea. Goodbye. Eek!'

Herman held his two children close by, and cried a big salty tear – not of sadness, but gratitude for the happiness he had enjoyed. At least now he would never be lonely again.

Although he did often spend longer than usual at the end of every day's fishing, gazing out at the grey waves, hoping to hear a friendly honk.

THE END

SHETLAND ISLES

The Silkie tale is set about as far north as you can get in the British Isles, so it won't be a surprise to learn that the island of Unst is not an easy or quick place to get to. Many people do make the journey, however, to experience the most northerly inhabited islands of Britain, a heart-poundingly raw, rugged part of our country. There are flights to Shetland from numerous Scottish airports, and a ferry from Aberdeen, and it's rare you hear of somebody regretting the journey, the area is so packed with natural beauty and historical fascination. You may want to take some rain gear with you, though.

visit.shetland.org

14. TALIESIN THE BARD

Snowdonia

We owe so much to the bards. They were the keepers of the stories for all the ancient British tribes, and if it wasn't for the songs they sang, celebrating great battles and feats of derring-do, maybe Britain wouldn't have any stories to tell at all.

We all celebrate William Shakespeare, 'the Bard of Avon', as the nation's greatest poet, but by far the greatest bard of ancient times was a clever chap known as Taliesin. His power with verse was so strong he was said to have been a valued friend of a whole host of British Kings, including Bran the Blessed. But his beginnings were far more humble.

The bard's real name was Gwion Bach, or 'Little Gwion', and he was a lowly lad in service to a great enchanter named Ceridwen, who lived on the shores of Lake Bala in Snowdonia. She was said to have once been wed to none other than the wicked Tegid Foel, who drowned in his castle under the lake, but she was left with two children, a boy and a girl. Her daughter Creirwy was as clever and charming as she was beautiful, but sadly the same could not be said of Creirwy's little brother Morfran, and folk cruelly laughed that he looked like a plucked crow. This wouldn't have mattered so much had the boy been gifted with brains to make up for it, but his mother also had to admit that he had the intelligence of a mound of sheep poo.

Luckily, being a witch, Ceridwen knew what to do. She got out her magic cauldron and put in all the ingredients of a special potion – newt's noses, ferret's eyebrows, tomatoes, that sort of thing – which would eventually confer everlasting wisdom on anyone who drank the first three drops. However, all the rest of the brew would be poison.

This potion needed to be stirred almost constantly for a year and a day, and of course, the job fell to wee Gwion, while the fire beneath was tended by an old blind man with nothing better to do. This was exhausting work for the servant boy, but he did as he was told, until the recipe was finally ready.

Alas and indeed alack, at just that moment, three drops splashed out of the cauldron onto Gwion's hand, and he squealed in pain! Then, as he put his hand to his mouth to stop the burning, Gwion suddenly felt enormous power spreading from his finger, up his arm and throughout his body, coming to rest, of course, in his brain, which suddenly pulsated with a very clear and important wisdom. That wisdom was that the very powerful and very annoyed Ceridwen would KILL HIM when she found out what had happened.

Fortunately, the lad's new-found cleverness also gave him the excellent idea of grabbing Ceridwen's spare wand – a fine model carved from pear-tree wood – and the further idea of turning it on himself so he could change shape at will. Gwion tore off in the form of a hare, desperate to get as far away from his boss as possible. But Ceridwen was born clever, and after a wave of her own wand, she quickly took off in hot pursuit as a big slavering hound.

And so the chase went on – the boy turned into a salmon and leapt into the lake, but there was the angry enchanter in the shape of an otter, hot on his fins. Then he flew up into the air as a sparrow, but Ceridwen the sparrowhawk soon had him in her sights. Finally, exhausted, little Gwion tried to hide as an ear of corn – and his employer gobbled him up in the shape of a big black hen.

You'd naturally expect that to be the end of poor Gwion – very few people turn into an ear of corn, get eaten, and live to tell the tale. But all that new-found wisdom could not just die so easily, and he began to grow anew within Ceridwen, whose belly was soon swollen with the servant she wanted dead.

However, when the baby was born nine months later, and instantly began to sing so sweetly about how blue the sky was, and how green

14. TALIESIN THE BARD

the grass, and how white the sheep, even the mighty Ceridwen could not bear to do him harm. And so, she placed the baby in a leather coracle – a sort of round boat – and set him out to sea, where the fates could deal with him as they would.

Before long the baby was discovered by Prince Elffin the Unlucky, who had been heir to the lands of King Gwyddno before they were lost under the Irish Sea. The homeless Prince saw that the tiny singing baby was so clever that his head positively glowed, and so he called him 'Radiant Brow' – or, in the old language, 'Taliesin'. And this Taliesin sang:

'I am the one who will sing of your fame,
My songs are heard in the four-turret fort,
Forever to come, folk will know well your name,
And bring you an afterlife not to be bought...'

With clever Taliesin by his side, Elffin was no longer unlucky, and he won many wagers and horse races by following the young bard's advice. When Taliesin was old enough, he began to travel the land singing his songs and telling his tales, and performing services for the greatest Kings of all time, and he never had to turn into any animal, vegetable or mineral ever again.

To this day, folk follow in Taliesin's footsteps, and call themselves bards, continuing the tradition of storytelling and singing. They still get together every year at festivals called Eisteddfods, and when they do, you can be sure that glasses will be raised to the memory of clever Taliesin.

THE END

SNOWDONIA

When visiting Wales, Snowdonia has always been something of a no-brainer — the huge national park with its mighty mountain has inspired bards for millennia, and is a popular tourist destination to this day. We could have chosen so many Snowdonia tales for this collection, and the shores of Bala are like a magnet for folklore lovers. Perhaps more people go there for the hill-climbing than to stand on the spot where the servant

---

boy Gwion made his fateful cookery faux pas, because not everybody is clever enough to know about it… But now, you are.

visitsnowdonia.com

15. THE MARRIAGE
OF ROBIN
REDBREAST

Ayrshire

M any eons ago, when there were still Kings and Queens in the lands of Ayr in western Scotland, every peasant, merchant, animal and bird in the land owed their loyalty to the person with the crown. And when, as happened one snowy wintertime, the King of Ayr announced that he was going to get married, every creature was duty bound to help with the festivities.

None, however, was more important than the beloved Robin Redbreast, especially at the time of the Winter Solstice, when his bright ruddy chest and beautiful song was most highly prized. And so, one December 25th, Robin set off to the King's castle to sing for him upon his wedding day.

Robin had not flown far when he was called down to the ground by an old grey wildcat. Robin flapped down to talk to the four-legged stranger, but made sure to stay in the air.

'Where are ye going, wee Robin?' asked the cat.

'I'm away to the King to sing him a song this good yule morning, auld moggy!' chirruped Robin.

'Well that's grand. Afore ye go,' the cat purred in reply, 'just swoop down here and I'll show you the bonny white ring around my neck.'

Robin twittered a laugh. 'No, no! That may work on the mice, pussy, but it won't work with me! Cheery bye!'

And on he flew, towards the castle.

Feeling a little tired, Robin flew down to a windowsill to eat his tiny birdy sandwiches. Suddenly, mid-chew, he felt a big, scary presence next to him. It was an enormous kite! No, not the gaily-coloured flying toy, but a vicious-looking bird of prey.

'Ah, hellooo! Where are ye going, wee Robin?' asked the kite.

'I'm away to the King to sing him a song this good yule morning, auld Kite!' Robin chirped back.

'Good for you, son! Afore ye go,' the kite smirked, 'come over here and I'll show you this incredible magic feather I have in my wing.'

'No no!' Robin chuckled again, quickly flapping out of harm's reach. 'You greedy auld Kite, that might work with linnets and sparrows, but it won't work with me! Cheery bye!'

And away he sped once again.

Next, he flew over a craggy hillside with a burn – a Scottish word for a small, lively brook – which was bubbling away through the contours of the hill.

Robin paused awhile, as a cheeky looking laddie shouted his name: 'Hey, Redbreast! Where are ye going, wee Robin?' asked the laddie.

'I'm away to the King to sing him a song this good yule morning, wee laddie!' Robin replied.

'That sounds daft!' said the little boy. 'Afore ye go, why don't ye fly down here and I'll give you some breadcrumbs out of my pocket?'

But the Robin did not trust the laddie. 'No no,' he shot back, 'I'm no fool, you'll put me in a cage and I'll never fly again. Cheery bye!'

And with a single trill, he was gone once again.

Before very long Robin Redbreast flew up to the King's castle, where His Majesty and his bride-to-be were kissing on the ramparts, awaiting the arrival of their traditional Christmas guest.

'Aha, and where would we be today without wee Robin Redbreast?' smiled the happy King.

'We could not be wed until his song was heard!' his partner replied.

And as the royal bridegroom held his blushing bride in his arms, the little red-chested bird fluttered down to a small tree beside the lovers,

15. THE MARRIAGE OF ROBIN REDBREAST

and sang his heart out for them. It was the sweetest melody, warm and romantic, and as slushy as the snow was crisp:

'O my Love's like a red, red rose, that's newly sprung in June:
O my Love's like the melody, that's sweetly played in tune...'

When the final note of Robin's song had stopped echoing around the chilly ramparts, the Queen applauded, and said to her husband, 'My dear, what can we do to repay this brave Robin for his Christmas song? I think we should give him wee Jenny Wren to be his own wife, and they can be as happy as we are.'

'My darling, how are you always so right?' the King agreed, adding that this was the best idea he had heard, and knew that it would be one of many many great and wise ideas that his fair Queen would have over the years.

And so, that Christmas Day, Robin Redbreast and Jenny Wren were married alongside the King and Queen, and they sang together for the dancing at the party afterwards, and both couples lived long and happy lives together. No thanks to a certain cat, a kite and a cheeky wee laddie.

THE END

AYRSHIRE

The islands and coastline around Ayrshire need no added bonuses to be treasured holiday destinations — but the Bard of Scotland, Rabbie Burns, was born here in 1759, so as the home of Burns devotion, there are dozens of fascinating museums and sites to visit. 'The Marriage of Robin Redbreast' is an old tale that was told to Burns when he was a small child. You can also visit the mysterious Brodick Castle, but whether that was the site of Robin and Jenny's wedding, we cannot say for certain.

ayrshire-arran.com

---

16. JACK O'KENT
AND THE DEVIL

Abergavenny

There's a lot of confusion surrounding the old Welsh tales of Jack o'Kent. First of all, as you all surely know, Wales is the land beyond the western edges of England, which hides from the Atlantic behind Ireland's back. On the other hand, Kent is a county far off to the east, leering out towards the Low Countries. But the old wizard Jack o'Kent has remained famous in his Welsh home of Abergavenny for the longest time.

Abergavenny is a mysterious place of mists and mountains, a town built in the midst of seven hills – most of which seem to bear Jack o'Kent's signature, so great an enchanter was he. Some of the stranger locals insist that he stood several yards tall, with the sleekest of golden manes flowing into his luxurious beard in a way which thousands of years later would have been called 'so cool'. Everyone in Abergavenny knew Jack.

Most of Jack's tales also directly involve a grand nincompoop who is only known as 'The Devil', although in those backward days people called almost anything they didn't like 'The Devil', so this one could have been any kind of demon, boggart or general git. One thing's for sure, this 'Devil' bloke really had it in for Jack o'Kent.

Being such a clever spellcaster, Jack had no problem making this magical villain appear with a snap of his fingers, but to The Devil there was a different game afoot. He could not bear to think that anyone was cleverer than he was, and the way the villagers went on about Jack o'Kent's gigantic brain and genius wizardry every day, the demon knew he had to beat this charmer in a fair deal.

On his first meeting with the wizard, The Devil found Jack out in his wheat field happily sowing seeds, and watering every last one with a never-emptying watering can. Jack did not look at all surprised to see this peculiar little scarlet demon pop up, all horns and hairy bits, and was no more surprised when the stranger offered:

'Tell you what, clever-clogs-so-called-Jack-o'Kent, I can ensure that your seeds take root and grow in double abundance, and then we can split the crops fifty-fifty. What do you say to that?'

'Done!' Jack beamed, and The Devil shot back:

'Yes, you have been done, mate! I'm keeping the top half of the crop, and you can have the bottom! Hahaha!'

The top half of a wheat crop was of course the tasty bit, while the rest was just straw. And so, with a clearly well-rehearsed devilish laugh and a clap of thunder, the demon's twist was revealed.

'Oh dear, what a foolish Jack I have been!' Jack grinned, but what The Devil hadn't taken into account on this occasion was that Jack had actually been planting turnip seeds. And Jack was very happy, when harvest came along, to hand over useless turnip leaves to The Devil, as he filled his barns with the juicy turnip roots.

The Devil was not the kind of mythical figure to fall for that kind of prank two harvests running, obviously, and the next sowing season he made sure to call for 'bottoms!' the moment the self-same deal was struck… Just as surely as Jack o'Kent was certain to plant wheat that year.

Having got the measure of the silly demon by that point, Jack o'Kent was to outfox The Devil a thousand times over his long life – just ask the people of Abergavenny; there are dozens of stories featuring the two of them, and the silly games they played. They were said to have played bowls with giant boulders – a sport which Jack always won, while The Devil left a large gash on the mountain known as the Skirrid, when he tried to take his last shot and fell bum-over-horns into the valley below.

However, the final trick came when Jack wanted to build a bridge up in the clouds, from the tip of one mountain to another. He realised that he could only do something so dangerous with The Devil's help.

'Okay then, Jack, I will build you this bridge,' The Devil grinned, 'but I will have the SOUL of the first to cross it! Mwahahahahaha! Haha! Ho!'

Perhaps The Devil should have twigged that this deal had some flaws from the way Jack so quickly and smilingly agreed to it: 'You're on, my scarlet friend!' he laughed. But they shook hands on it, and The Devil nearly broke his back putting together the impossibly high bridge. When it was completed, there he stood on the Sugarloaf mountain, panting with exhaustion as Jack beamed at him from the other side.

'Lovely job, Devil, thank you!' cried Jack, and having admired The Devil's handiwork, he added just one word – 'FETCH!' – and hurled an old bone across the bridge, right into The Devil's yawning mouth.

Through the mist and across the bridge scampered Jack's ancient, yappy, slobbery and incontinent dog, Idris, and the happy mutt jumped on The Devil to give him the licking of his lifetime. The exhausted Devil had been fooled again.

But then, The Devil looked into silly old Idris' big brown eyes, and realised that what he had really always wanted was a furry pal just like him. And so, he granted Idris eternal life, and treats, and they disappeared into the mist together, happy to let Jack be. Certainly, nobody in Abergavenny heard of 'The Devil' again, and the great Jack o'Kent was happy to come and go across that bridge in the sky whenever he liked. Sometimes he can still be seen somewhere peeping above the mists high up in the Abergavenny hills, no doubt cooking up further clever-clogs plans...

THE END

ABERGAVENNY

Abergavenny is exactly as described in the tale — a misty town set amidst truly gobsmacking mountain views in every direction. There's even a stone circle to behold, created to celebrate the town's Eisteddfodd. Simply visiting for a pot of tea and to look at those majestic views is enough, but then of course there's the challenge of following in Jack o'Kent's footsteps,

16. JACK O'KENT AND THE DEVIL

and exploring the higher slopes... But it can be very dangerous up there, so be like Jack — and be clever!

visitabergavenny.co.uk

17. TAMLANE OF CARTERHAUGH WOOD

Selkirk

Much gossip has been spun about the beauty of the fairies, their earthy spellbinding appeal that can send humans mad... But then, just as often, we hear of humans who are so desperately desired by the fairies that they steal them away for forever and a day... So perhaps we do have something going for us after all.

Queen Titania, the almighty ruler of the Faerie Kingdom, is famous for her passion for the human form. She and King Oberon once had a terrible falling out over a small Indian boy who they both wanted for a servant. But it turns out he was not the only human desired by the Queen of the Faeries...

The vast forest of Carterhaugh, in Selkirk, not far north of the Scottish border, was once given as a birthday present to a young maiden called Janet. Her father, a wise local chieftain, told her tales of the forest's mossy beauty, its shadowy glens, mysterious trees and refreshing wells. But he also gave her a clear warning:

'Oh my dear Janet, be careful how you roam in the wood – if you see a white horse, it will belong to Tamlane, and you must flee from him without delay!'

'Why, who is he?' replied the curious birthday girl.

'A youth of beauty, or so the legend runs,' the old man replied,

17. TAMLANE OF CARTERHAUGH WOOD

'but a menace that no man can catch! It is said that any maiden who meets him in the wood loses something – sometimes it is a ring, sometimes a lock of hair... but more usually, it is her maidenhead.'

Janet's eyes grew large and wide at the thought of meeting such a brute, but she heeded her father's warning, and then set off on her pony to see her new wood all for herself.

The stories of Carterhaugh's intoxicating beauty were shown to be true to Janet after just a brief canter through the trees. Above all, the flowers took her breath away, and she happily rode through her property, picking the prettiest she could find.

But then she spied the most luscious of all – a red rose bush which blossomed in a clearing with an old stone well where the water ran fresh and clean. Dozens of the blood-red blooms grew out among the razor-sharp briars, and the plant wound itself tight all around the trunk of an old tree... And there, tied to the tree, was a fine white horse.

Trembling a little despite herself, Janet dismounted from her pony, and began to tiptoe over to the roses, just to pick one or two to take home and revel in their perfume. But no sooner had Janet picked just the one flower when a tall, slim and beautiful youth appeared from behind the tree, smiling at her in a curious way, and half talking, half singing...

'Why do you come to pick my flowers, Janet? And why do you come to Carterhaugh Wood without my say-so? So? Say.'

Janet knew the man's name, of course – it was Tamlane. But how he knew hers, nobody will ever guess. However, Janet was no wallflower, and she refused to be spoken to by such a man, and in her own wood!

'Carterhaugh Wood is now mine, Tamlane, my father gave me this land for my birthday, and you should leave... yes, absolutely go away, right now! Or I will call... all the knights of the kingdom to come and remove you by force! I will come and go here as I wish.'

'As you wish,' Tamlane replied with a broader smile, which flashed like the sun. This was the smile which had led him to be imprisoned in the wood in the first place. Few people could resist that flashing smile, and many hearts had been blown up like balloons on seeing it. Janet fell in an instant, and the result of this bedazzling and bewitching smile was that before either knew where they were, the two youths were lying under the rose bush, naked as the day they were born, encircled in each other's arms, and legs.

They lay there long in each other's embrace, but when Janet eventually managed to tear herself away from the wood with tears and promises and ride home, she made sure not to tell her father or anyone at court about what had happened.

What she failed to say with her mouth, however, her belly soon began to betray. Her maid Margaret knew the signs at once, and in a very quiet whisper – because she could not bear for kind Janet to get into trouble with her father – she explained, 'I see your petticoat is getting shorter. I can tell there is a baby growing inside you, Janet, and something will have to be done, one way or another. My Granny taught me that the only remedy, to allow the memory of this Tamlane and the time you spent together to be only a distant dream, is to eat the root of the nutmeg tree, which is found only in Carterhaugh Wood. The root will make you just sick enough to end your worries, and all will be well that ends well enough.'

And so Janet rode back to Carterhaugh, and instinct led her to the nutmeg tree in question – the very tree where the roses grew, and where the white horse was still tethered.

Janet took a knife and was digging up a root from the tree when she realised once again that she was not alone. This time, when Tamlane appeared from behind the tree, there was no flashing smile. 'If you need that root,' he began, still in his half-song voice, 'then I know the cause, Janet. You mean to destroy what we have created here together with our love. Yes, I see. I do understand the need, and know it is your power alone to decide what happens within you. I honour whatever you decide, Janet... but please hear my story.'

'Once I was as free as you,' Tamlane began, 'but now this wood of Carterhaugh is my only space within the world of men and women. I am not faerie, and no longer man. Seven years ago – I have no idea if they were seven human years or faerie years, or even which is longer – I rode merrily into this glade to pick a rose, just like you.

'My horse threw me, and I landed roughly. But there, waiting for me in a bower entirely made up of meadow flowers, was Her Majesty, Queen Titania, the ruler of the land under the green hill – she who must be obeyed. As I was well brought up, I gave her a smile, and found myself embraced from every direction by her overpowering fragrance, in a daze, under her spell, and inside her heart.

'"I've had enough of faeries, and of asses!" she declared to me, "Thou art the only boy who passes." And I have remained ever since a subject of the Faerie Kingdom, forever at her rhyming call. I have been treated as a Prince in Titania's court, but I still return here to Carterhaugh, to gaze out at all that I left behind.

'But now it is Hallowe'en, Samhain, the Faerie's Feast, and word has been poured in my ear that every seventh year, a human must be sacrificed by the Queen of the Faeries – for what reason I have never discovered. And that human can only be...'

'Nobody is sacrificing me, Tam!' Janet roared.

'No – me!' Tamlane protested. 'But I have a hope. Would you help me escape my fate, Janet?'

Janet paused, and looked at the muddy root in her hand. She had no qualms about eating it, and reclaiming her own freedom. But then, perhaps if Tamlane could be helped back into the mortal realm... Could she love him? Could he love her?

'What's the plan?' Janet asked, quite prepared to take on Queen Titania with her bare hands.

'You must wait here, only an hour or so for you, and as the first flicker of twilight appears, the royal procession will come through this glade, to lead me to the sacrifice. You must first let the black unicorn pass, and the brown, but then run to my milk-white steed and pull me to the ground. Then hold me, Janet, hold onto me with all your might! Only love is the answer, and I believe that the worst of spells will need to be broken before we can be together.'

The following hour passed slowly for Janet, but eventually the piping of the faerie procession fanfare could be heard close by, and along came Titania, a Goddess of perfect form – whether she was a mile tall or the size of a rabbit, she seemed to radiate all ideas of beauty, of flowery fragrance and nature's joys. Titania sat abroad a huge black unicorn, and sang out, 'Such joy we shared here, you and I, Tamlane, it's a shame you have to die!' Behind her on his own unicorn cantered the King, Oberon, a gloomy-looking brute as gorgeous in his coldness as she was in her warmth. And then there came the milk-white steed.

The horse bridled as Janet rushed forward and wrestled Tamlane to the ground. Queen Titania roared, and the pipers squawked, and all was bedlam. 'Too slow, you unicorns, time to gallop!' Titania boomed. 'Who is this rough and uncouth trollop?'

Janet had no time for poetry – locked tight in her desperate embrace, suddenly there was no Tamlane any more, but instead, she found herself wrestling a huge and very slippery giant newt!

The newt was so slippery, but Janet held on. Then suddenly the newt changed, and clasped to Janet's bosom was a slithering adder!

The adder was so slithery, but Janet held on. And in a flash, she found she was struggling with a big grizzly bear!

The bear was so grizzly, but Janet held on. Bear? The bear had disappeared, and in its place was a huge burning hot lump of coal.

The coal was so hot, Janet thought she would go up in flames. But she had a brainwave, and leapt into the cool waters of the well. And there, as the steam rose, was a pale and naked young man in her arms. It was Tamlane. Janet cloaked Tamlane in the green mantle of her dress, and stared across at Titania with a victorious gleam in her eyes.

Queen Titania was not a woman to be trifled with. 'TAMLANE! NO! That girl must go! Shame betide your ill-fared face, and let you limp away, you've taken off the cutest man that ever I did play! Had I but known, Tamlane, my boy, what now this night I see, I'd turn your eyeballs into oak, your heart to stone... HEY, LISTEN TO ME!'

But Janet had saddled up her own horse and hoisted Tamlane up behind her, both dripping wet and exhausted from their ordeal, and they were already galloping out of the grove, and out of Carterhaugh Wood, never to return. They had a life to make together.

THE END

SELKIRK

Just as the tales of Thomas the Rhymer and Tamlane (also known as 'Tam-Lin') share many themes — both being ex-boyfriends of Titania — so they arose out of much the same part of the country, and you can easily travel from one story location to another on a fine afternoon. If you travel about a mile west of Selkirk you'll be in the right area, with Janet's great forest now only a small wood, and nearby, the Ettrick bridge is said to be the site where she wrestled Tam from his horse. If you explore the wood,

17. TAMLANE OF CARTERHAUGH WOOD

you may find that the very grove can still be found there, and near the road you will find Tamlane's Well, which runs with fresh and clean water to this day. If you see any roses in the wood, though, think twice before picking one.

visitsouthernscotland.co.uk

18. THE GIANT WHO HATED SHREWSBURY

The Wrekin

You will find the border county of Shropshire where the Welsh hills blend into English ones – although it's very hard to tell the difference, as they're all lumpy and green. Shropshire's county town has long been known as Shrewsbury, but the problem is, although the home team is called 'The Shrews', and Shropshire folk pronounce the name like a berry belonging to a small rodent, the debate rumbles on, century after century, as to whether the place should be pronounced 'Shroosbury' or 'Shrosebury'. This is annoying… but it's not reason enough to try and drown the whole town.

Try telling that to the foolish giant in this story.

It was a warm Tuesday afternoon and the sky was white and dappled with grey, like a vampire's skin after a fight. On the bumpy horizon, you could not fail to spy a particularly angry young giant, name of Reeky, who was making his way through the Welsh hills and valleys, galumphing moodily over the border and into the Shropshire countryside.

In truth, nobody can now be sure why Reeky was so set on getting his revenge on Shrewsbury, although it may as well have been because of an argument about how the town's name was pronounced. It's not that likely that Reeky himself had any idea why he hated

18. THE GIANT WHO HATED SHREWSBURY

Shrewsbury so much, he was just a very angry giant, and simply knew he had to kill everyone who lived there.

And so, to that end, he had picked up a gigantic spade and scooped up an astonishing mountain of earth. His plan was to create a dam, dumping the dirt in the Severn and redirecting its flow so that the great river would crash into the town and drown everyone in it, even on the highest hills – which is where the Mayor himself lived, the main target of Reeky's humungous anger.

'I'LL SHOW THAT NO-GOOD MAYOR!' he thundered, without stopping to think for a moment why he actually hated the Mayor of Shrewsbury so much. That was Reeky all over for you.

Giants can travel a lot further than humans, but by the time Reeky had stomped further into Shropshire, and was somewhere on the road between Wellington and Shrewsbury, the muggy weather and heavy spade of earth had made him terribly sweaty and ready for a bit of a sit down.

Just as he found a field large enough to park both his enormous buttocks in, he spied one of those tiny pink human things coming along the road towards him. This little fellow was a cobbler from Wellington, name of Urkle. A brave fellow this Urkle was too, as he waved happily to the terrifying giant, and wished him a merry day.

'Where are you off to this clammy Tuesday, big man?' asked the cobbler with a smile.

'I AM GOING TO KILL SHREWSBURY!' Reeky replied.

'Um… that's er… why?' asked the cobbler with as straight a face as he could muster.

'THE MAYOR IS A GREAT BIG… WELL, HE IS A LITTLE TINY… I HATES HIM! I AM GOING TO DROWN THEM ALL! THAT WILL SHOW THEM! THAT WILL SHOW THEM HOW TO BE DROWNED!'

'Drowned???'

'YEAH, MATE. I HATES ALL THE SHREWSBURY PEOPLE AND ESPECIALLY THAT STINKING MAYOR, SO I'M GOING TO MOVE THE SEVERN WITH ALL THIS MUCK AND LET IT FLOOD RIGHT INTO THE TOWN. THEN I'M GONNA WATCH EVERYONE DROWN. STANDARD TUESDAY, MATE.'

'That sounds a little bit, um…' the cobbler began, but he could see the look of bloodlust in the giant's massive eyes, and quickly changed

his tune. '… a little bit… understandable and perfectly reasonable!'
The cobbler did not fancy being squished like a midge that Tuesday.

'YES. THEY WILL ALL DIE. HOW FAR IS IT TO
SHREWSBURY?'

Now this Urkle was a shrewd fellow. He was on his way back from
Shrewsbury himself, with a sack full of scuffed, dirty and broken old
shoes which the townsfolk had given him to repair by the end of the
week. Most of his work came from mending Shrewsbury shoes, and
if the town was flooded, he would be skint and homeless! Besides,
he added to himself, he didn't like the idea of innocent people being
drowned. He should probably have had that thought first. But at
least he could do his bit to prevent such an unnatural disaster from
happening.

With very little pause for thought, Urkle replied to Reeky:
'Shrewsbury? Why, my good giant, even with legs as long as yours,
you have a loooooooooooong long long LONG journey ahead of you!
Long, it is, if not longer! You'll never get there, not today nor
tomorrow. I mean,' he continued, opening up the contents of his sack
and letting Reeky see all the terrible old shoes and boots he was
carrying. 'Just you take a look at how many shoes I've worn out on
the road since I set off from Shrewsbury a WEEK ago!'

Reeky took a good look, and let out a low groan. 'IF IT'S REALLY
THAT FAR AWAY,' he roared in reply, 'THEN FRANKLY IF THEY
WANT TO BE DROWNED, THEY CAN BLEEDIN' WELL DO IT
THEMSELVES! I CAN'T EVEN REMEMBER WHAT I HATED
THEM FOR NOW. STUFF IT!'

And so, the giant rose up, took his big spadeful of earth, and
dumped it right where he stood. There was so much soil, the pile made
a huge extra bump on the horizon all around, and suddenly the cobbler
found himself standing next to a hill from nowhere. Not only that, the
miffed giant took his own boots off, as they were also packed with
mud and dirt, and emptied them right beside the first pile of earth,
creating a smaller hill.

Then, without so much as a goodbye, he stomped off in the
direction he came from, and was never heard of again.

The cobbler went on his way, filled with relief that he (and all the
people of Shrewsbury!) had survived to tell the tale forever more.

As the anecdote was told and retold, year after year, grass grew on
those two piles of earth, and now we know them by the names of The
Wrekin, and there next to it, the smaller heap, Ercall. Either one of

18. THE GIANT WHO HATED SHREWSBURY

them make for a gorgeous climb on a sunny day – so who says that giants are good for nothing?

THE END

THE WREKIN

The Welsh border is studded with many beautiful and awesome (in the truest sense) 'Blue Remembered Hills', as beloved by A. E. Housman. The south of Shropshire is dominated by Titterstone Clee Hill, but in the north, The Wrekin has its own claims to fame — not least being lovingly referenced by P. G. Wodehouse in his 'Mike' school stories, while evidence of an Iron Age hillfort on the top suggests it was a major centre for prehistoric Salopians in its day. Although the giant obviously never got there, Shrewsbury itself has many famous attractions, being the home of Brother Cadfael and Charles Darwin!

shropshiretourism.com

19. RHIANNON

Narberth, Pembrokeshire

A t first, good King Pwyll of Dyfed thought the glimmer of gold which caught his eye that misty morning was a bird, maybe a skylark. The handsome young King was sitting on a grassy mound, where he had been told he would happen upon something very important, when he heard the song of the birds, and the rhythm of hooves. Then she galloped by, closer than seemed possible, flitting between banks of thick mist.

She was a tall woman of regal bearing, clad in a long golden dress and riding a muscular white mare. Songbirds perched on her shoulders, and she looked serene, cantering slowly from cloud to cloud. She offered Pwyll only the briefest glimpses – but that was enough.

The King was in love, and so he leapt into his own stallion's saddle and raced off in fiery pursuit of this golden woman who had already wrapped herself around his heart, brain and other bits. He galloped into the mist and eventually caught that glimpse of gold again. But no matter how furiously his horse raced, she never drew nearer. And when he dejectedly slowed to a canter... suddenly there she was, only feet ahead, looking back at him with a sly smile! Pwyll geed up his horse, and approached... but then the woman in gold disappeared once again!

Eventually, exhausted, King Pwyll cried out, 'O maiden, for the sake of whoever you love most, stay awhile!'

And there, out of the mist, she rode. 'I will stay gladly, for you,' she smiled.

'I rode harder than thunder to reach you!' Pwyll panted.

19. RHIANNON

'You should have said something,' she replied. 'It would have saved your poor horse a lot of bother. I am Rhiannon.'

To Pwyll, the name seemed to ring out like a bell in the night. He was smitten, if ever a King was smote. 'Wh… where are you riding to, madam?' he garbled.

'I journey on my own errand,' Rhiannon replied, 'But I am glad to see you, Pwyll. My father, King Heveydd Hèn, has dared to promise me in marriage to Gwawl, a rich man whom I despise, but I spied you long ago, King, and I made my choice then.'

'You mean…?' Pwyll's jaw flapped open.

'We will be married,' Rhiannon replied, 'but first there is much to do…'

For many happy couples, this would mean booking reception venues and ordering cakes, but Rhiannon was more busy escaping her arranged marriage in the year that passed before her marriage to Pwyll. Nevertheless, when the day came, Pwyll's great hall was finely bedecked with all the hallmarks of wedding festivity, and the wedding breakfast was being enjoyed by all.

There was an old tradition that bridegrooms could not deny any favour asked of them on their wedding day, and so Pwyll just smiled when a lanky ginger stranger approached and asked for a favour. He did not know this ferrety fellow, but he knew his duty.

'I cannot say no, I swear before my noble guests: name your boon, ferrety fellow!' Pwyll laughed.

'It is but one thing, Pwyll,' the stranger replied. 'I want my promised wife, Rhiannon, as her father and I agreed. We shook hands on a deal worth much gold. I am Gwawl, son of Clud, and I am very rich.' He smiled a gruesome smile.

Everyone groaned. Some people just can't help but ruin parties, and Gwawl had always been unpopular, a preening and oily bully. Pwyll was lost for words. As silence plunged the wedding breakfast into gloom, all too late Rhiannon saw what had happened, and heard Pwyll's oath. 'Yes, you can be silent,' she rolled her eyes at her love. 'Never did man make worse use of his wits than you have just done.'

There was nothing else for it but for Gwawl to take Pwyll's place on the top table, pop a carnation on his tunic, and wed Rhiannon. But the angry bride did have time to usher Pwyll out of the great hall and whisper some directions to him before reluctantly returning for pre-wedding toasts and merriment.

Eventually, another stranger presented himself at the top table, with a big floppy hat and enormous bushy beard, and holding aloft a small sack.

'I claim my boon from you, Lord Gwawl!' this figure loudly announced, but the groom just snarled. He was chatting up one of the bridesmaids, and didn't like being interrupted.

'Get on with it then, beardy,' Gwawl drawled, 'I've no option but to say yes anyway.'

'Sir, all I ask is to fill this sack with a little food and wine.'

'Ha, help yourself,' Gwawl replied. 'There's more than any of us can eat.'

And so with a whoop, the stranger began cramming all the opulent fruit and meat and cake he could into the sack, all the gourds of wine and suckling pigs. Gwawl's eyes widened when he saw the small sack never seemed to be full, and yet before long every scrap of the wedding breakfast was gone!

'How did you do that, you hairy oik? It must be witchcraft,' Gwawl complained.

Rhiannon gave him a timely dig in the ribs. 'Why don't you go and have a look for yourself, husband-to-be?'

'I will as well,' Gwawl cried, and approached the stranger. 'How the blimey have you managed to – WARGH!' This last noise was the sound of Lord Gwawl falling bum over chin into the sack as he bent in to look, and disappearing from view!

King Pwyll pulled off his floppy hat and false beard, and held the bulging sack up, prodding it as it twisted and turned. 'That's the right place for you, boyo,' the King laughed, and Rhiannon called the wedding party to attention.

'As it's my wedding day,' she announced, 'we will play my favourite game, Badger In The Bag!'

'How do you play that, then?' her Auntie Gwyneth asked.

'You get a badger, in a bag, and then you hang it up and everyone gives it a whack, or a kick!'

'That sounds a bit cruel, what's in it for the badger?'

'Oh, the badger LOVES it!' Rhiannon replied. 'In fact, I think it was a badger who invented the game. It's such fun! So, who's first?'

And so the whole wedding party lined up to boot Gwawl up the unmentionables as he struggled in the sack, and only after Rhiannon and Pwyll were safely married was he allowed out, bruised and outfoxed, and made to swear by Rhiannon to 'Go away and never even dream of exacting any kind of revenge on any of us for this –

19. RHIANNON

you deserved every kick! I am no pony for you and my father to barter with. Be gone!'

And as Gwawl made his promise and limped away into the night, a happy ending seemed secure for all.

But happy endings can be awkward like that: they glimmer on the horizon one minute, and before you know it you're back at the bottom of the snake. Within a year of saying 'I do', Rhiannon had given birth to a fine healthy son, in the castle at Narberth. Rhiannon, Pwyll and all at court were so happy they had a huge party to celebrate, and afterwards, the whole court slept like a forest of logs: Rhiannon in her bed, her six waiting women around her, and by the window, the baby in his cradle.

Some terrors, however, are too horrifying ever to be named, and so nobody has ever sworn what kind of hideous monster it was who came to Narberth that night. Whatever denizen of bad dreams was creeping through the Welsh countryside, it must have been huge, as it snatched that baby out of its cradle from the tallest tower window, and disappeared back into the nothingness of the night.

When the six ladies in waiting awoke at dawn, the sight of the empty cradle set them all to shaking. 'What'll we do?!' whispered one. 'Is there some kind of rulebook for this situation?'

'Yes there is,' replied a second woman confidently. 'The stag-hound has just had a litter of puppies. If we tear one up, smear the Queen with blood and sprinkle a few bones all over her bed, she'll get the blame and we won't be burned to death!'

'Murder a puppy?' replied a third. 'Are you sure that's the only option?'

But these gentleladies were driven mad with fear, and they quickly arranged things so that when King Pwyll came by to wish everyone a good morning, the empty cradle and bloodied Rhiannon would tell him all he needed to know.

'SHE ATE THE BABY!' squealed one waiting woman nonetheless, unnecessarily.

Rhiannon awoke with a start, and roared with horror at the bloody mess surrounding her, leaping out of bed and into Pwyll's arms. Though their hearts were breaking together as they processed the cruel awakening, her eyes met with her husband's, and he knew she was innocent.

'You cannot think that I have done this!' Queen Rhiannon

thundered, as she wiped the puppy blood from her chin. 'You silly women, if you are afraid of being accused, I would defend you! Some outside fiend has stolen our Prince, but I do not eat babies!'

Nevertheless, gossip travelled rapidly even in those days, and mud still stuck fast, and so the ancient laws of the Kingdom decreed that the monstrous Queen had to pay penance.

In his grief-numbed haze, Pwyll could only nod his assent when it was announced that Rhiannon would remain at Narberth for seven years, sitting at the bottom of the hill, where she would be forced to tell this story to all who visited the castle, and offer to carry them up the hill and through the gate.

So there she sat, by the old horse trough, with her friends the skylarks roosted around her – though few visitors had the gall to accept the offer of a piggyback from such a noble woman. For some time, this would have been the sad tale that Rhiannon told you had you visited, if it hadn't been for an eventual stroke of luck.

In nearby Gwent, on that doom-laden birth night, a lord named Teyrnon had been waiting patiently in his stable. Every year, his finest mare would foal, but by the morning, there was never a trace of the little pony that had just been born. Thunder and lightning cracked and flashed as the rain lashed the stable, but Teyrnon held his vigil, as his mare gave birth to a tiny healthy colt.

Suddenly, the window crashed open and a gigantic skeletal claw knifed into the stable. Teyrnon couldn't see what the hand was attached to, but as its bony fingers felt for the foal and tried to haul him out of the window by the mane, Teyrnon stepped forward and chopped with his deadly sword, for all he was worth.

An unearthly scream rang out which silenced the thunder and lightning in its agony, and there in the straw lay the claw, twitching and dead. Whatever monster it was that had been stalking the humans of South Wales that night hared off who knows where one final time, and Teyrnon breathed a sigh of relief.

This was soon followed by a sigh of delighted surprise when the claw opened to reveal a healthy baby boy, swathed in satin, and giggling at the wee horse beside him as it tried a few faltering steps.

Teyrnon raised the boy as his own, naming him 'Gwri Goldenhair', and he grew so fast and so strong that he was riding that horse born on his birthday before he was three.

By this time, of course, the story of Rhiannon's unjust penance was well known in Teyrnon's kingdom, and as a kind-hearted man, the unfairness of it worried him. As an old friend of Pwyll, Teyrnon knew Rhiannon was no baby eater. And as his boy grew, the resemblance to Pwyll became more and more impossible to miss.

And so Teyrnon and the lad rode to Narberth castle one day, and greeted the poor figure that awaited them by the old horse trough.

'Go no further!' Rhiannon arose and declared, 'I am to carry you on my back up the hill, because I killed and ate my son, apparently.'

'My Lady Rhiannon, you are strong, but my weight would snap you like a wishbone! I will not be carried,' said Teyrnon, and his little blonde companion was just about to insist the same, when Rhiannon caught sight of him.

'PRYDERI!' she cried, which in her language meant 'Care' – we could debate at length why she cried this, but Rhiannon knew what she meant. The boy was not at all befuddled when this strange lady fell to her knees and wrapped him in her arms, tears rolling down her face. King Pwyll was summoned and his tears mingled with hers, and the boy joined in until they were in danger of drowning in happy salt water.

Teyrnon was thanked for his care of the boy, and the newly-named Pryderi was raised to follow Pwyll as a wise and valiant King of Dyfed when the time came.

When the time did come, this happy ending took a different course. But that is another tale, because lives like Rhiannon's can never be wrapped up with a simple happy ending.

THE END

NARBERTH, PEMBROKESHIRE

Pembrokeshire is the county at the very south-west tip of Wales; and one of the first towns you will come to, from the east, is the ancient and pretty town of Narberth — so compact, ancient and pretty indeed, it is even twinned with the English town of Ludlow, which is only just over the border! Visitors to the area can enjoy the multicoloured architecture, perhaps go and visit the Folly Farm Adventure Park... but with Rhiannon in mind, it's the castle you will want to visit, or at least what's left of it. Even the ruins are 13th-century Norman, but they were built on top of a much older castle, and it's here that you would once have had to turn down Rhiannon's offer of a piggyback — if you had any manners at all!

visitpembrokeshire.com

20. MERLIN AND
THE DRAGONS

Dinas Emrys, Gwynedd

I t may disappoint you to learn that there was probably more than
one 'Merlin' – or if you prefer, 'Myrddin', with the two D's
making a 'th' sound. It's probably not so much that different folk
took on the role of Merlin in the same way a superhero steps into
another's shoes; perhaps wizardry was just a family tradition. It's
even slurred in some quarters that a Merlin built Stonehenge in
Wiltshire all those thousands of years ago. Then there was Merlin the
Wild, a sixth-century bard who messed up an important battle for his
master one day and ran out into the woods to spend the rest of his life
as a gibbering grizzled hermit, forever spouting forth his endless
poetic prophesies that generally translated as 'Watch out!'

But the most celebrated Merlin, the Merlin Emrys who folk say
taught Arthur so well, was born, according to many, in Caernarfon in
Wales. Caernarfon is a stupendously ancient town whose name means
'sea fort', so it seems the Merlins took their name from the place –
Caer Merddyn – not the other way around.

This very bright boy of Emrys was, so gossips gossiped, the son
of a demon of some kind, who had seduced his poor kind mother
Adnah. That was why this young Merlin was so weird, they said. But
fifth-century peasants can be so cruel. What Merlin Emrys was, was
talented.

When Merlin was a lad, the ruler of much of Britain was called King
Vortigern, and he was a bad King. Truly rubbish. Nobody could say

for sure that he was a bad person, but it's clear that his crown did not fit his big head – he lost all his battles, and even the King's Speech he gave every winter solstice was really boring.

Since the Romans had packed up and gone home, Vortigern was in charge of a kingdom with Picts bearing down on him from the north, pirates all around and endless tribal uprisings, and so he made a historically stupid decision.

Actually, it's worth pausing for a moment to add that the decisions Vortigern made weren't necessarily his own, but came from a council of self-claimed 'Wise Elders'. Where once Britain had been dominated by the ancient wisdom of the Druids, since the Romans had killed most of them, these weirdoes were all that remained. Nobody had voted for these officious officials, and they all had very curious ideas of how the world worked. There were three of them, all men, and all had long white beards, long robes, and short attention spans.

'If only you big burly fellows would travel over to Albion, I, King Vortigern, would happily give you a tasty slice of Kent, in return for fighting all my battles for me – Picts, pirates, that kind of thing. Basic security. Hope to see you soon – love, King V xx.'

The invitation was hastily accepted, but once these shaggy English-ish invaders arrived on British soil, they found the place very comfy indeed, thank you very much, and decided they'd rather like a lot more of it! And if the rubbish bighead King Vortigern didn't like it, they asked him, whose army was going to stop them?

King Vortigern and his gaggle of daft wise men ran away, out far west like so many Britons, to the hills of Cymru – 'Cum-ree' – or as these Saxon invaders called it, 'Wales'.

Once a likely hill had been found to set up a new court, Vortigern couldn't even build a simple castle on top of it, that's how bad he was at being King! Every time one stony tower had just about been built on the top, and the cement was just beginning to set... there would be a crack, and a tremendous eruption of some kind would wobble the whole hill, until it all came tumbling down!

'THAT'S THE THIRD CASTLE THIS MONTH!' Vortigern squealed with frustration, and turned to his advisors. 'What am I doing wrong, lads?'

20. MERLIN AND THE DRAGONS

The three beardy-weirdies ummed and ahhed and conferred with each other in the corner of the rubble. Before long, urgently whispered cries of 'Well I don't know!' and 'Perhaps a supporting joist?' and suchlike were heard. Eventually, the tallest advisor turned and told his boss, 'It's terribly simple, sir. The only way to build a proper castle here is to find, somewhere in the land, a young poor person, preferably one born of a demon in some way. Bring them to this spot, naked, and then tear out their gizzards and fling them all around the foundations of the castle. That ought to do it, don't you think?'

'Um... Well, yes, since you happen to mention it, yes,' Vortigern replied. 'Pretty obvious now I come to think of it, which I do...'

And so poor Merlin Emrys, aged no more than 14, was dragged from his mother's home, which was in a dell just to the north of Vortigern's construction site. Merlin was tall for his age, and a sallow-looking boy, with long hair and flashing eyes which bore into everyone he flashed them on. But there was always at least half a laugh in his every word and look.

The situation was explained to him. 'So,' he responded at length, 'you think that successful castle construction is down mainly to child murder and random butchery?'

'That's right,' smiled Vortigern, reaching up yet again to prevent his crown slipping off his bulbous head. 'I'd be terribly grateful to you, you know, if you could just see your way clear to, you know...' And he giggled, poked out his tongue and ran a finger across his neck. The tallest advisor removed a very sharp and shiny blade from the folds of his gown and gave Merlin another very wide – but very insincere – smile.

'Now, hang on a moment,' Merlin began, 'That sounds like a very silly way of going about things to me.'

The old wise fools looked very offended at this, but they had no time to interrupt, because Merlin was already having one of what his mother called his 'moments'. Somehow the awkward young lad had always been blessed with strange moments of great insight, and now he had one to share with the king.

There was a loud cracking sound, and the hill wobbled once again.

'I can see why your castle cannot be built here! Or rather, I can't see it, but I can hear it and feel it under the stones. Follow me, and bring plenty of spades!'

So the whole throng followed young Merlin down into the foundations of the hillfort, and at the boy's suggestion, they instructed the workers to prise up a large rock in the centre of the pit. Beneath the rock was a lake. Well, it was more of a puddle, really. But the water wasn't important, it was what was splashing around in it that made everyone gape.

The cavern reverberated with gasps as all assembled saw two little but fierce lizard-like creatures. One was a deep red, the other a pallid white, and both had scaly wings and tiny puffs of fire protruding from their noses. These two dragons were having a battle, hammer and tongs, in the middle of the hole. First the white one slapped the red one right across the chops with an almighty thwack, next the red one came back with a meaty punch which set the whole cavern rumbling.

'You, my lord, have a bad case of wyrms!' Merlin laughed.

'They look like dragons to me,' simpered King Vortigern.

'Very closely related cousins, sir,' Merlin went on, 'as are these two. These are the dragons whose noisy screams forced Old King Ludd to seal them up in this very hill. The white fighter is from over the seas, belonging to these English, who you so kindly invited over to kill and pillage the people, my lord.'

Because of the dazzling smile with which this was said, Vortigern did not even have time to work out that he was being offended before the sparky young Merlin swept on:

'The red dragon has been here for a lot longer, and will remain. In fact, both will remain upon this island for centuries to come, and both will keep fighting, until a great person is found who can unite them both, and build a Britain of peace for all. I'm afraid to tell you,' Merlin concluded, with a stylish bow, 'that that great person is never going to be you, King Vortigern. Sorry about that. But we can't all be beloved legendary figures, I suppose.'

It was an eloquent and important speech, but few of Vortigern's old advisors paid it much heed. All three long-bearded men were frozen with fear at the sight of the fighting dragons. They had all pulled their robes up tight around their thighs, and were dribbling a little in terror at the idea of one of the tiny dragon cousins flying up their pants.

'Master!' the tallest one cried, 'let us leave this place and build elsewhere! Maybe a bungalow!'

'Quite right,' agreed Vortigern, 'I don't want to live in a place infested with WORMS! Okay then, you can keep the place, my lad. Right ho, come on everyone, chop chop, castles to build,

20. MERLIN AND THE DRAGONS

battles to lose – sorry, I mean win, obviously – we'd better pack up camp and move... I don't know, over there somewhere, west. Further away from those horrible Hengist and Horsa guys. I tell you, you think someone's a friend, and then they turn around and...'

King Vortigern's prattling grew quieter in the dusk air, and Merlin Emrys smiled, and replaced the mighty rock over the warring wyrms with a simple wink to them both. He had lived to tell another tale, and the spot where he stood was to take his name: Dinas Emrys.

However, as he turned to trudge back home to his mother, Merlin frowned. He knew that those two fighting wyrms meant many a bloody battle still lay ahead between the Britons and the English, and if there was only one good ruler out there to lead the fight for freedom, it was going to have to be his job to find that person, and teach them all he could to make them a kind, wise leader of the people. Only then would the white and red dragons be forever at peace, at last.

Well, except perhaps when it came to rugby championships.

'Rugby championships?' Merlin puzzled to himself aloud, and shrugged. His work, whatever it was, was only just beginning.

THE END

DINAS EMRYS

Not all folktales are evenly distributed around the country, and this one corner of North Wales has Beddgellert and the legendary site of Merlin's first great trick at a pleasant walk's distance. The real Dinas Emrys is one of the most popular places to visit in all of stunning Snowdonia, rising mistily above the town of Beddgellert itself. But if you also want to sample any of the tributes to Merlin in his proud hometown of Caernarfon, it's only twelve miles away, and well worth your time.

snowdoniaheritage.info

---

21. THE SWORD IN THE STONE

Tintagel, Cornwall

E very nation needs one great hero – Britain, as you can tell, has more than its fair share of them. But none greater are remembered by the people of this strange little island than King Arthur, the brave and noble ruler of the Britons.

People can argue and fight for centuries to come about whether Arthur ever really ruled at Camelot, if he was married to Guinevere and sought the Holy Grail and suchlike. But whether Arthur was a shiny knight in armour or some kind of Romano-British warlord, only the very most boring historians entirely deny that there was a real person who inspired the legend.

There are many regions of Britain which lay claim to being the site of Arthur's great achievements, both north and south. But no claims are more intoxicating than those deep in the South-West, from Wiltshire down to Cornwall. And in Tintagel, they go so far as to boast of it being Arthur's birthplace.

The legend runs that Arthur's father Uther Pendragon was a brave and beloved ruler somewhere in the South-West. The youngest son of King Constantine, pretender to the Roman throne, Uther and his brothers Constans and Ambrosius Aurelius had been battling all their lives to see off the Saxon invaders led by rampant warriors Hengist and Horsa – and also to stop the clueless tyranny of King Vortigern, who invited the English over in the first place, and lost the country to them in the process.

21. THE SWORD IN THE STONE

When, after many battles, Uther was the last brother left, he became known as a great defender of the people, and never a bad word was said about him. That was until the day he clapped eyes on Igraine, wife of Sir Gorlois, Duke of Cornwall. Cupid's arrow stuck deep in his heart with just one glance, and suddenly nothing mattered more to him than taking Igraine for his own wife.

The wizard Merlin – that old trickster of Vortigern's, now grown into a tall and impressive master of all arts, sciences and magicks with a K – was also Uther's best friend, with high hopes for the British hero; and when he saw the change in the King, Merlin despaired for the country. Uther of course begged Merlin to use his darkest and strongest powers to get him what he wanted, while a meaningless war was waged on Gorlois' Cornish forces at Tintagel Castle – a tall palace jutting out over the ragged crags of the north coast of Cornwall, or as the locals call it, Kernow.

Merlin did all he could to dissuade Uther from ruining everything for the sake of a wild passion, but no power is stronger than love at first sight, and, realising he was beaten, Merlin promised to help his friend. He prophesised: 'Uther, you and Igraine will make a baby on your first night together, but I will bring up this boychild myself, and teach him all the sorcerer's ways. You will see neither of us ever again.' Uther would have agreed to anything at this point, and so with one puff, the wizard released a blizzard of secret ingredients, potions and pollens, which found its way into Tintagel's water supply and drugged the guards and people of the court, making everyone there believe that Uther actually was Gorlois!

Uther marched up to the front gate without any trouble, was swiftly let in, and then the foolish lover was free to visit Igraine before anyone could blink twice. Meanwhile, the poor Duke of Cornwall himself was thrown into the sea by Uther's victorious knights.

Everything fell out as Merlin predicted, as everything always seemed to. The baby was called Arthur, and nothing Uther could say had the power to stop Merlin from taking the baby away, as promised. Gorlois and Igraine already had one daughter, little Morgana, otherwise known as Morgan Le Fay, but they never had any more children. Before long, realising how he had let his heart rule his head, Uther simply wasted away, and died of a cough.

Little Arthur was brought up as a humble squire in the home of Sir Ector, a kindly knight who already had one son, a large boisterous lad called Kay, who teased the adopted boy and called him 'Wart' – but Ector nonetheless raised Arthur as much like a second son as he could. With Uther gone, the Saxons were marauding the kingdom unchecked, moving further and further west, but Ector was one of many Britons who fought to keep the people safe.

Everyone awaited the day that the rightful King of Britain would arise, and save them from invasion and tyranny. This wasn't just an idle hope, either – Merlin had, with great ceremony, revealed to the yeomen and yeowomen of Britain... Excalibur! Known to the Welsh as Caledfwlch! The sword which would deliver them all from Anglo-Saxon murder and plunder!

The wise magician explained to them all: 'Nimue, the mystical Lady of the Lake, cast this mighty sword herself from a unique ore found nowhere else on the planet! Excalibur's strength is that of several armies, but only one person can wield it to any effect...'

High up on an ancient hill, a large grey rock rose out of the grass, and there, firmly wedged deep into the stone, was the shining silver sword. Underneath, in marks clear to them all, was written:

WHOSOEVER PULLS THIS SWORD OUT OF THE STONE IS RIGHTWISE KING OF ALL BRITAIN.

An excited harrumph ran over the gathered crowds, as eyebrows rose and lips pursed and a queue of the beefiest and buffest Britons formed, each contender confidently prepared to show the world that they were The Chosen One to rule the land.

Sir Ector gave the sword the first tug, but he was an old man by now, and laughed off the minor hernia the attempt gave him. Next came Sir Derek, then a blacksmith called Wayne, and then Lady Mim of the Tall Castle – none of whom could get the mighty Excalibur to even budge. For days on end, the most muscle-bound, big-headed, ambitious and deluded warriors among the Britons all rode up to the sword in the stone, determined to yank the mighty blade out of its rock and show everyone that they were The Chosen One! When, of course, they all failed, some took their failure in good humour while many started fights with anyone who giggled, but all of them went home again, leaving Excalibur apparently hopelessly stuck in that stone forever more.

But Merlin, of course, knew that only one person was chosen to wield Excalibur, and he had been tutoring the young Arthur since infancy to make him the best King he could possibly be. While those

21. THE SWORD IN THE STONE

around him believed in nothing but jousting, and fighting, and gold, Arthur learned not only the important basic stuff like mathematics and runes and home economics, but how to be as wise as King Solomon and as brave as Alexander the Great, while remaining more modest and true-hearted than any King had ever been.

All Arthur wanted to be was a knight in shining armour, just like Sir Ector was, and young Kay was going to be. Kay treated Arthur like a servant – he was not a cruel lad, but thoughtless, and, like so many before him, certain that he would be the one to budge that sword. When the day came for Kay to try, of course Arthur was by his side.

'Out of the way, Wart!' Kay grumbled, 'This is knightly business. O people of Britain, now I, Sir-Well-Almost-Sir-But-King-Soon-Probably-But-Let's-Say-Sir Kay shall prove that I am your rightwise King!'

And young Kay took hold of the glinting hilt of Excalibur, feeling a tingle of power running up both his arms as he found a strong grip. He pulled. His brawny arms quaked with the effort of heaving and tugging at the sword... Until he realised that he would either have to let go, or leave both his arms there forever, torn off at the armpits. He was beaten.

'That's it, the whole country is doomed, nobody will ever be crowned King again!' sulked Kay, kicking the stone in anger and immediately bursting into tears at a broken toe.

The kindly Arthur was just examining Kay's poorly toe – Merlin had given him the best medical training – when a voice was heard:

'Go on then, Arthur, it's your turn next, boy!'

'Arthur?' snarled Kay through his tears, 'He's just a servant, and a weedy little one at that, there's no point in him bothering to even touch the sword.'

But Merlin, appearing from behind an old gnarly oak tree, was not to be dissuaded. 'Well, we're here now, young Kay, why not have some fun? Go on, Arthur, just give the sword the once-over. Hold the hilt. Feel the power. Try your luck.'

And so, as Kay nursed his big toe, young Arthur mounted the hill and did what his wise teacher advised. He felt the handle of Excalibur in his hand for the first time. He felt that same tingle of unmentionable power that Kay had felt, travelling up his arm. But, he told himself, it was just a sword. A piece of metal. The whole thing was frankly silly, and there was no point in—

'FSHOOM-TING!'

With one clean movement, Excalibur slid out of the stone with a pleasing sound, and Arthur found himself holding the heavy sword high up in the air, as all around him gasped with suitable melodrama. Peasants hurrying to and fro stopped and went 'Ooh!' Mighty knights in armour pinched themselves to check if they were dreaming. But it was undeniable. This one small young man had retrieved the sword from the stone, and had to be the one true King of All Britain, sent to deliver them from invaders and tyrants! This young lad really was… King Arthur!

Everyone fell to their knees and swore to follow the young ruler from that day forward, and all of Merlin's wise teachings set the young King in good stead. Of course, Kay was the most sulky about the whole turn of events, but Arthur treated him like a brother, and made him the first of his Knights of the Round Table, a brave band of soldiers all sworn to protect the people of Britain from injustice and violence wherever it shook its ugly head.

There were many fights ahead, many battles, many feasts and many jousts. But it all began the moment that the sword left the stone, in that woody clearing in Cornwall.

THE END

TINTAGEL

Any visitor to Cornwall who doesn't include Tintagel on their itinerary must be eccentric, to say the least. The craggy coastal castle ruins may be Medieval, but it's likely to have been chosen as the ideal spot due to much earlier fortification in Romano-British times, and also features in Tristan and Isolde. Whether you believe that any form of Uther's saucy sally ever happened here or anywhere in the first half of the first millennium is up to you, but the whole region will certainly make it easy to free your imagination, thriving as it does on every possible allusion to Arthurian myth, from Merlin's Cave to a number of reputed sites of Camelot itself. All you need is the Cornish scenery and a little willing suspension of disbelief.

visitboscastleandtintagel.com

22. BRAN THE BLESSED

Harlech

I f you think 'The Mabinogion' sounds like something someone would say with their mouth full, then you probably don't speak Welsh. It is perhaps the oldest collection of stories from Britain, and we are glad to have the precious text, thanks to the long history of gossip in the western lands.

'Welsh', you see, is the Saxon word for 'stranger' – which is incredibly rude, when you think about it, to invade someone's country and call them the stranger. It's like a burglar waking you up and telling you to get out of their house. But Wales is the place where the British have been pushed for the longest time, invasion after invasion, and the British turned every news item into stories around the campfires of Wales, until they found their way into The Mabinogion at last.

And that is how we still know all about Bendigeidfran, otherwise known as King Bran, the Blessed.

Despite sounding like a kind of breakfast cereal, the name 'Bran' also meant 'Raven' in the old tongue – although the man himself was anything but flightworthy. Over 100 feet tall by some exaggerations, Bran was the largest King of the Britons of them all, built like one mighty army all stuck together with putty. A brave, burnished, brown-bearded and benevolent bloke, Bran was the strong, silent type, blessed with the love of all his people, the sheep in the fields, the wolves in the forests, and of course, the ravens, who roosted within the circle of his enormous crown.

Everybody loved Bran. So why did he end up as just one enormous head?

The trouble really started when the Irish Prince Matholwch sailed across the sea to Bran's castle in Harlech, begging to marry Bran's charming sister Branwen. She admitted to being as enraptured with the Irish Prince as he was with her, and so Bran silently nodded his approval, and sent the newly-weds back across to the emerald isle with a smile.

Their hot-headed brother Efnysien was less happy about the marriage, and more interested in fighting the Irish than loving them, and so on the wedding night, he did unspeakable things to the bridegroom's horses, which nearly sparked a war right away. Efnysien loved war, and fights, and if neither was available, just causing trouble. To make up for Efnysien's crime, King Bran gave Matholwch and Branwen a very expensive wedding present – a huge cauldron that could bring back the dead. But he would quickly grow to regret buying it for them.

Gazing out over the waves that beat against the Gwynedd coast one day, Bran was startled to be addressed by a starling, nervously perched amid the ravens on his broad shoulder: 'Erm, excuse me King Bran? I'm Sally the Starling, hello.' Bran, of course, said nothing, but the starling went on: 'Sorry about this, but I've been taught to speak by your sister, and she's sent me here to tell you she's been having a really nasty time over in Ireland. Her husband treats her like a kitchen slave, feeds her on scraps, and all in all, well, she wanted to see if you could maybe pop over and give her horrible other half a flipping good pasting?'

Bran did not need asking twice – he loved his sister almost as much as he loved fighting epic battles, and so the game was on.

The British armies set sail west to Ireland, but no ship had been built which could stay afloat with big Bran on board. Luckily, the gigantic warrior was so lofty he simply waded out to sea, carrying half the army's weapons and supplies in his special bumbag, and even taking his own troupe of musicians on his shoulders so he and the ravens could enjoy some tunes as they travelled, with an armada of Britain's finest warriors sailing in Bran's wake.

Many campaigns were fought in the ensuing years, and many brave folk fell in the hideous battles. Even with a giant general like Bran to lead the British army, cracking tiny skulls left, right and centre, laying down over chasms to provide handy bridges for his troops, punching castles in the face until they collapsed and so on, it was no walkover for the British. This was mainly because the Irish had the magic cauldron, and so as fast as Bran and his armies could kill all the enemy soldiers, they just came back fighting, only with a few bits missing each time.

To cut a long, bloody war story short, it was only when a berserk Efnysien leapt wildly into that magic cauldron and sacrificed himself by bashing it to pieces from within until it exploded, and him with it, that the day was finally won, and the British were victorious.

But at what cost? The finest fighters of a generation had fallen on both sides – and yes, that included even Bran. Slashed on the shins with a poisoned sword, Bran's enormous body was quickly filling with venom when he had the rather daring idea of cutting off his own head before the poison got that far. He simply counted to ten, gritted his teeth, and – WHOP! – his head was off. Normally, this would of course kill you anyway, but as we have seen, Bran was anything but normal.

One strange side effect of this unique medical marvel was that, for the first time in his life and/or death, King Bran became incredibly chatty. The doctors did not know why, because they couldn't even work out how the head was still alive. And not only that, but big old Bran the Blessed's head was LOUD.

'OOH,' he would thunder, 'DID YOU SEE ME CUT MY OWN HEAD OFF, LADS? HAHAHA! PRETTY QUICK BIT OF THINKING, THAT, EH? YOU KNOW, THERE'S SOMETHING STRANGELY CALMING ABOUT NOT HAVING A BODY TO WORRY ABOUT ANY MORE. AND I CAN EAT WHAT I LIKE WITHOUT HAVING TO WORRY ABOUT GETTING FAT! HAHAHAHA!' And on he would go, you would have said 'laughing his head off', if he hadn't already done that.

Bran's faithful band of supporters, the few survivors like Pryderi and poor Branwen, took Bran's big boisterous bonce with them on their travels around the Kingdom, until they made their home on the mystical island of Gwales, a grassy atoll where they shut themselves away and sang and drank and remembered old times for almost a century, while hardly ever feeling time passing at all.

After that century or so had passed, though, some of Bran's stories were starting to become a little bit repetitive – after all, the King was *very* loud, and did go on at great length – 'HAHAHA REMEMBER THAT TIME THAT WE TRIED TO BOMBARD THE IRISH WITH DISEASED POODLES, BUT THE POODLES EXPLODED IN MID-AIR, AND POOR OLD MANAWYDAN GOT SPLATTERED WITH GALLONS OF POODLE JUICE? WAHAHAHAAA! IT WAS QUITE CRUEL REALLY, COME TO THINK OF IT, BUT NEVER MIND, EH…'

And so the elderly band of loyal followers carried Bran's head all the way to the south-eastern city of Londinium, where they perched it atop a precipice known as Gwynfryn, the White Hill, facing out to sea, in the hope that Bran would loudly fend off any invaders from France with his long, booming stories.

'HERE, YOU FRENCH PEOPLE WANT TO HEAR ALL ABOUT THE TIME MERLIN AND TALIESIN HAD A COMPETITION TO SEE WHO COULD TURN INTO THE FUNNIEST SQUIRREL? OH, THOSE WIZARDS, BOY, THEY DON'T HALF MAKE I LAUGH. NO, DON'T SAIL AWAY YOU FRENCHIES, LISTEN TO OLD KING BRAN, COME BACK NOW, HAHAHAHAAA…'

In time, even poor old Bran seemed to run out of juice, and the earth slowly grew over his noble head. One day, the English built a tower on top of Bran's hill, the White Tower, which we now know as the Tower of London. And from that day to this, Bran's beloved ravens have made their home in that tower. It's said that if they ever fly away, the country's done for. Or perhaps it means that Bran is preparing for his comeback.

THE END

HARLECH

There are three or four main sites connected to the mighty chieftain we've come to know as 'Bran', the Tower of London perhaps being the most obvious, while there is also an Iron Age hillfort in Cornwall named Caer Bran in his honour, and the 12th-century castle at Castell Dinas Bran in Denbighshire was once thought to be his home. The North Wales coastal county of Gwynedd also claims Bran as its own, and it is at Harlech that he was said to have seen poor Branwen off on her doomed honeymoon. The mystical isle of Gwales is believed to be the island of Grassholm, part of the modern-day Pembrokeshire Coast National Park, out in the middle of the Irish Sea. If you want to know whether time still stands still there, you'll just have to visit for yourself.

gwynedd.com

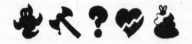

23. TRISTAN AND ISOLDE

Fowey, Cornwall

The legend of the Cornish knight Tristan and the Irish Princess Isolde is world famous, and has been turned into operas and films and who knows what else. And the reason for this lasting fame? Because it is a story about two very sexy people who have a really bad time. Just look around you at the most popular stories of your day, the papers and the scandals – things have still not changed in the millennium and a half since this sad history first became the subject of fireside gossip.

Tristan was a dashing and gorgeous young knight of the court of Kernow, far down in the south-west of the island. The favourite nephew of the Cornish King Mark who kept his court at Tintagel, Tristan was the King's go-to man for all the most valiant and exciting missions that befell the Kingdom. He was always handy in a scrap with a belligerent giant, the first person you'd think of if a demon was ruining your birthday party, and let's just say that he hadn't met a single fire-breathing dragon he hadn't either tamed, or killed.

Kernow's relationship with Ireland, the smaller British island to the north, was very important indeed in those days. Tristan had faced the great Irish knight, Morholt, in single combat at a recent All-British-Knights-Bashing-Each-Other contest, and literally wiped the floor with the poor goon. This wasn't exactly the best way to stay on the right side of the King of Ireland, and so when a particularly murderous dragon was reported in the south-east of the land, it struck

23. TRISTAN AND ISOLDE

Mark as a good idea to send Tristan over the narrow Irish Sea to deal with the problem.

In the end, it wasn't a very murderous dragon after all; the poor thing had just been going through a grumpy period and was goaded by some tourists who were pretty much asking for it. Tristan simply had a good chat with the scaly pest and convinced it to fly far away to the chilly north, where its fiery breath would be more appreciated, and then he told everyone in the Irish court that the dragon was dead. And there was much rejoicing.

Tristan had not escaped his face-off with the grumpy dragon completely unscathed, however – one sneeze from the fire-breather had partially roasted his shoulder. The King of Ireland revealed that there was only one thing for it.

'My hugely, vastly, astonishingly clever, beautiful, talented, gentle, funny and friendly daughter Isolde is the person to take a look at that, young man!'

'She sounds nice,' replied Tristan with gritted teeth, as his blistered skin stung beneath his armour.

'Takes after her mother, so she does,' replied the King, 'and there's nothing she doesn't know about healing wounds! She went to the best Wise Woman University that Irish gold can buy, and is quite the medicine woman. Hey, Isolde!'

It's such a cliché to say that time stood still at that moment – and it's also very inaccurate, as at the very most, time can only pass very very very slowly. But clichés are usually only clichés because they are the closest we can get to expressing a feeling for which there are no simple words. So when Tristan turned, and saw Princess Isolde sail down the grand staircase to join them, time passed so slowly for the singed knight that he felt he could have painted a whole gallery of paintings of her beauty before she even reached the bottom step.

His jaw sagged. His roasted shoulder was forgotten. He gaped.

'Hello there, brave sir knight,' she smiled, 'what seems to be the problem?'

There was no problem, Tristan felt, as he lost himself in her shining amber eyes, and there never could be, as long as she kept smiling at him like that. The problem only became clear when Isolde began to tend to his wounded shoulder, and he fell deeper and deeper in love, while she seemed to be, at the most, professionally jovial with him. Tristan knew that even a dashing knight like himself could not hope to marry a Princess, and so he was careful not to make his feelings too obvious. He decided he would just have to hide his love away, no matter how bitterly it grew, and work off his frustration on armies of giants, dragons and unruly knights.

However, in his letters home to King Mark in Tintagel, Tristan really let rip and wrote all about Isolde's mesmerising beauty, her incredible intellect and her ability to heal even the trickiest wound. In fact, so lyrical and passionate was his review of the Princess' charms, he knew he only had himself to blame when the reply came back from King Mark:

'Dear Tristan. This Isolde sounds absolutely lovely. Tell you what, bring her with you when you come back home next week, and I'll marry her. Sound fair enough? Thank her Dad from me! All the best, your pal, Uncle King Mark. Kiss kiss.'

Isolde was miffed, to say the very least, when she realised she was being married off to some King she'd never even met, but her father insisted that King Mark was very handsome, and lovely, and wise, and above all, Kingly, and nothing could be more auspicious than to unite Ireland and Kernow in loving wedded bliss like this.

'And if you have any doubt come the wedding morning,' added Isolde's mother, who was her own kind of Wise Woman, 'just you take a big glug on this bottle. It's a peachy juice I've created which will make everything seem much better right away.'

On the choppy journey back to Great Britain, Isolde gazed mournfully out at the grey sea and grey sky, and wept for the loss of her freedom. In fact, she decided, never had she more needed everything to seem better right away, and so she grasped her mother's bottle, and took a big swig.

There was a knock at her cabin door. It was Tristan. She looked into his piercing blue eyes, and fell extravagantly in love with him.

Four eyes. That was all it took, and in the meeting of those gazes, the fate of Tristan and Isolde was sealed. It was love, and love could be the greatest thing in the universe – or the most destructive.

In truth, Isolde already liked Tristan a great deal, but she had never been in love and did not know how it felt. Her mother's potion simply removed all the doubt and worry from her mind, and within at most half a trice, she had grabbed young Tristan and folded him in her arms, covering his startled (but extremely welcoming) face with burning kisses.

23. TRISTAN AND ISOLDE

The love potion was only supposed to last a few hours, just long enough to get Isolde married to King Mark; after that, she would have to deal with the consequences. But by the time Tristan and Isolde were back in the court at Tintagel, a whole day later, she was as in love with Tristan as ever she was, and he was more in love with her than anyone had ever been with anything in the history of the world – and he was happy to smite anyone who said otherwise.

King Mark was an honourable and wise ruler, but he really wasn't the most observant lover in the history of romance, and although Isolde wept all the way through the service, and best man Tristan audibly groaned as the marriage of King Mark and Queen Isolde was solemnised, Mark barely noticed a thing – and now, Isolde was his wife.

The tragedy was, no amount of noble chivalry could keep Tristan and Isolde apart, no matter how they wept at every lie they were compelled to tell good King Mark. Each night, they had to flee to the dark woods, where Tristan would play Isolde sweet and sugary songs on his harp. They could only declare their love in the dark, and then by a flickering flame, they gazed soppily into each other's gorgeous eyes for hours on end.

Gossip all around the court about the closeness of the King's nephew and the Queen could not have been kept away from the King's ears forever, but even when King Mark overheard the rumour about Tristan and Isolde, he refused to believe it. It was only when his sleep was robbed from him by endless dreams of his wife and Tristan kissing and cuddling, that the King decided to take action. He laid flour at the doorstep, and in the morning, he could easily tell which footprints were his wife's, and which his nephew's. Both headed into the woods, and he had all the proof he needed.

That night, King Mark was waiting in the shadows, heavily camouflaged, when Tristan and Isolde arrived for their harp session. The King lingered, and listened, and realised the depth of the lovers' feelings for each other.

'We cannot go on like this, my love,' Isolde whispered.

'I would rather a thousand and one stolen nights like this than never to see you at all, Isolde,' Tristan whispered back.

'If only the King were a horrible tyrant,' Isolde replied, 'this would be easier, but Mark is a good man. It breaks my heart that we are breaking his.'

'There is nobody who means more to me in my life than my uncle – except you. But you are right, the time is coming for us to…'

'To die, my boy! To DIE!' Mark thundered out in the darkness. He had arrived with a poisoned sword to do away with his rival, but even with surprise on his side, he could not bring himself to kill his beloved nephew. Nonetheless, his guards were there in a second to part the two lovers, and march them back to Tintagel, where the law demanded Tristan would be burned for his treachery.

As the young knight was marched along the side of the cliff, however, he took his chance. He spun round, kicking the guards away, which gave him just enough time to leap off the cliff – a leap to certain death, but better than the fate which awaited him.

To his surprise, the Cornish wind caught his cloak, and slowed his fall just enough for him to roll on the ground and stand, free, gazing up at his heartbroken Uncle and the love of his life flanked by guards. Love can be the most destructive force in the universe, and the only thing which vanquishes it is hate. But there was no hate there among them. Instead, King Mark sent all the guards away, and roared:

'Tristan! I should destroy you and grind you into the mud for the disservice you have done me. I never believed what the people said about you two, but I have been too trusting. By rights I should burn you at the stake, my dear, and have this boy hung like a puppy. But I know that you would only escape every time, Tristan, and swing in to save her like the hero you are, so there is no point. Instead, my boy, you will leave my court – no, Kernow – no, the whole of Britain! – and you shall never return! Go and live in Brittany and fight French ogres or something, but you will never be welcome in my company again! Isolde, you are coming home with me.'

All three of them cried bitter tears, but Mark's word was final. That night, as Tristan was marched onto the first ship leaving port, Isolde broke through all the bounds between them to share one deep farewell kiss with her love. But both felt certain that this would be the very last meeting of their lips.

Isolde could never be happy as the Queen of Kernow, but as time went by, with her always at King Mark's side, she learned to hide her feelings. As did King Mark, who never spoke an unkind word to his wife – after all, war between Ireland and Kernow was the last thing anybody wanted.

Over on the French coast, Tristan was beloved for his bravery and chivalry, and was soon given the hand in marriage of a particularly pretty young damsel, in return for saving her father's castle from a delinquent kraken. Weirdly, her name was also Isolde, and she was naturally head over heels in love with her handsome husband.

But that was not to say that Tristan hadn't collected many enemies over the years, and one day his luck finally ran out. He chanced upon six huge and brutish knights, who were all determined to steal away the innocence of a young milkmaid in distress. Tristan would not stand for this, and of course he swung into action, saving the young virgin and the day, and laying waste to all six knights... But not before one of them had attacked the brave hero from behind and run him right through the belly with his lance.

Tristan staggered home and collapsed into his wife's embrace, and it was clear there was very little life left in him. In fact, they both knew there was only one person with any hope of curing Tristan's wound – and she was the Queen of Kernow.

While breath remained in his body, Tristan begged for word to be sent to Queen Isolde, to come and heal his deadly wound as she had tended to his burns all those years ago. He asked for the ships returning from Cornwall to carry white sails if Isolde had agreed to come, and black sails if not. Hour after hour after day after day passed by, Tristan weakening by the minute, until...

'They are here, husband!' announced Tristan's wife.

'At last!' the dying knight coughed, 'I knew she could not let me down! Tell me, wife, are the sails white or black?'

This weeping second Isolde was not a bad person, but she had always known that she was not, and never would be, the one true Isolde as far as Tristan was concerned, and this fact stuck in her craw and turned to poison. She stared out to the approaching ships, all sails shining bright white, and Queen Isolde gazing fearfully out from the prow of the leading ship... and she replied:

'Black sails, Tristan. They are black sails. Queen Isolde has left you to die.'

This was all Tristan needed to hear. And the last thing he ever heard. His wife had not even ended her sentence before his heart broke, and gave up, and he was dead.

His wife was no healer; there was nothing she could do. And when Queen Isolde finally arrived, it was too late even for her own healing powers. She had fled from King Mark's side to save Tristan's life, and had been too late. Isolde needed no poison, no weapon, no potion – her own heart broke at the sight of her dead lost love, and her lifeless body fell over him in an embrace that nobody would ever part.

Tristan and Isolde were taken back to Kernow and buried together just as they were. Before a year had passed, the stone which marked their grave was encircled with the branches of two trees which grew out of the soil – a hazel, and a honeysuckle. No matter what anybody ever did, the two beautifully interlacing plants could never be separated. Some things just belong together.

THE END

FOWEY, CORNWALL

Many people who call themselves experts when it comes to legends, mythology and ancient history will tell you that there never was a Tristan, nor an Isolde, and that the tale of doomed lovers was invented somewhere on the continent, and regurgitated in Cornwall years later. But the wisdom remains that at some time halfway through the first millennium, at roughly the same time that Arthur was said to be fighting his battles, there was a real warrior who we now know as Tristan. Tintagel has become more famous as an Arthurian site, but one of the greatest clues we have to this tale's truth can be found on the road into the picturesque Cornish town of Fowey, where a stone from the sixth century reads, in Latin: 'Drustan lies here, of Cunomorus the son, with the lady Ousilla'. The names may have changed a little over the years, but although the stone itself has been moved around many a time (so there's no point in digging beneath it for evidence), the memorial certainly gives lovers of the tale pause for thought.

fowey.co.uk

24. GAWAIN AND THE GREEN KNIGHT

Swythamley, Staffordshire

Christmas has been celebrated in the isles of Britain for a lot longer than anyone has called it 'Christmas' – whether you prefer names such as 'Winter Solstice', 'Yule', 'Mithrasmas' or the Roman 'Saturnalia', the beginning of the coldest season has always been a time for families and folk to flock together in the warm, under glittering candlelight and in halls festooned with the richest evergreen boughs, to toast the successful bringing in of the harvest, and be together as the temperatures plunge and the countryside freezes.

This was much the same even in the days of King Arthur and his court at Camelot. One dark New Year's night, all of the Knights of the Round Table, their wives and families, squires, jesters and wizards, all came together in Arthur's Great Hall to see in the new year with wassail and feast and cheer, and have a wonderful time. So green were the bowers which hung around the Great Hall, it was some time before anybody realised there was a stranger in their midst.

'King Arthur!' came the cry, deep and demanding in the fireside glow, and all looked to see the tallest knight they had ever beheld, clad all in green with a mighty horned green helmet, and carrying in his hands a sprig of holly, and a large sharp axe, which glinted by candlelight.

'I am he,' returned the King, swallowing a mouthful of particularly tasty pheasant. 'Who wishes to know me, and strolls casually into my protective circle on such a winter's night as this?'

'You shall know me as The Green Knight,' replied the stranger. 'And as it is Christmas, my lord, I have come here to propose a merry game for one of you brave, famous Knights of the Round Table.'

A hush had descended throughout the previously rowdy throng, and those present were all ears to hear of the Green Knight's festive pastime.

'It's a very simple game,' continued the Green Knight. 'I give this axe to one of you strapping fellows, and then you can have a go at me. Just one blow, mind! But I cannot flinch or protect myself. And then, if I survive, I get to return the blow.'

The Knights, from Bors to Lancelot to Bedevere, all remained silent. The first bit of the game sounded easy enough, but too easy – there had to be some kind of catch, and they didn't like the idea of it.

'None of you?' boomed King Arthur with disbelief. 'I have gathered together the bravest and most noble men in the Kingdom, and not one of you feels up to accepting this frankly suicidal offer from the Green Knight? Well, in that case, my green sir, it seems it must fall to myself to accept this New Year's challenge!'

However, no sooner had Arthur stood and begun to roll up his sleeves than he heard a gentle cough from the corner of the room. It wasn't a cough anyone generally paid much attention to, but it had fallen so silent, Arthur heard it. It came from his young honorary nephew, Gawain.

'Gawain, you have something you would like to say?'

'Um, well, perhaps, sire!' the thin young man stammered in reply.

'You would face this challenge?'

Gawain had always wanted to be a fully-fledged Knight of the Round Table, and this, he realised, was his chance. 'Yes, I will, my lord!' Gawain stood.

'Offer open to Knights only, mind you!' The Green Knight warned.

'Gawain my boy, come here!' said King Arthur, and his nephew knelt before him. 'For having the bravery to cough when all around you remain silent, I now dub you Sir Gawain! I just hope you keep the name for longer than the next few moments.'

And so Sir Gawain took the Green Knight's axe, and the stranger knelt before him. With one mighty thwack, Gawain razored the axe through the Green Knight's neck, and the mighty helmeted head toppled terribly onto the ground.

Everyone held their breath. And then, the Green Knight arose, picked up his head, and held it aloft, red blood dripping down his green tunic, and addressed the feasting merrymakers.

'Well done, Gawain, that was an excellent swing! Took my head clean off. And now, it is my turn to return the blow. But as I can see you are still young and only newly ennobled, we shall see each other in one year and one day, in the Green Chapel where I reside. Only then perhaps will you be ready to face my axe.'

And with little more ado, the Green Knight squidged his head back onto his body, and calmly rode away from Camelot.

Gawain had a busy year, training and adventuring, until he felt that he deserved the title of Knight of the Round Table. This didn't just mean building up his muscles and perfecting his sword skills, but training his brain, and learning all the ways of chivalry, and how a Knight must behave.

Just as he was beginning to feel he was getting somewhere, Gawain realised that very nearly a year had passed since he had been knighted, and the arrival of evergreen decorations at Camelot told him it was yuletide once again. He had to turn his face from all the merriment of the season, and ride north, to where the Green Chapel was supposed to be. Before him he held his shield, bedecked with a green pentangle – a five-pointed star symbolising Gawain's five-strong bond of faithfulness, and chivalry.

As he galloped off, the snow began to fall, prettily at first, but then in heavy blankets which made it hard for him to see where he was going; his poor horse had to struggle through snowdrifts higher than his nostrils!

Luckily, a castle was hard by, with warm light glowing invitingly in the windows, and Gawain knew that he would surely freeze to death if he didn't seek shelter and comfort with the strangers who lived there. And after all, it was the Solstice; who could turn away a Knight in need on such a night?

He was proved right that nobody would leave him out in the cold, and the lord of the castle welcomed Gawain in like a lost favourite nephew. 'A Knight of the Round Table right here in the castle of Hautdesert! What an honour at this merry time of the year!' beamed the lord of the castle as he introduced himself and his handsome young wife: 'We are Lord and Lady Bertilak!'

There was also a wizened old lady who sat spinning at a wheel in the corner of the hall, but nobody seemed to notice her, or mention her name, and Gawain didn't like to ask.

Gawain was given mulled wine and roast goose and warmth from the crackling yule log in the enormous fireplace, and soon he was exhausted and ready to be shown to his bed. 'The Green Chapel is but a mile or two from here,' Lord Bertilak reassured his guest. 'You can ride out as soon as the snow will allow. But until then, Sir Gawain, you are welcome here, welcome to our food, our wine, our warmth – what is mine is yours!' And at this, the lord of the castle laughed a loud and lusty laugh, and Gawain followed Lady Bertilak up to the fine bed he had been given, where he soon fell fast asleep.

The next morning, Lord Bertilak was up early and ready to set off hunting by the time Gawain had stirred and arisen. He was yawning his way down to breakfast as his host greeted him.

'Good morning, Sir Gawain!' the lord thundered. 'I presumed, with your busy quest to worry about, you would not be interested in going for a Boxing Day hunt, so I am just on my way out. But you must keep warm, help yourself to anything. In fact, here's a game for you – I will happily give you whatever I manage to catch, on the condition that you give me whatever you might gain on this day. Does that sound a fair deal?'

'Well I have no plans to gain anything except perhaps a little extra sleep,' replied Gawain, looking out at the thick snowdrifts blocking off his journey north. 'So you have yourself a deal!'

They shook hands, and Gawain ate a little bacon and returned to bed. But it was only a few minutes later that he heard a knocking at the old oak door to his room, and before he could reply, Lady Bertilak had let herself in, and stood there in the firelight.

'Oh, brave Sir Gawain!' the buxom hostess said, 'how long and tough your journey north must have been. Is there anything I can do to make you feel better? Anything at all?'

'No, you've been very kind, thank you.'

She lay on the Knight's fur-festooned bed, and continued, 'Your quest has been so hard, will you not come and rest your head on my bosom?'

Sir Gawain composed himself, lest his stuttering response give away his panic at such a suggestion, before replying, 'My lady, I fear it would show scant respect to my host to do such a thing. Lovely though the offer is!' And he gulped.

24. GAWAIN AND THE GREEN KNIGHT

'Come, I thought the Knights of the Round Table were lusty and would be denied nothing they desired?' Lady Bertilak said. 'I see you are virtuous, but will you not at least lie with me?'

Very cautiously, Gawain lay on the bed, at a careful distance from his hostess. 'Well, this is nice,' he ventured to add.

'Isn't it?' she replied, 'It's even nicer over on this side of the bed.'

'Very comfy here too,' Gawain insisted.

'If you come closer, fair Knight, I will reward you with this ring.' And the Lady Bertilak held aloft a glittering jewelled ring. But Gawain would not even hear of such a thing.

'I need no jewel or reward, my dear hostess,' he said, 'I simply need to be pointed towards the Green Knight's chapel and to do my duty as one of King Arthur's Knights.'

Lady Bertilak sighed, defeated. 'Your chivalry is famous throughout the land, but I did not believe any man could be so honest until now. However,' she went on, 'one thing you must accept from me, for your quest.' She began to undress, and Gawain went all red and began to protest, but she silenced him with a finger to his lips, and showed what she had to give: a green girdle, a kind of belt which wound around her waist, and seemed to glisten with an indefinable power. 'This you must have from me, and to refuse would be more unchivalrous than to take. Believe me, you will need it.'

And so despite his oath, Gawain made no complaint as she wound the girdle around his waist – and even as she kissed him on the lips when it was fastened. And then, she was gone, and Lord Bertilak was at the gates, blowing his hunting horn.

Gawain descended to the great hall to greet his host, who carried a great brute of a wild boar, the result of his day's hunting.

'As promised, Gawain, here is my day's bounty. What do you have to offer me in return?'

After a brief pause, Gawain decided to keep silent. He approached Lord Bertilak, and gave him a kiss, without a word about where it came from.

This went on for some days, Gawain forever refusing the temptations of Lady Bertilak, until he awoke to find the sun shining in a blue sky, and the snow and frost thawed enough to allow the young Knight to continue his quest towards the Green Chapel. With thanks to his hosts at Hautdesert Castle, and the green girdle wrapped twice around him, the chilly but chivalrous youth mounted his horse and galloped off due north.

It was the grating sound of a mighty axe being sharpened that led Gawain to the Green Chapel, a leafy and luscious grove deep in the middle of a bare and wintry forest. There in the grove stood the huge imposing figure of the Green Knight, who greeted his valorous visitor with a silent salute, and gestured towards a gnarled stump that was to act as Gawain's execution block... Or was it?

'I have arrived to receive your return blow,' Gawain said, but no reply came. 'Happy new year to you as well,' Gawain added, as he knelt and revealed his neck to the Green Knight's axe. It would not be true to say that Gawain was immediately brave, and on the Green Knight's first swing, the young victim visibly flinched. The Green Knight shook his head, and pointed for Gawain to return his head to the block... But then, on the second blow, it was the Green Knight's turn to flinch, and he missed Gawain altogether.

This was too much for Gawain, whose nerves were all a-jangle, and he thundered, 'Do it! This is your game, Green Knight, and I am not afraid to die. Bring down your axe and have done!'

In less than a second, the mighty Green Knight lifted his axe, and brought it down thunderously on Gawain's fleshy neck... And it bounced right off him, leaving just the slightest nick in his skin!

Thanks to the magical green girdle, honour had been served, and Gawain was just beginning to thank his stars and leave the Green Knight for good, when the tall axe-wielding magician began to laugh: a deep, fruity laugh which echoed around the Green Chapel, and seemed somehow familiar to Gawain.

Removing his disguise, the Green Knight admitted, 'Yes, Gawain, it was I, Lord Bertilak of Hautdesert Castle, all this time! I see you have been saved by my wife's green girdle. You should of course have told me about that, but now I see how fearless you are, to travel all this way and submit to my axe, I do not blame you.'

'Yes, well done, Sir Gawain,' said the mysterious old spinster of Hautdesert Castle, stepping into the Green Chapel with a cackle, and removing her own disguise. 'You have proved me wrong. I thought that my brother Arthur's Round Table Knights could not be as brave as the ballads said they were. And so I arranged a test for one of you. If you are typical of these Knights, then my brother truly has created a chivalrous court, though perhaps not an honest one. You may return to him now, and give the green girdle to Arthur from his sister, Morgan

24. GAWAIN AND THE GREEN KNIGHT

Le Fay, with all blessings. Wear it to remind you of your dishonesty at this turning of the year.'

Gawain did not need telling twice. He missed Camelot, and was still a fresh recruit as a Knight. There were quests to undertake, battles to win, and maybe even damsels who might be in need of his professional services.

On his return south Gawain stood before the smouldering yule log and told his frankly weird tale to the whole court, leaving nothing out, and after careful pondering, the other Knights agreed to forgive Gawain the deception of Lord Bertilak, as they had all learned from the young knight's deceptive mission. From that day forth, all the Knights of the Round Table wore scraps of the green girdle knotted on their armour, to remind themselves that bravery and chivalry may be important, and above all, respect for women... but that humans will always make errors – and as long as they are made for the best reasons, that's something we must all accept, with liberality.

THE END

SWYTHAMLEY, STAFFS

There are numerous Arthurian locations detailed elsewhere in this book, but there are also sites that have a strong claim to being the real Castle Hautdesert and the real Green Chapel in the Peak District area of Staffordshire. The first version of Gawain's tale is written in a West Midlands dialect, and so the area of Swythamley, and particularly the mysterious green caverns known as 'Lud's Church', have long had strong connections to the legend, and are well worth a visit, in sunshine or snow.

peakdistrictinformation.com

25. AVALON

Glastonbury, Somerset

The problem with folk who don't understand how history works is that they often fail to grasp the crucial fact that life as they know it will not last forever. Are the seas really rising? Will the British end up one day sitting at the top of lamp posts chewing on locusts? It's hard to say for sure, but anyone who could see the watery lands of Britain as they have developed over the last few thousand years, water levels rising and falling, would see the wisdom in stocking up on locusts, just to be safe rather than sorry.

A perfect example of the ever-changing landscape that surrounds us can be pictured at Glastonbury – that famous corner of the Somerset countryside which vibrates with music and magic. There on the horizon, seen from town and festival alike, you cannot miss Glastonbury Tor, an ancient pock-marked hill with a medieval church tower atop it. But had you been gazing at this hill around the time of King Arthur, in the fifth or sixth century AD, you would be looking at an island – the Isle of Avalon, also known as the Island of Apples – rising eerily from the vast watery stretches which went on for miles in the winter, where now we walk on reasonably dry land.

This Isle of Avalon has many claims to fame – some have long insisted that the Welsh King of the Fairies, Gwynn ap Nudd, hides a special door to his underground kingdom there. But above all, it will be forever known as the final resting place of Arthur, King of the Britons.

The Romans had fled the land which they had thoroughly drenched in British blood, and thanks to Vortigern, the way became clear for another round of vicious invasions – this time from the deadly

25. AVALON

English, the Angles and Saxons. Brave Arthur and his death-defying band of professional British fighters became the last line of defence against this blonde, bloodthirsty bunch from over the seas.

Arthur's greatest victory was the Battle of Mount Badon, an epic scrap which took place quite possibly in the hills around Bath, the gateway to the south-west. It is sometimes said that on Badon Hill a hundred hundred Saxons fell to the swords of Arthur and his Knights, and briefly in that area, peace reigned once again. A magnificent court was created, with a Round Table encircled by honourable knights, and the British felt quite safe... for a while.

But such a moment of peace, like the shape of the landscape, cannot last forever, and eventually the noble ruler Arthur was to be brought down by his own family. Some say the twisted trouble-making usurper responsible, Mordred, was Arthur's nephew; some say he was his full-blooded son – but whichever it was, there was little love lost between the twisted noble and the mighty ruler when they faced each other in the snow, one frosty winter solstice.

After many years of jolly jousts, valiant errands and memorable feasts at the court of Camelot (with the odd search for the Holy Grail thrown in to spice things up), things eventually seemed to start going wrong for Arthur whichever way he looked.

Perhaps the problems had all started when his trusted adviser, the wise wizard Merlin, was spellbound and imprisoned in an old gnarly oak tree by Arthur's half-sister, Morgan le Fay. Morgan was a skilled healer and sorcerer who just happened to also be Mordred's mother. One by one she wheedled every secret and magic trick from Merlin's spellbook, until the day came that she was his equal in every regard – whereupon she tricked the usually untrickable magician into imprisoning himself forever!

The gossip ran that it was only with Merlin frozen in sleep that Arthur's greatest heartbreak came – Camelot's most handsome knight, a Gaul known as Lancelot of the Lake, fell in love with Queen Guinevere and persuaded her to flee home to his French castle with him. The Queen was so torn she felt her heart would smash into pieces, but she could not deny the passion that pulled her to Lancelot like a moth to a candle.

When word finally reached Arthur of the treacherous couple's elopement, who should be the bearer of this bad news? Mordred, of course. Mordred had been a sickly child, and had grown into an even more sickly adult. He was blonde and pale, with thin lips that rarely smiled, but when they did, it was not attractive. 'My lord,' the little troublemaker began with a hideous grin, 'I have shocking news. The Queen, your wife, has fled over the sea with your best friend, Lancelot. They have been making a fool of you, Uncle Arthur. Are you going to stand for that?'

A gallon of red-hot tears pricked at King Arthur's eyes, but he quenched them with a burning fury – and believed every word Mordred said. Guinevere was a traitor, he heard. No fit Queen. An insult to Britain. Something had to be done. With no to-do, the King decided to ride off in pursuit right away, fuelled by jealous righteousness. But who could be relied upon to keep an eye on the court of Camelot while he was away? There was only one choice.

'Mordred my boy,' said Arthur, 'Simply keep your hand on the tiller of the land, for my briefest absence. Care for the people, see justice done where necessary, and I shall return with my Queen before another moon arrives!'

'Don't worry, your majesty,' drawled Mordred, 'I'll know just what to do when the time arrives. Your land is safe from dread, with Mordred...'

But then, as the King galloped away and disappeared over the horizon, Mordred added, '... Don't hurry back!'

Arthur had made a big mistake. The ambitious Mordred soon discovered he rather liked being the boss, bathing in fresh creamy milk and kicking peasants, and with the King so far away, he decided to make the job more permanent. Soon word reached Arthur that he had lost his Kingdom to the traitorous young regent, who was mercilessly mistreating the British people and ravaging the land, and doing both with the greatest glee.

Mordred had decided to raise the taxes by a thousand percent, and melted down every penny he could to create himself a thick golden suit of armour which shone so dazzlingly bright he could see his simpering pale face in every plate. The poor were starving, and Mordred simply loved laughing at starving poor people.

Of course, the noble King Arthur had no option but to turn away from his heartbreak in France, and speed back to free his kingdom from Mordred's cruelty, his sword Excalibur always at his side. By the end of the year, at solstice-tide, which was normally a time of great feasting and fun, Arthur faced the young pretender to the British crown in a field of blood, known as Camlann.

All the Knights of the Round Table rallied to Arthur's cause – Sir Gawain fought bravely, as did Sirs Bors, Galahad, Bedivere, Kay, Valiant and more. Excalibur positively smoked in Arthur's grasp as his enemy thrust forward his shield. The legendary sword had dispatched armies of Saxon invaders and villainous warlords, but on this day, in the aging King's hand, Excalibur somehow finally seemed to founder. Long bouts of butcherly duelling in the swirling snow had worn Arthur down more than ever before. Mordred caught Arthur many times with his own sword, and the blood ran freely down the King's burly but bruised body. But this was Arthur! Holding Excalibur! Somewhere deep down, no matter how exhausted and deathly the beleaguered King felt, he knew he could not lose.

'Ha! See the great King Arthur bleed and groan in the ruddy snow!' sneered Mordred, young and lithe, though with a fountain of sweat filling his preposterous golden armour. 'Maybe it's time for you and your Knights to hang up your spurs, Uncle... Or should I say, FATHER!' And with his face a horrifying mask of unspeakable hatred, Mordred screamed and lunged towards Arthur for the kill.

But then, his face changed, from hatred into... confusion? Pain? Fear? Mordred gazed down to see the trusty Excalibur's hilt neatly glinting as the broad blade sheared through his glittering belly like it was butter. Gold could not stop Excalibur. Mordred dropped down in the snow, blood and dirt, dead as dung.

This time there was no loud 'hooray', no feasting to celebrate the victory – because Arthur himself was clearly mortally wounded as he collapsed in the red-splattered snow and the solstice sun set over the frosty waters around Avalon.

It's quite possible that Arthur died that very moment. But that is not how the story goes.

Suddenly, swooping onto the battlefield, arrived Morgan le Fay, that so-called wicked sorcerer. This butchery had never been the plan. Her son was dead, she could see, but her brother the King still had breath in his body. Morgan was, above all, a healer, and she was the leader of nine skilled sisters who lived atop the island of Avalon itself. These sisters of Avalon carried Arthur's failing body onto a long boat, and they sailed away, westwards, until they reached the island of apples.

Many have told tales of how Arthur then called to his side his most trusted Knight, and one of the only survivors of the Battle of Camlann, Sir Bedivere, and ordered him: 'My brother, brave Bedivere, take Excalibur from my scabbard and return the sword to Nimue the Lady of the Lake, she who first placed its British blade in that stone for me to retrieve all those years ago...'

Taking his leave from his King, Bedivere carried the mighty Excalibur out to the lapping waters of Avalon... however, he found he could not bring himself to throw the sword into the water – surely Britain would need its strength again? He hid it under the snow and returned to Arthur to tell him that the job was done, that there had been a big splash, and all was well, but Arthur knew that there would be more to tell, if Bedivere really had obeyed his order.

'Do not worry, Bedivere,' Arthur said, 'This is the way it has to end, but the sword will return when it is needed by the people of Britain.'

And so, with tears tearing down his scarred face, Sir Bedivere finally gained the courage to hurl Excalibur far out into the misty waves. Just as it looked set to make a big splash, a silvery hand shot out from the water, and grasped the famous sword! The hand held Excalibur aloft for just one shining moment, and it glinted one more time in the sunset's rays, before sinking back under the waves.

When Bedivere told Arthur about this, the King knew the job had really been done.

Legends can take many forms, but what actually happened to King Arthur next forks one of two ways. Perhaps the brave warrior died from his wounds and was buried there on Avalon...

But then, perhaps he didn't. Even today, folk still believe that it was on Avalon that Morgan healed her wounded half-brother, and that once he was safe, she froze him in time, just as she had with Merlin. This was not an evil spell, but part of an important promise to all the people of Britain – that when the time comes, when the wise, just, and brave King Arthur is needed once again to protect his people, the people of Britain, in their time of greatest need, he will rise once again – with Excalibur in his hand, and Merlin by his side.

And you know, some days, it does feel like he might be a little bit overdue.

THE END

25. AVALON

GLASTONBURY

Nobody needs telling that Glastonbury is dense with millennia of storytelling mysticism and historical mythology — least of all the multitudes of music lovers who rock up to the region every summer to have fun at the Glastonbury Festival. The town itself is a treasure trove of mythological and mystical magnificence — not to mention mumbo jumbo. Glastonbury Tor cannot be missed no matter what your reason for visiting the area, however, and is a fair (and steep!) signposted walk from the Abbey. Glastonbury Abbey ruins have enough non-Arthurian tales of their own — Jesus of Nazareth's uncle Joseph of Arimathea is said to have planted a holy thorn here two thousand years ago, but although there is a legend that this Middle Eastern tin trader did have links with Britain, it's a tough tale to believe. Equally hard to credit is the reputed discovery of King Arthur and Queen Guinevere's graves within the Abbey in the 12th century. This was very probably a monastic con trick, designed to please the King of the Day and increase the glory and wealth of the Abbey... but if you can't give your will to believe free rein in a place as mystical as Avalon itself, then there's no hope for you.

glastonbury.co.uk

OTHER ARTHURIAN SITES

There are many many places laying claim to being 'the real Camelot', in England, Scotland, Wales and even France — but of course, the South-West, with its wealth of Arthurian traditions, tends to be the loudest claimant of them all. It does help that one of the ancient names for the hillfort of Cadbury is 'Camlat', or something very similar. Winchester also has long claimed to be the home of the real Round Table.

If you're in Scotland, however, besides Edinburgh's famous Arthur's Seat, the small town of Camelon outside Fife was once on a wall dividing England from the Picts, and the similar name speaks volumes. Merlin's Grave can be found in the border town of Drumelzier, and near Dumfries you will find Loch Arthur, where Excalibur was said to be cast, and Stirling has its own claims to the Round Table.

Wales' insistence on being real Arthur country is perhaps the most vociferous, and Arthur's legend in print does begin with Welsh texts. There aren't many Welsh areas which don't make Arthurian claims, but the strongest can be found at Caerleon, an old Roman fortification north of Newport, which may have been Camelot. Then in Snowdonia you'll find Cadair Idris — a warrior's throne said to be Arthur's — and Llyn Llydaw, a lake where that famous sword may have ended up. Plus of course, Merlin is one of Wales' famous sons, and many places, like Carmarthen, are proud of their connections to him.

legendofkingarthur.co.uk
kingarthurslabyrinth.co.uk
undiscoveredscotland.co.uk

133

26. CADOC AND
THE MOUSE

Brecon

Not long after King Arthur's heyday, in the hilly Brecon area of central Wales, there was a small but respected school in the tiny valleyside village of Llanspyddid. The students there were of all ages and abilities, but the brightest pupil of them all was probably Cadoc.

He's more commonly known as Saint Cadoc, but young Cadoc was certainly no saint. He yawned through his classes, gazed out of the window daydreaming at clouds, and spent more time doodling than studying. This wasn't because he was a bad lad at all, he was just far too bright for the lessons taught by his boring old teacher, Bachan. Cadoc had already travelled through Britain and Ireland learning much about life from many angles, but he had returned to his Welsh home and was forced to sit through tiresome lessons such as...

'And that, boys and chaps, is how we know that God created the mermaid to test us all. Now, get out your Science textbooks, and I will tell you all how flat the Earth is, and how quickly the sun spins around it. ARE YOU LISTENING TO ME, CADOC?'

Cadoc's gaze left the window, and he turned to face his teacher in a flash. 'Sorry, sir, no sir, I wasn't!' the dreamy lad replied – proving that he was anything but a liar. The teacher sighed, and continued to drawl his bad lessons to the dozy class.

It wasn't just that Cadoc was bored of hearing these silly 'facts', he was quite certain were all far from correct, either. It was a humming hot day and everyone in the classroom had only had half a handful of green oats and a few hawthorns to eat that week, and it was nearly

134

suppertime. The whole valley for miles around was in the grip of a terrible famine, and no grain was being grown in the rotten fields. Cadoc's ribs were sticking out of his tunic, and sometimes he got so hungry he was tempted to teach himself how to eat leaves, like the goats.

Suddenly, the teacher Bachan squealed, and leapt up onto his chair. 'Eek! A mouse!' he screamed, and pointed with terror at a small, white, whiskery mouse who had appeared out of a hole somewhere in the classroom. 'Someone deal with it, please, it's looking at me funny!'

Cadoc sighed, and picked up the timid little rodent. Being a clever lad, he knew not to be afraid, but he also noted something very interesting. For miles around, the cows were bony in the fields, the horses were hungry for hay, and cats and dogs were positively eating each other in their craving for food, any food... And yet, this little mouse seemed rather plump and well fed.

'Get rid of it, get rid of it!' begged Bachan.

'Sir, hang on, I've had rather a good idea for a wheeze here!' Cadoc replied, and fetched a long ball of string from his desk. 'If I gently connect a length of this thin twine to the mouse's leg, and then let her go outside...'

'Yes yes, do it please, quick!' the teacher cried.

'Then maybe, if I just hold onto the string, and see where the little thing goes...'

The mouse pelted off towards the old hillfort at Coed Fenni-Fach, just up the hill from the school, and Cadoc followed the string to a small hole in the ruins of an old castle which once had stood there.

Kneeling down on the grass, Cadoc began to dig at the hole, deeper and faster, until suddenly, he struck a hollow cavern of some kind, stone-enclosed and crumbling, and as he peered in, and let the sun shine through to the dark cavern inside, he saw it was absolutely filled with...

'WHEAT!' cried Cadoc with the biggest smile he had managed in weeks. In a cool, dry place, wheat can survive for many decades and still be edible. Nobody knew who had hidden all the wheat in the secret granary at Coed Fenni-Fach, but once it was all scooped out, it made enough bread, and cakes, and biscuits, to keep everyone safe from starvation for months, until the harvest finally came in again and they could feed themselves. There was even enough to share with the little mouse and all her family!

The teachers at Llanspyddid school decided that this was so clever of young Cadoc, they would give him an A star grade for all his classes, and he could finally graduate and get on with his life. He was always much better at teaching than being taught by other people, anyway. And his lessons were always fun.

THE END

BRECON BEACONS

For those of you who love a bit of adventure and going up and down very steep hills, the Brecon Beacons are a very exciting place to travel to, as well as eye-wideningly epic. There are a thousand and three different places to visit in this picturesque mountain range in South Wales, but if you're keen to walk in Cadoc's footsteps, you can pay a visit to the tiny village of Llanspyddid, and follow the mouse's route up to the Iron Age hillfort of Coed Fenni-Fach. The grain has all gone now though, so it's best to take some sandwiches.

fforestfawrgeopark.org.uk

---

27. JACK AND THE BEANSTALK

Wilmington, South Downs

This island once echoed from shore to shore with the grunts, belches and poor poetry of GIANTS, as you know. Some could be as big as the Tower of London, others only a measly eight feet tall, but for centuries, they roamed Britain's hills and valleys. And somebody had to deal with them. This would have been a rather unfair way of seeing these huge folk, who had been here long before any of us, if it wasn't for the fact that almost every giant on record was, to put it bluntly, AN ABSOLUTE GIT. They scoffed down innocent tourists as if they were jelly babies, greedily hoarded the gold, hard-quarried by 'the little people', as they called us, and generally terrorised the countryside, the seaside, and any other kind of side they felt like walking all over.

Nobody knows for sure why the giants were quite so grumpy and greedy, but the big natives were never happy about having to share the island with stubby little interlopers, even if they were quite tasty to eat. Some say they lashed out because they were here first, as Albion's children. Others say it was simply the difficulty giants had in finding comfortable shoes in their clod-hopping foot size that made them so angry. But whatever the reason, these giants were a menace to our very survival.

The human settlers tried in vain to live happily with their lanky neighbours, but too many greedy midnight raids on too many villages meant that the people of Britain needed some security. The most

137

27. JACK AND THE BEANSTALK

famous hero of all to be remembered down the centuries was Jack, the Giant Killer, a smart Englishman with the wit and guile to send any murderous ogre packing. Many tales are told of Jack's mighty giant-battling feats, but none repeated so jubilantly as his very first mission, at the top of the famous beanstalk.

The English were especially hated by giants, as they had come to Britain later than anyone else, in the middle of the first millennium, and made it their own. Jack knew nothing of this, being born on the island, and only a lad when his career began. He lived in the heart of the Sussex countryside with his widowed mother and a rather saggy old cow. This cow, Milky White, was Jack and his Mum's one and only asset, her milk their only source of food besides what few turnips Jack could grow in the rubble outside their crumbly cottage, and his Mum made butter to sell at the market, when there was enough to go round.

But one sad day, with the rain pouring in through the roof and both of them starving hungry, Jack's Mum could stand no more. 'There's nothing else we can do, Jack,' she sighed, 'We shall have to sell poor old Milky at the market, and use whatever she fetches to feed ourselves, and fix the cottage, and hope for a better day.'

'But Mum, Milky is all we have!' Jack cried, 'Who will want such a poor sack of bones anyway?'

'Less of that, lad, she can hear you!' his mother snapped back. But they were both upset – Milky was more like one of the family than livestock. With her mind made up, however, Jack's Mum was not an easy woman to argue with, and so she gave Jack a raw turnip for his breakfast, sadly kissed the tip of Milky's nose, and sent them off on the day of the Lewes market.

Jack took hold of Milky's bridle and reluctantly pottered down the lane, hoping against hope that he could prove himself an excellent salesman, and get a good deal to please his Mum. But as he looked in Milky's big sad brown eyes, he realised that what he would like more than anything else was to find his old beefy friend a happy home for her remaining years.

It was then that he saw the man. Jack lived in quite a lonely corner of the country, and rarely saw anyone except his Mum, but this curious fellow would have caught his attention in any crowd. First of all, he seemed to be an unusual shade of green from tip to toe, with a fiery ginger beard hanging low from his chin and woven into his jacket and trousers, looping around both his spindly legs. His eyes, as they swivelled round to Jack's own, were bright and sparkly.

'My – my – MY! Now that is what I call a cow!' the fellow thundered, delightedly. 'Never have I seen such a noble and intelligent creature! Is she bound for the market, Jack?'

Milky blushed. Jack wondered how the fellow knew his name.

'Aye, she's a fine friend,' Jack returned, his dreams of being a trader quickly forgotten, 'But she's not really much of a Sunday roast, sir, I'll be honest with you.'

'Sunday roast?' gasped the fellow, aghast. 'Why, don't even say such a thing in jest, my lad! It is a friend I see before me, if not two friends. I would be honoured if I could call this splendid cow a friend, and yet...' The loopy-looking stranger shook his head. 'I suppose you're wanting plenty of gold for such a fine four-legger? Hmm. I wonder if you know how many beans make five.'

'Two in each hand and one in me mouth!' Jack shot back, and the fellow grinned. 'I really have to get everything I can, sir,' Jack went on, 'Milky means ever so much to me, and...'

'MILKY!' boomed the fellow with a grin. 'Oh, yes, of course she's a Milky through and through, you can see it on her nose, I should have guessed. Now please hear me out, lad. What I can offer you is...' He put his hand into a pouch somewhere in his tummy and pulled out a handful of... 'BEANS!'

'Beans?' Jack replied, puzzled.

'Some beans,' the fellow corrected.

'Oh, SOME beans? Well why didn't you say?' Jack grouched.

The strange fellow raised a ginger eyebrow. 'These aren't the kind of beans you just have on toast, lad! You will never find any beans of this kind anywhere else on this island, believe you me, and believe me you. They are exotic, and strange, and – for want of a better word – magical.'

Jack was just preparing another sarcastic reply when he saw the jumble of large purple beans heaped up in the strange fellow's hands, where they seemed to be wriggling, and – yes, he really did see that – glinting, like stars. He was bedazzled.

'Not only that,' the stranger pleaded, 'But I promise you from my very bottom that I shall take the best care of this magnificent creature. She shall be a friend to me and my family, and frolic in our pastures, and never be hungry again.'

Jack could only take so much of this sales patter – he was no businessman, and this ginger geezer had described exactly the life Jack wanted for dear old Milky. He did the deal.

'You, my lad, are far cleverer than anyone will ever understand,' the odd fellow chuckled, 'This is the very best decision for everyone concerned. Take these beans – be careful they don't wriggle out of your pocket, mind! – and just wait for your good fortune to spring up all around you.'

Jack hugged his old friend Milky goodbye, patted her nose and whispered to her that now she would be free and happy, and accepted the curious, fizzy-feeling beans from the weird chap. He carefully popped them in his pockets, and felt them dance around. When he looked up, both strange stranger and dear old Milky White had completely vanished.

Long before his planned turnip break, young Jack arrived back home to excitedly show his Mum what a clever deal he had struck. When he unloaded his sparkling reward onto the kitchen table, however, his Mum pulled a face that looked like she had mistaken a cowpat for a delicious bowl of porridge. And she only said one word.

'Beans?'

'Magical beans!' Jack insisted.

Jack's Mum did say lots of other things at this point, but barely a single one of them would be polite to repeat in this story. It's enough to say that she completed her loud reaction to poor Jack's magical deal by grabbing the beans, screeching 'Here's what I think of your so-called magic beans, you stupid ha'porth!' and hurling them out of the kitchen window, where they wriggled and disappeared out of sight, somewhere in the rubbly patch where nothing but turnips had ever grown.

Jack was sent to bed without any supper that night – but then there wasn't any supper for him or his Mum anyway. It was a stormy, rain-sodden night, but somehow, for all their worries, and for all the drip-dripping of the rain through the holes in the ceiling into an array of rusted pots and pans, both Jack and his Mum slept deep and long, and awoke to blue skies and a blaze of sunshine.

Also, as Jack's Mum noted with a scream as she opened the curtains that morning, there was a GIGANTIC BEANSTALK in their rubbly turnip patch! Well, the beanstalk was rooted in their garden for sure, but its thick tendrils stretched far beyond the extent of their rough scrap of land, and as they gazed up, its leaves and branches sprouted high up into the sky and disappeared far off into the clouds.

The poverty-stricken pair had no words, but they did have a dance, and a scream for joy, that now they would be in bean feast heaven! They would never be poor or hungry again! All they needed to do was harvest the beans, and then…

'Where are the beans?' Jack's Mum wailed. 'What use is a five-mile-high beanstalk with NO BEANS ON IT?' And, a tough woman at the best of times, at these highs and lows of excitement and disappointment, she finally caved in and began to wail, loudly, big fat tears bursting out of her in all directions.

'Don't cry, Mum,' Jack said, brightly, 'Look at how massive this plant is! It's bigger than any tree! All I need to do is shin up to the higher branches, and there's bound to be something worth having up there!'

Jack's Mum was far too busy dramatically blowing her nose into her apron to stop Jack as he shoved a turnip into his pocket, hitched up his pants, and, taking a firm grip on the strong stalk, began to haul himself high up into the lush green foliage.

'What are you doing now, you clod?' his Mum yelled, 'You'll be killed!'

But nimble Jack was already up so high he could barely hear her cries of consternation, and with a single holler of 'Bye Mum, be back later!' the young daredevil was lost in the clouds.

No beans could Jack see anywhere – but then, being swamped in thick white clouds, he couldn't really see very much of anything. Whether the beanstalk had twisted and bent in the mist, carrying Jack over onto some rocky crag or cliff-face high up above his cottage, he could not tell; but he was certainly surprised to put his hand out and touch solid ground, hidden underneath the swirling white. The brave lad cautiously tested his weight on the surface, shakily lifted himself up onto his feet, and looked around.

If finding solid ground in the clouds was a surprise, it was nothing compared to what Jack saw next. An almost unimaginably huge dry stone castle, with turrets and towers stretching up to the very edge of orbit, grew out of the clouds only a minute's sprint ahead of him. Jack's mouth sagged in stunned admiration as he goggled at this impossible fortress.

If you want to get over a shock, another shock is as good as any remedy, and so the sudden earthquake fixed Jack's goggling. Crumbling tremors sent vibrations through the ground and up Jack's quaking legs. And then came the great roar:

'FEE-FI-FO-FUM! I SMELL THE BLOOD OF AN ENGLISHMAN!
BE HE ALIVE OR BE HE DEAD, I'LL GRIND HIS BONES TO MAKE MY BREAD!'

There, galumphing round the west wing of the castle, came the mighty Giant. He was so enormous he didn't even have a name, and always insisted on being known as THE Giant. Nimble Jack could barely have jumped up to touch his knees, even if such a mad thought had been likely to grip him. Jack had tiptoed from the safety of the beanstalk's foliage, and was standing in clear view, so there was no way he could have spent more than a couple of seconds looking at the Giant, but that was more than enough. Those slavering lips! Those brown and crooked teeth! Those hands, each claw-like fingernail the size of a canoe! And worst of all, that HIDEOUS haircut!

Before this bone-milling ogre could sniff out the petrified Jack, the crafty young adventurer pelted towards the far side of the castle, hid in the shadows, and, just to be certain of not being found, hurried up a drainpipe, scurrying like a rat.

The Giant sniffed in a confused manner, gave his unreliable nose a gloopy, deep bogey-picking, and forgot all about it.

It was not especially nice up the drainpipe, but at least Jack knew that his bones would be safe up there. He cautiously inched his way up until he found himself climbing out into a dirty sink, full of rotting food and filthy plates. He instantly knew he was being watched.

'Gor! A clean little pink 'un in my lovely dirty sink!' cried the most enormous woman Jack had ever seen. Though not a patch on the monster outside, this big crumpled scrubber must have been a dozen feet high. It was lucky for Jack that she appeared to be more fascinated than angry – or hungry!

'Please, er, madam, all I was doing was looking for some beans, and…'

'Beans? What d'you want beans for? I probably got a tin full of 'em somewhere you could have. If you could carry it.'

'Thank you. B-but then just as I was looking, I saw this HUGE monster…'

'Oh, you mean me husband?' she replied, with a snarl of

exhaustion and regret. 'Yeah, bit of a shocker, ain't he? I can barely stand to look at the big 'orrible blighter meself. I was such a happy girl, frolicking among the oak trees, back when I was so-high to a dinosaur, but then, married to that villain for ten minutes I was, and he had me in this kitchen, cooking his humans, dirtying his floors just the way he liked 'em, creating that horrible smell he's so keen on... My life's just not my own any more. I tell you – hush!'

The large lady froze, and gestured her tiny visitor into the holes of a nearby hunk of stinking cheese. Jack held his breath as the kitchen shook with:

'FEE-FI-FO-FUM! I SMELL THE BLOOD OF AN ENGLISHMAN!
BE HE PINK OR BE HE SPOTTY, I'LL CHOMP HIS TOES AND BITE HIS BOTTY!'

'Oh there you go again with all the 'Fee-Fi-Fol-de-rol' rubbish,' the Giant's wife shot back at him, 'You're always saying that. And seeing as you got me to make four Englishman pies, a Scotsman flan and German sausage just yesterday, I'm not surprised the smell's still lingering.'

'FAIR ENOUGH,' admitted the Giant. 'ANYWAY, WIFE, IT'S HALF AN HOUR SINCE BREAKFAST, AND I'M FAMISHED!' With this, he dropped onto the table a string bag containing half a dozen cows, still mooing in a very annoyed way. 'BOIL THEM UP AND GET ME A SPOON, WIFE. I'LL BE BACK WITH MORE.' And with that, he thundered off to burgle and terrorise more farmsteads for miles around.

'I'll boil up his beef for him one of these days,' Mrs. Giant grumbled. 'He don't care what he takes, what he eats, which house he stamps on. It's all a laugh to him. Just look at all the wonderful things he's stolen...'

The Lady Giant opened a cupboard and Jack had never seen such riches, pouring out in a glittering wave – gold and silver coins, every precious jewel you could imagine in every colour under the sun, crowns, pearls, fascinating thingummies and bejewelled goblets galore.

'You must be the richest giants in all the land!' Jack gasped, up to his knees in gold pieces.

'Don't mean nuffin to us, love,' returned Mrs. Giant. 'He only likes 'em because of the sounds of misery coming from the people he takes it all from! It just sits in that cupboard taking up space. Here,' she continued, scooping up most of the messy riches into an enormous

27. JACK AND THE BEANSTALK

stocking, 'you'd be doing me a favour by getting rid of it for me. He won't notice, he'll be too busy eating his cows. You'd best be scurrying off anyway, he'll be back for his elevenses in no time. But you hurry back, young pink 'un, for there's more rubbish for you to take!'

Jack thanked the Lady Giant with a sincere bow, and jumped back into the plughole, zooming down the water slide with his sock full of bounty behind him, until the pipe pinged him out at the tip of the beanstalk.

Holding tight onto the sturdy twisting tendrils of the plant, with his heavy swag weighing him down, Jack the nimble lost no time in speeding his way down to the cottage, where his Mum was waiting with eyes ready to burst out of her head in astonishment.

'Jack! It's been raining gold and jewels! And it's been your doing?' she squawked, as Jack allowed the Giant's ill-gotten gains to spill out of the stocking. 'We're rich, Jack! RICH! JACK! We are RICH! RICH WE ARE! JACK!'

Jack's Mum could easily have gone on repeating the words 'Jack' and 'rich' for hours, had her kindly son not stopped her in her tracks. 'Well it's not ours really, Mum,' he admitted, 'I will be trying to find out whose it was and give it back to them! It was stolen by, oh Mum, the biggest, ugliest, most horriblest GIANT you ever did see!'

Whatever loud and angry things Jack's Mum had to say about giving back all the lovely jewels, and a tiara she had only just begun to admire and try on for size, this stopped her in her tracks. She had never ever seen a giant before, and didn't much like the sound of them now.

'Now look here my lad, I don't know much about giants, in fact I didn't even believe they existed until just now, same as I never believed in magical vegetables that stretch up to the sky, or raining rubies. But what you and I are gonna do is buy an 'orse, and run away as fast as that 'orse's legs can carry us.'

'Sorry Mum, I can't, I promised a nice lady giant I'd take more of these stolen riches off her hands.'

'You can't be messing around with lady giants Jack, I forbid it!'

But Jack was not to be dissuaded, and after a couple of strengthening bites of turnip he was swinging himself back up and up the mighty beanstalk as if he was born to it.

Back at the top, he spied the Giant setting off once again to terrorise some poor Saxon settling. The Giant stopped. He sniffed. He boomed.

'FEE-FI-FO-FUM! I SMELL THE BLOOD OF AN ENGLISHMAN!
BE HE BLONDE OR BE HE GINGER, I'LL SCOFF HIS TOES AND CRUNCH HIS FINGERS!'

Jack winced. That was the worst rhyme he had yet heard. Luckily, the Giant just sneezed, pulled out a bag of dry-roasted Vikings, and went on his way, crunching as he went.

What greeted Jack when he once again surfaced in the dirty kitchen was still a surprise, on that day of non-stop surprises. It was a chicken.

'No, that's not just a chicken,' Mrs. Giant laughed, 'this is The Hen That Lays Golden Eggs.'

'I thought that was a goose?'

'Don't be stupid, those are white with long necks and who's ever heard of a goose laying golden eggs anyway?'

Jack had to admit it did sound slightly weird.

'Go on,' continued Mrs. Giant, flicking the Hen at Jack from the palm of her hand as if it was a pea, 'get it gone with the rest of this shiny rubbish, and there'll be one load more before I've got all my cupboard space back!'

Jack caught the discombobulated Hen and looked at it. The Hen looked back at Jack, gave an ear-splitting cluck – BER-KAWK! – and plopped a perfectly egg-shaped nugget of purest 24-carat gold right into his hand...

'Jack! Well now I really have seen everything, ever, that it is possible to see!' Jack's Mum gasped when she saw the Hen repeat its glittering party trick ten minutes later. 'Tell you what, boy, one week of eggs from this little darling and you can give back all the jewels you want, she'll set us up for life! No more holes in the roof! No more turnips for breakfast, dinner and tea! No more cleaning the windows with me old knickerbockers...'

But while Jack's Mum chattered on, her brave lad was already making his final journey up into the clouds.

There was no Giant lying in wait for him this time, but he scurried up the drainpipe as before to see what the big brute's wife had in store this time.

145

27. JACK AND THE BEANSTALK

'There you are, and about time too, that big get will be home for his dinner any moment and I need you to get shot of this annoying whatsit for me!'

There in the cupboard Jack was introduced to a tall golden Harp. She was fashioned into the shape of a nymph along one side of the frame, so she could play her own strings as she sang, loudly and in a never-ending melody: *'Yes, I am the most beautiful magical musical instrument that you will ever meet,*

My voice is as lovely as sugar is sweet,

My beauty it dazzles – I know you're impressed,

When it comes to being awesome you know I'm the best...'

Jack hoisted the Harp onto his shoulder and accepted the final scraps of stolen booty from Mrs. Giant with warm gratitude.

'But won't your husband be angry when he sees that all his riches are gone?' he asked, kindly.

'Oh he's always angry,' Mrs. Giant groaned, 'I just want it all out of my sight, especially that noisy big-headed Harp. Now let me get on with my floor dirtying, and I'd better get some smells on before you-know-who returns for his bloomin' dinner.'

Once again, Jack took the water slide route and was shot right out into the safety of the beanstalk's leaves, with the outraged Harp singing constantly about how disgraceful it was that someone so beautiful and talented should be manhandled in such a manner.

However, he had to clamp his hand over the Harp's mouth when he once again felt that familiar earthquake of the Giant's footsteps, and heard the bellow:

'FEE-FI-FO-FUM! I SMELL THE BLOOD OF AN ENGLISHMAN!

BE HE SOUR OR BE HE TASTY, I'LL MASH HIS GUTS INTO A PASTY!'

'HA – CALL THAT A RHYME? YOU BIG WASTE OF TIME!' sang the Harp, before Jack had even noticed his hand had slipped. The Giant turned his way, and roared:

'THE ENGLISHMAN IS OVER THERE! JUST YOU WAIT, YOU CHEEKY... I CAN'T THINK OF A RHYME, I'M TOO ANGRY!'

And the Giant began zooming across the wispy white, full pelt, the clouds trembling with every massive bound!

Jack did not stop to watch this terrifying sight – he was headed down, down, down, his mind racing with a hundred desperate plans to escape from the terrifying oaf. The Giant couldn't climb down the stalk, surely? His weight would topple the whole thing! But no, the enormous brute was headed down directly after Jack, and the mighty stalk was still standing tall!

'How dare you treat me like your chattel? Don't shake me up like I'm a rattle!'

'Shut UP!' roared Jack, leaping down from leaf to gigantic leaf as fast as he could. Then he had an idea. He thrust his arm through the Harp to secure it to his shoulder, and decided to stop jumping, and start sliding. He held onto a tendril of beanstalk like a fireman's pole, and WHOOSH, down he surfed, leaves clattering around him as he zipped towards home.

This bought him precious seconds, before the Giant could follow him down and begin using his cottage for football practice. If the Giant saw Jack's Mum festooned in his jewels and crowns, they would both be an in-between-meal snack for him without a doubt! There was no time to explain.

'Mum! Get the axe! Quick!'

'What did I tell you about messing around with giants?' shrieked Jack's Mum, but she clattered off, weighed down with gold and jewels as she was, and returned with their rusty old wood-chopper.

'Stand back!' the young lad yelled, and began rapidly, desperately hacking at the sturdy beanstalk. His Mum chipped in with her bread knife, sawing through as best she could without even a 'How do ye do?' to the Harp, who was still melodically whining about the way her day was going. *'This will not, cannot end happily! Why is no one paying full attention to me?'*

They must have had no more than a couple of minutes' head start on the Giant, but it was just enough – his enormous feet could just be seen emerging from the clouds above when the beanstalk finally began to give, and to sway, first towards the old cottage, then towards the sea, before – CREAK, CRRRRRASHHHH!

The beanstalk fell out across the shore, and there, far in the distance, Jack, his Mum and the finally dumbstruck Harp could see the Giant, the enormous bully who had devastated the countryside for hundreds of miles around, fall to Earth like a bomb going off on the horizon. And that was the end of him.

As for Jack, he was as good as his word, and scoured the country to put right all the wrongs of the vicious Giant, whose landing site

27. JACK AND THE BEANSTALK

was marked with a huge chalk outline on the slopes of Windover Hill. He couldn't be sure that every single jewel got back to every single victim of the Giant's thievery, but he did his best, only taking a few golden eggs from the Hen before the poor witch who owned her was tracked down – although the wizard who had to reclaim the Harp didn't seem too happy about it for some reason.

Jack would have many more adventures, and vanquish many more murderous giants in his celebrated career, but at the end of every mission, he would always be able to return home to his Mum in their prettily redecorated little cottage, and he would stand on the stump of that enormous beanstalk, and tell everyone all about his exploits.

But the beanstalk never grew again, and all that ever sprouted up from that rubbly patch, forever more, was turnips.

THE END

THE SOUTH DOWNS

Historians and archaeologists have not done too well in identifying the historical site of Jack's mighty beanstalk, but if a chalk outline indicates a place where a murder has happened, it seems a fair bet to imagine that Wilmington was where the famous Giant Killer's career began. Modern archaeology suggests that the Long Man carved into the side of Windover Hill in the South Downs is only a few hundred years old, and no mention of it is made before the 18th century, but the possibility that Georgian antiquarians were simply renovating a much more ancient drawing is very real — it's certainly clear that Britons have enjoyed scribbling all over the landscape for as long as they have existed, and no journey to the South Downs is worth making without a visit to this mysterious example.

visitsussex.org

---

28. JACK THE
GIANT KILLER

St. Michael's Mount, Cornwall

J ack had only ever wanted a quiet life, once he and his Mum had
dealt with the infamous beanstalk Giant – but as soon as word
of Jack's triumph had spread across not just his own kingdom,
but the whole land, people came from far and wide to plead
with the poor lad to help them with their own giant problems.

After several years acting as an ogre extermination service, Jack
was no longer a boy, but a strapping, well-equipped and grizzled
warrior, far from afeared of any big bully he might come across. It
helped that his adventures had brought him a whole host of handy
tools to help him: a lightweight giant-ripping sword, a cloak of
invisibility, shoes of swiftness, and so on.

But when he took on the job of stopping the cow-crunching,
peasant-stamping villainy of the giant Cormoran, a particularly
belligerent, violent and downright rude brute who lived down at the
very bottom tip of Cornwall, people thought that Jack might have met
his match.

Jack left his little cottage on the South Downs and headed south-west
to what he hoped would be his last job. Eventually he arrived in Cerne
Abbas in Dorset, where he saw a large man-shaped chalk drawing
etched into the hill, very like the one he had at home – but ruder.

'Ah, that were old Blunderbore,' a grizzled and tooth-hungry local
told Jack. 'He used to terrorise the countryside, scoffing a dozen cows
in one mouthful and refusing to ever wear any clothes. You could hear

the horrified screams for miles around, and nobody could beat him! One day he choked on a Roman legion and dropped down dead right there.'

'Well, that saves me a job!' Jack replied. 'I am off to fight the Cornish giant Cormoran.'

'What? Not even Jack the Giant Killer could beat Cormoran! Compared to Cormoran, Blunderbore was just a pussycat! Why, he is ten miles high and twenty armies strong! Goodbye, stranger, you will be dead before I see you again.'

Jack heard the old hick chuckle as he passed on his way, and continued his journey south-west.

After many more days' trek, Jack arrived down on the coast in Plymouth, where two gigantic body outlines were marked. He was not surprised to find another wizened old local there to greet him.

'These two used to be known as Gog and Magog, dear,' she sort-of-smiled at Jack. ''Twas Prince Corineus who vanquished the pair of horrific brutes! Right here on the seafront, that Corin splatted them both and made the people safe.'

'Well, that saves me a job!' Jack replied once again. 'I am off to fight another Cornish giant. They call him Cormoran.'

The old lady's crinkled face fell into a look of sheer horror.

'No way, sonny,' she replied, 'Not even Jack the Giant Killer could defeat Cormoran. Even Gog and Magog working together would have been lucky to even hurt Cormoran's feelings. Cormoran has muscles the size of the moon and breath that burns hotter than the sun! Bless you, son, but you take him on and you're a goner. Goodbye.'

And with that, she was gone. Jack gulped, and carried on south-west.

Before long, Jack ran out of land to traverse. The tide was in, and just over the waves he could see a white granite island rising out of the horizon.

'That's where he hides, and waits,' warned yet another wrinkly old local lady. 'The giant Cormoran. Fifty fathoms high he stands, with arms like forests and claws as sharp as...' Luckily the old lady was saved from having to think of anything especially sharp, as Jack silenced her with a snort.

'I don't care how tall, strong, evil or smelly the giant Cormoran is, I am Jack the Giant Killer, and he has met his match!'

'You're mad!' The old lady replied. 'Even Jack the Giant Killer couldn't...'

'But I just said, I am Jack the Giant Killer.'

'You'll wish you were when Cormoran wakes up!' cackled the aged local, and scurried away to whatever safety she could find.

A few hours later, as dawn arose over Mount's Bay, Jack was tired and muddy, but he was ready. He stood up on a hill towards the village of Morvah, a fair distance from the sea, and blew his giant-annoying horn. There was an almighty cough, almost enough to cause an earthquake, and a growling sound that made it clear that something not even remotely nice was headed Jack's way. And then, there above the white granite island, arose Cormoran himself, easily eighty feet tall with rippling muscles, hair sticking out all over his body, and a look of wild hungry rage in his eyes.

Cormoran gazed down to see where the blast of the horn had come from. 'WHAT IS THIS, LITTLE SQUIT?' Cormoran roared. 'WHO DO YOU THINK YOU ARE, WAKING ME UP, AND WHAT DO YOU WANT AROUND HERE?'

'I am Jack the Giant Killer, and you have met your match!' the comparably tiny Jack replied.

'NOPE, DIDN'T CATCH A WORD OF THAT,' Cormoran grinned back, eerily, 'BUT IT DON'T MATTER ANYWAY, BECAUSE WHATEVER YOU CALLS YOURSELF, I CALLS YOU BREAKFAST!'

And with that, the mighty murderer pounded and splashed across the sea to where Jack was calmly waiting, splish, splash, thunder... CRASH!

All of a sudden, Cormoran seemed to entirely disappear from view! What looked like a rubbly expanse of beach was just a trick. Jack had spent the whole night, assisted by a number of enchanted spades and pickaxes, digging the biggest hole ever carved into the earth, and then lightly covering the trap with a specially woven cloth, disguised with sand, pebbles and driftwood – and Cormoran had fallen right in.

'You see, the thing is,' Jack said to the startled Cormoran as he hopped onto the stuck-fast giant's head, pickaxe tightly gripped in his hands, 'Everyone has been going on about how big you are, how evil and murderous and angry you are, how sharp your claws are and how impossible to beat in battle it all makes you...' The brave little man lifted the pickaxe. 'But what nobody mentioned even once, in all my

28. JACK THE GIANT KILLER

travels, was just how very stupid you are, Cormoran. If anyone had told me you were clever, I would have been terrified! But as it is...'

Jack brought the pickaxe down onto the giant's skull with an almighty 'CRACK! SPURT!' and killed the enormous monster with one blow.

'... As it is,' Jack continued, 'You have had the misfortune of running into Jack, the Giant Killer, and now your days of terrorising the people of Britain are over.'

There are many more tall – in fact, incredibly tall – tales told of other fights Jack got into, and won, with murderous ogres, giants and huge beasts of all kinds. Some say he became friends with one of King Arthur's sons and was invited to feast at the Round Table. Some say he travelled the world, saving folk from murderous giants.

I won't be the one to say that none of this was true. But the one thing I do know for sure, once the Cornish giant Cormoran was defeated, is that Jack travelled home to his old cottage by the roots of the beanstalk, put his magic boots up, and had a very well deserved rest.

THE END

ST. MICHAEL'S MOUNT

Cornish and south-westerly folklore is so thick with giants, it seems a fair bet to imagine that this was exactly where the famous Giant Killer stood. Plymouth Hoe has definitely always been closely associated with Britain's gigantic natives, and once upon a time two huge chalk figures were carved into the landscape to mark the site of the vanquishing of Gog and Magog. Unfortunately there is little evidence left of giants in Britain these days, although they do say that a Plymouth grave was found in medieval times which would have suited a man eleven feet tall! Besides the Long Man of Wilmington, other giant chalk outlines litter the British landscape, including the Cerne Abbas giant in Dorset, but we can't show you him because he's not wearing any pants. Mount's Bay itself is a glorious holiday destination when the weather feels like making it so, with Michael's Mount a fairytale island festooned with historic buildings bang in the middle. When the tide is out, you can walk there, and look for any miscreant giants yourself! One place to look would be the village of Morvah, where Cormoran's remains are marked by a huge rock, called the Giant's Grave. If you listen very closely, at dawn, it's said that the still-not-quite-dead giant can be heard demanding to be let out...

stmichaelsmount.co.uk

29. DUERGAR!

Simonside Hills, Northumberland

Giants are hard to miss, but the people of Britain have long been convinced that there are older, smaller settlers hiding in every corner of the country as well. Even if you start out by deciding that there's a clear difference between pixies, elves, fairies and dwarfs, there are so many names for each category of magical squirt that we could be here all day.

Take the dwarfs – the hairy ones who tend to go mining for precious stones and metals, and are also said to have the worst reputations. Fairies might suckle your cattle or whisk your wife away to a strange land for a thousand years, but at least they don't roam around in the dark looking for innocent humans to club around the head. Some nasty little ruffians can be classified as dwarfs, but others call them bogles, brownies, goblins, you name it – and each of the terms would be very offensive to them if they heard you use it!

The little people of the Simonside Hills in Northumberland, only a short ride from the border between Scotland and England, would have been even more offended if they heard what the people around there said of them. They were known in that area as 'Duergar' – and when you heard someone shout that word, you knew that something had gone wrong, and the dwarfs were being blamed.

Everyone in the town of Rothbury blamed everything on the Duergar: 'Nasty, smelly, hideously ugly little hairy people!' the tittle-tattles insisted. 'The Duergar roam the hills late at night with their little torches, leading good folk into peril just like Will-O'-The-Wisps, stealing all of their precious things and generally pushing anyone foolish enough to trust them – to their DOOM!'

Of course, none of these folk had ever seen one of the Duergar, let alone caught one and got it to admit to these crimes – but everyone knew they were out there. And they were really useful scapegoats for all sorts of crimes and disasters...

However, there was one person who refused to believe all this. In fact, this young girl, an orphan called Jay, was so brave and clever, and so certain there were no Duergar out there, she told all her friends that she was going to show everyone once and for all that there was no such thing.

Jay waited until dusk, packed herself a sandwich or two, wrapped her shawl around her against the early autumn chill, and marched confidently up to the hills.

It was craggy and dangerous on the path she chose, but Jay had walked that way a thousand times or more, and had no fear of getting lost. 'No fear at all,' she said to herself, 'I should be just coming up to the old gnarled sycamore now, and a short stroll west from there is the signpost, and from there...' But her monologue soon petered out as the darkness bit sharp, and she realised she hadn't come across any sycamores at all, and she was... she hated to admit it to herself... LOST!

Jay was not the kind of person to give up and cry at the first sign of trouble, so she stood stock still and tried to formulate a plan. Just as she was wondering whether it was too early to have a sandwich, something caught her eye. There, only a few yards away from her, a light appeared, bouncing up and down in the darkness, giving out very little glow besides the bright flame itself. Then Jay heard a soft whistling that was somehow both jovial and haunting at the same time.

'DUERGAR!?' she wondered to herself out loud, more glad that something exciting was happening than afraid. Jay had many good qualities, but perhaps her best virtue was also a rare one – she was very happy to be proven wrong on any subject. Many humans seldom admit even to themselves when some belief they have always treasured turns out to be tummy-rubbish, but always being ready to learn the truth and drop false beliefs should be one of the most important things about being a human.

In her excitement, Jay swiftly but cautiously set off after the little bouncing light, and it soon led her to a very poky but warm craggy cottage, with a heavy-smelling peat fire smouldering in the grate. She also saw two stones set before the fireplace as chairs, and two thick old fenceposts.

There was nobody else in the cottage when she arrived, and took her place by the fire, having collected a large bushel of brushwood from around the cottage's entrance. She decided to feed the fire with it, and stay awake to see what happened next.

Suddenly she froze where she was sitting. Into the cottage waddled a tiny bearded fellow who stood no taller than her belly button. He came right over to where she sat and plonked himself right next to her without ever once glancing in her direction. It was as if she was not there, and with wide eyes, she drank in all she could about this curious little fellow.

The dwarf's name was actually Roarie, and he was the chief of the Duergar in that area. But she was never to know that. What she did take in was his natty little lambskin trousers and jacket, the long gold beard which sprayed out from his chin, and the smart mossy hat he had perched on his head with a feather sticking out of the top. As Roarie gazed into the fire, she had to admit he was not at all ugly – just very small, very serious, and rather quiet, though he was mumbling under his breath: '*Duergar they say, Roarie's my name, no manners, some humans, we're not all the same...*'

Jay was trying to make as little noise as possible, but eventually the cold began to sting, and so she dared to place some brushwood on the fire, cracking each stick over her knee before they went in. Still without in any way acknowledging Jay's presence, her little silent host plucked one of the thick fenceposts out of the earth, and broke it over his own knee as easy as if it were a twig before throwing huge chunks onto the fire, which immediately began to crackle and roar warmly.

Jay was never sure if it was the fire which lulled her to sleep, or the gentle lilt of the tiny bagpipes Roarie then began to play, but sleep she certainly did...

And awoke all on her own! In fact, not just all on her own, but out in the open, surrounded by morning mist, with dawn breaking over her. Where had the cottage gone? She was still seated on the same cold stone, and there next to her was the rock the little man had sat on, and beside it the one remaining fencepost. But where the fire had been, all Jay could see was... a terrifying drop, hundreds of feet, to jagged rocks below!

For one rare moment, Jay felt a shudder of belly-wobbling fear shoot through her, as she realised just how close she had come to falling to her certain death! Just one more step and she would have been gone in the dark, forever. And who had saved her? None other than the so-called Duergar! That one quiet but kindly dwarf had somehow pulled her back from the edge, and kept her safe until it was light enough to see her way home.

Never again would Jay suggest that there was no such thing as the Duergar – but what she did do, any time her silly neighbours started blaming bad things on the 'ugly, spiteful' little folk, was put them right about one or two things. These people, she insisted, were their friends, and her very existence was proof of that. And nothing was ever blamed on the Duergar ever again.

THE END

SIMONSIDE HILLS

This rugged expanse of border country is a magnet, mainly for extreme sport enthusiasts — as the tale shows, there are lots of craggy cliffs to scale up, and brave high-jinks to get up to! But if you do explore the Simonside Hills near the town of Rothbury, up above the Coquet Valley, and if you do go and try and find the Bronze and Iron Age carvings, or even the little stone huts which look just like the cottage in Jay's story — make sure to go during daylight! If you get lost in the dark, you cannot guarantee that the Duergar will be around to help you home.

visitnorthumberland.com

---

30. THE EYE OF LEWIS

Lewis

Lewis is the largest expanse of land in the Outer Hebrides, the string of islands off the west coast of Scotland, and has an astoundingly rich history, having once been part of an ancient Norse Kingdom. The very name 'Lewis' means 'song house', the home of hundreds of ballads. But one of the oddest things about the isle is that it used to be somewhere else entirely.

The Last of the Giants was responsible for the relocation of Lewis, but although you may have become aware that giants were frankly unpleasant beings very nearly without exception, this one was different. He was just as gigantic and fearsome-looking as any other giant, but this huge fellow looked around at the devastation and cruelty of his fellow skyscraper-sized British natives (that giant who hoarded gold and fell down a beanstalk, the pair of brothers who clobbered each other to death over treasure, all those nasty brutes), and this giant despaired.

'STOP BEING HORRIBLE TO THE LITTLE PEOPLE!' he would cry whenever he got the chance, unafraid of any hills or castles the other giants could throw at him. 'CAN'T YOU SEE THEY'RE HERE TO STAY, AND ARE MUCH QUICKER THAN ANY OF US? WE SHOULD BE FRIENDLY WITH THEM, ENGLISH, SCOTTISH AND WELSH, OR WE'LL SOON FIND OUT THAT THERE ARE NONE OF US LEFT TO TELL OUR TALES!'

As it happens, this one giant was as quick and clever as any human, which is how he had worked out that living peacefully alongside the new settlers was their only hope. But of course, the other giants sneered, spat and roared at the poor Giant of Lewis. Until one day, he decided he'd had enough.

Nobody knows for sure where Lewis was in those days, but this big fellow decided it was far too near the last remaining violent, stupid giants for his liking. And so he headed out to the coast and poked one enormous finger through an outcrop of rock, creating the Eye of Lewis. Then he threaded through it the strongest thread the world had ever seen, gave an almighty tug and waded through the northern seas, dragging the Isle of Lewis far north and west, until it reached its current destination.

There this sad giant sat and sang, and lived out his days in peace with all the 'little people' – which is what he called us humans – who had also made their homes on the island. Nobody knows how long he lived, but he survived longer than every other member of his violent species, who were eventually wiped out by human giant slayers like Jack, who felt they were defending themselves from the brutish natives. The Giant of Lewis was right: his species was endangered.

However, uniquely among all of his kind, you can be sure that there were many tears shed by the little people of Lewis when the Last of the Giants died, and he is buried there to this day. No need to look for his grave – he was so big, the entire Isle of Lewis marks the spot.

THE END

THE ISLE OF LEWIS

You can reach Lewis' metropolis of Stornoway by ferry and by air, and a great bus service makes transport surprisingly easy once you get there — because, just like the giant in the story, nobody comes to the Outer Hebrides to be in the centre of things. The beauty of the landscape, the unique antiquity of the society, with Gaelic still the prevalent tongue, makes Lewis an ultimate getaway. Through standing stones and Norse remnants, the most intrepid explorers can find their way up to the north coast, west of the Port of Ness, where the Eye should still be visible offshore, eroded through the craggy rocks.

isle-of-lewis.com

---

31. THE KNUCKER

Lyminster, West Sussex

I don't half fancy a pie, don't you? Not loads of them, obviously, just a nice hot crispy one for tea. Everyone loves pies, don't they? Let's tell a story about pies.

Back in the times when things like this still happened there was a Knucker. Not a Knocker, and certainly neither a Knicker nor a Knacker, but a Knucker. This was what the people of Arun – on the south coast of what they now call West Sussex – called him, anyway. But the Knucker was a water dragon.

This huge, vastly unlikeable beast lived in a Swiss-cheese labyrinth of watery tunnels just outside the village of Lyminster. He came in and out through three round bottomless pools, known as Knuckerholes, where he would bask and loop-de-loop his long scaly body from hole to hole, like a huge thread weaving in and out of a button. The pools could never grow dry, but could never be drunk nor indeed swum in, so toxic was the Knucker's pong. He really was breakfast-reversingly smelly!

When he wasn't diving around being smelly, the Knucker was frankly ruining the lives of the poor folk of Lyminster and the surroundings: stomping into town, easily the height of the steeple at St Mary's church when he drew himself up, and just as easily able to stomp right through the roofs of any bungalows which stood in his way.

'Boo!' he would shout, as he went round gobbling up dogs, cats, sheep, and of course the slower villagers. The Knucker could not breathe fire, but oh dear, you should have smelled his breath! Or rather, you shouldn't, because one whiff would have killed you stone

160

dead. And as for the teeth, his treacherous black fangs could chew right through a cottage and not even need flossing.

The thing is, when this monster did these things, he wasn't even nice about it. The Knucker was the most terrible gloater! 'Haha, I like yer cottage!' he would gloat, making horribly rude gestures as he whipped himself through the air in great leaps, like he was still floating in water. 'Looks really nice now you've got no roof, dur-brains! Hope you've got umbrellas! Hahahaaaa!' And off he would fly, back to his Knuckerholes.

'Knucker been in town again, then?' one villager would grump.

'Aye, this time he took four pigs, two cats, all the ducks on the village pond, and the baker's eldest, Ralph,' replied his neighbour.

'Aw that's a shame, he'd only just learned the trumpet too,' the other replied. They all agreed: 'Something must be done!'

The Mayor of Arundel decreed a decree: 'Whomsoever will deliver the countryside from this really horrible stuck-up monster will receive a golden guinea for their troubles! And also, quite probably the hand of my beautiful, intelligent and charming daughter Hazel! – as long as she actually fancies them.'

And so the challenge was on – but as time went by, all the poor champions who dared approach the Knucker's three pools could be found littered in numerous unattractive pieces around the surrounding countryside. The folk all agreed that they would just have to be careful, that's all.

One of the things the villagers had found, however, was that though the Knucker liked chomping on cottages, they were nothing to him when compared to a nice hot crispy pie – preferably with a few sheep and a PE teacher in it as a juicy filling. And so they agreed that the baker would just have to bake the biggest pies possible for the Knucker, and send his bravest delivery boys out to the three pools to dish them up. Then perhaps he'd leave them alone.

The baker's in Lymington was the finest in the county, and it was called 'Pulk's'. Mr Pulk's young apprentice was a lad called Jimmy Puttock. Jimmy Puttock had quite a belly on him, and was a bit embarrassed about his new job, because the less pleasant of the other boys and girls at school used to sing at him:

'Who ate all the pies? Who ate all the pies? Jimmy Puttock, Jimmy Puttock, he ate all the pies!'

31. THE KNUCKER

'It's not fair,' poor Jimmy would say, 'I can't help being chunky. And it's not even a rhyme, you're just saying 'pies' twice!'

But though it really wasn't Jimmy's fault that he was a big lad, you should have seen the speed with which he scarpered off the first time he had to take a big pig pie to the Knucker. The Knucker's enormous jaws chomped down on that steaming pie – CHOMP! – sending the dish flying and Jimmy pelting off through the woods faster than he ever thought was possible.

Jimmy was a wily lad, though. He felt sure he couldn't carry on taking these pies to the Knucker without getting into some serious trouble, probably in the form of becoming dinner. And so, he reasoned, why not serve the Knucker up a real pie – the final pie he would ever eat?

Therefore, on the very next pie day, with the distraught baker's reluctant blessing, Jimmy took the biggest pie dish ever created, kneaded some fine crumbly shortcrust pastry, and filled the middle of the pie dish with the most horribly dangerous and disgusting filling you could imagine: wolfsbane, deadly nightshade, arsenic, toadstools, rotten cabbage, month-old scrag-end, coriander, and his Uncle Peter's rancid long johns, which hadn't been washed since the dinosaurs. With a peg secured surely to his nose, Jimmy baked up this foul pastry, and when it was golden brown and humming slightly, he heaved it up onto his cart and set off to the three pools.

'Grrr! Oi! This pie had better be tastier than the last one, fatface!' the Knucker snarled as Jimmy's cart trundled near, 'You didn't put enough Maths teachers in there last time. I keep saying, I like nice juicy teachers in my pie!'

But then, without another grumbling word – 'table manners' meaning nothing to Knuckers – the huge foul dragon whipped up into the air and crashed down onto the cart right where it trundled, with one almighty 'CHOMP!' – and he almost took a slice out of the poor horse's behind as he did so. 'NEIGHHH!'

The Knucker chomped. He chewed. He licked his lips and he swallowed. He looked thoughtful. 'Not bad,' he growled. 'Perhaps a tiny pinch too much of the... POISON AND DIRTY PANTS!' The Knucker positively gargled and frothed with these last few words, before dropping down dead with a thunderous THUD!

As the Knucker didn't want his head any more, Jimmy Puttock stepped down to hew it off and take it back to Lyminster. But, oh no! As Jimmy brought down his sword, the peg fell off his nose and

162

the Knucker's head let out one last foul rattling posthumous belch – 'BLEEEEUUURGH!' The pong was so bad, Jimmy and his poor horse both went out like candles…

But then, there was light. The darkness cleared, and Jimmy could see that he was in the Lyminster village square, surrounded by delighted cheering villagers, all hooting Jimmy's name with glee: 'JIMMY PUTTOCK! JIMMY PUTTOCK! THE KNUCKER KNACKERER!'

The village doctor was bending over the poor lad, relieved to see him awake, and kindly said, 'Well done, well done, Jimmy Puttock, your cleverness has saved us all. And now you shall be rich and happy!'

'But the Knucker's breath…' Jimmy gasped.

'Oh yes, that will kill you,' the Doctor replied gravely. 'Nothing to be done about that. On the other hand, it is a very slow-working poison, so I'd give you maybe forty years to live. Perhaps fifty, if you don't have too many pies.'

'And therefore,' the Mayor beamed, 'you may have this guinea, and perhaps the hand of my wonderful daughter, Hazel. What do you think, Hazel?'

The charming and dazzling young lady sized him up. 'Yeah, go on then,' she smiled, 'I do like 'em chunky.'

And so, the brave and clever chunky Jimmy Puttock married, was wise with his wealth and lived a very merry and ripe life until a fairly old age. He is now buried at St Mary's church under the name of 'The Knucker Slayer', forever beloved for vanquishing the very last Knucker ever to be seen on these islands…

Of course, this was in the days before wildlife conservation.

THE END

LYMINSTER, W SUSSEX

When it comes to holidays, Brighton has always been the main location for anyone heading to the south-east coastline of England, but the county of Sussex boasts many great days out beyond that city's rusty opulence. Lyminster is only a small village, but there's still excitement to be had trying to track down the lair of the Knucker — there are Knuckerholes

31. THE KNUCKER

still to be found! And at St Mary's church, you can even see the Slayer's Slab, where brave Jimmy Puttock is said to rest. Bring your own pies.

westsussex.info

32. SIGURD'S HOWE

Dornoch, Highlands

A warning should be warned – this is probably not a great story for anyone who isn't a big fan of severed heads. Those who are big fans of severed heads – perhaps you should seek professional help of some kind?

Sigurd Eysteinsson, the Norwegian lord who decided to call himself 'Sigurd the Mighty', was a huge fan of severed heads. Because Sigurd the Mighty was a Viking. They all had bloodthirsty names – Olaf the Merciless, Bjorn the Family-Smasher, and Conan the Serious Problem. But Sigurd the Mighty was one of the nastiest Vikings of all.

He lived up in frozen Norway, but while he and his brother Rognvald were sailing around in their longship one day they saw the green and pleasant isles of the Orkneys up in northern Scotland, and liked the look of them so much they and their band of equally violent and unpleasant Norse warriors stormed right over there, kicked the King of the Orkneys out (which is to say, sliced him into pieces) and declared the Orkneys their own private kingdom. This was the Viking way – in fact, they would soon decide to grab whole chunks of England in much the same spirit.

As Rognvald set off to find other countries to call his own, Sigurd remained behind to rule over the Orkneys. However, as a Viking, he soon got bored of all the paperwork, and decided to go and grab more bits of Scotland to add to his collection. He began snaking his way down the eastern shore, killing everyone who stood in his path.

Until, one day, he came upon the castle of Máel Brigte, otherwise known as 'Máel Brigte the Buck-Toothed'. You wouldn't have money on poor Máel Brigte to be the man to vanquish the mighty Sigurd. He was as skinny as a rake, no more than five feet tall, rather spotty and, as his name suggested, had big goofy teeth jutting from his overbite. When he saw Sigurd advancing on his castle, it was all he could do to stammer out:

'Who... whoooo... hoo-hoo... WHO GOES THERE?'

'It is Sigurd the Mighty, and your castle is pretty much mine already!' roared the Viking, to hooting laughter from all his soldiers.

'My castle is secure!' squeaked Máel Brigte. 'We shall defend it with all our might!'

'As I said,' Sigurd replied, 'all your might won't be enough, so I'm already trying to decide what colour to paint those ramparts.'

Máel Brigte's soldiers did not like being laughed at, and they nudged their lord.

'Go on, sir, we're as good as that lot, we can beat them! Tell him!'

'We won't give up that easy, Sigurd!' cried Máel Brigte, with growing confidence. 'Any man of this land is equally able as any of you Norse nuisances! We shall do battle!'

'Indeed we will, goofy!' Sigurd replied, to bigger laughs. 'Forty of my men will face forty of your men in the field of combat, and the winner gets the castle!'

'Forty men?'

'Only forty, yes.'

Máel Brigte did a quick headcount. He had a total of thirty-eight men. But there was nothing else for it. He gave a little scream, asked his old grannie and cousin Elspeth to put on some armour, and replied to Sigurd, 'Very well, let the battle commence at dawn!'

'Any time is good with me,' Sigurd laughed, 'but we'll see you in the morning, toothy-boy!'

The next morning, Máel Brigte and his forty soldiers waited, shields before them and swords drawn and sharpened. Out of the morning mist stepped Sigurd, and forty other figures stood behind him.

'I do love a bit of a morning scrap!' Sigurd laughed. 'Those are your forty men?'

'They certainly are, the finest fighters of the North!' Máel Brigte bravely replied. 'Each able to take on anything you throw at us.'

'They look as if they couldn't even plunder a carrot from a bunny rabbit!' hooted Sigurd with a snarl. 'In fact, they look like such weaklings we probably didn't even need to... cheat!'

And with that, each of the forty figures behind Sigurd suddenly doubled to eighty – half of them had been hiding behind another soldier's back! Máel Brigte barely had a second to react to this treachery before Sigurd's cry went up:

'VIKINGS! BLOODY SLAUGHTER BEFORE BREAKFAST! HAHAHA!'

And the fight began. It was not a pleasant sight. You certainly wouldn't have wanted to try and put a tent up in that field, not during the torrents of unspeakable violence which immediately burst forth, or afterwards, where barely a blade of grass was visible among the butchered remains of Máel Brigte's army.

Máel Brigte himself fell victim to Sigurd's own sword within the first 42 seconds of the battle, and true to form, Sigurd hacked off the poor buck-toothed loser's head for his collection before trotting off to claim the now empty castle for himself. He put Máel Brigte's head on his saddle, where all Vikings liked to show off the heads of soldiers they had killed, and he set off for home.

It was rather a long return journey to Orkney, though, and before too long Máel Brigte's big buck-teeth began to rub against Sigurd's rump. Sigurd was tough, of course; he barely noticed when the head's teeth broke his skin, and just thought he'd put some cream on it later when he got home.

But as they camped that night, the wound in Sigurd's leg seemed worse than he first thought. Máel Brigte's teeth had sheared right through the skin as the head jangled around on Sigurd's saddle, and the whole of Sigurd's bum was already looking blackened, and smelling nasty. In the morning, he tried to walk, but failed. All his soldiers backed away at the foul stench – and, to cut a sickening story short, the greedy cruel Viking never saw another dawn. He was buried where he died, near a small Scottish town now known as Dornoch, and his burial mound was called 'Sigurd's Howe'.

Máel Brigte had beaten the big bully Sigurd the Mighty after all! Admittedly a bit late for him to celebrate it in any way, but as Sigurd's servants gathered together his collection of severed heads after his funeral, they swore that one of them had a great big buck-toothed grin.

32. SIGURD'S HOWE

THE END

DORNOCH, HIGHLANDS

You would be easily forgiven for raising an eyebrow if a small town up in the far north Highlands of Scotland advertised itself for beach holidays. But Dornoch does have a distinct climate of its own, due to its sheltered position, which makes the usual perils of the frozen north less noticeable. It's an ancient settlement with a cathedral — where Madonna had her son baptised, no less. But if you want to find Sigurd's burial mound, you may need to cross a golf course or two to find Cyderhall Farm nearby, near the road to the disused Meikle Ferry. But as Sigurd Eysteinsson died in 892, there's not a lot to see besides a lonely mound.

visitdornoch.com

33. LADY GODIVA

Coventry

Tax, believe it or not, can be a wonderful thing. The idea is that everyone in the country who makes a living gives a portion of what money they have to help the whole nation – this pays for security, health and wellbeing for every last woman, man, child and pet in the land. The problem starts when the powerful people who collect the taxes become greedy.

Very nearly one thousand years ago, a little before the Normans invaded and decided that they liked England rather a lot and would have it all, thank you very much, times were hard for most people. The Saxon nobles could swan around in their jewel-encrusted trousers, setting up churches and feeling good about themselves, but for most peasants, scratching a living in the fields, survival from season to season was challenge enough. There were very few nobles who even gave these poor people a second thought. But then there was Godiva.

Lady Godiva was married to a very powerful Earl called Leofric. This nobleman wasn't necessarily a villain, and had happily used his enormous fortune to build a number of nunneries and suchlike in his Earldom of Mercia – a vast expanse of the English Midlands. Leofric and Godiva had also paid for the establishment of a monastery which had grown into the tiny city of Coventry.

The problem was that the King, Edward the Confessor (who wasn't always confessing to crimes or anything, it was just a silly nickname which had stuck) found himself forever fighting off Vikings and other invaders. This cost lots of gold, so the King was always crying out to his nobles to raise taxes to pay for it all. These posh Saxons could have easily footed the bill themselves, obviously, but it was decided instead that it was much more fun to make the lowest of the low all put their hands in their pockets and pay for everything.

Godiva was a tall, striking woman, with the longest blonde hair that stretched right down to her shins. She was inclined to be a little vain, and loved her rich gowns and fine clothes, but she was not blind to the world around her. As the kindly Lady Godiva rode her fine chestnut mare through the dirty streets of Coventry, she could see that few people could afford to house and clothe themselves properly, let alone pay for the King's endless battles.

The problem with people who have everything, like Leofric, is that they can easily forget that not everybody is quite so rich and cosy. Godiva was not like that. At bedtime one night, she brought up the subject of this tax unfairness with her husband, and the rich man groaned.

'Oh, they can afford it all right!' Leofric grumbled, 'I swear I once saw one serf wearing a shoe on EACH FOOT!'

'That is not funny,' Godiva replied. 'The taxes are too much! You have taxed their grain, their houses, their horses and their hats! You have taxed their beer and their cats and dogs and carts and their knees! It is not fair.'

'Well okay, darling,' Leofric laughed, 'How would it be if we were to only tax their horses from now on?'

'That would be a good start, my dear,' Godiva replied.

'Good. Then we will just add up all the taxes on the other things, and add that amount of money to the horse tax. Job done.'

'How does that solve the problem?' This was not at all a solution, as far as Godiva was concerned, it still that meant people would pay more than they could afford. Despite her husband's patronising smirk, she insisted that all the taxes had to be scrapped – and that Leofric would be well advised to go and sleep on the sofa until he agreed to it. At this, Earl Leofric laughed fit to bust. He ignored Godiva, and climbed into bed.

'I'll tell you what, Godiva,' he snorted, 'You love your fine gowns so much, I'll cancel all the taxes the day that you ride through the streets of Coventry stark naked! Not even a sock!'

And, still giggling, he turned over and slept. While Godiva formed a plan.

The next day at noon precisely, Earl Leofric stood in the city square preparing to order the people to pay his new ridiculously high horse tax. But what people? Where was everybody? The streets were empty, and silent besides the odd coughing dog.

Clever Lady Godiva had sent a message out to all the people of Coventry to stay in bed that day, to board up all their windows, and whatever they did, to definitely NOT look out into the streets until an hour past noon. Leofric did not know this, and was astonished to find himself completely without an audience. That was when he heard the clip-clopping sound of his wife's chestnut mare.

There, atop the horse, was Lady Godiva, modestly bouncing along the cobbles. Her long blonde hair flowed down to cover up her more private areas, but Leofric could see, without any doubt, that she did not have so much as a sock on her body. Naked she rode along the high street, giving her astonished husband a wink as she passed, before geeing up the horse and trotting calmly back to their castle – after all, it was quite a chilly day!

As a sportsman above all, Earl Leofric could not go back on his word, and he did indeed take Godiva's advice on the taxing of the poor from that day forward. He learned his lesson that just because a woman like Godiva was beautiful and noble, it did not mean that she was ignorant of the needs of the many, rather than the few – or that she would not do everything within her power to fight for justice. The poor people loved them both for the change of heart, but Lady Godiva most of all. And when they thought about exactly how she won the battle for them, they all just smiled.

Of course, every last person in Coventry had sworn not to look out of their windows that chilly day – but there was one little lad, a tailor's apprentice called Tom, who could not behave himself. At just the moment Lady Godiva was trotting on her way back to the castle, he peeped out of his window and got the surprise of his life!

This was rather naughty of Tom – but if he hadn't sneaked a look, perhaps none of us would know the story of Lady Godiva at all! From that day on, once he had convinced everyone that he wasn't lying about what he saw, the fellow was known by all as 'Peeping Tom'.

And that's still the name we use for nosy people to this very day. Or, at least, it's one of the nicer names we have for them.

33. LADY GODIVA

THE END

COVENTRY

The Coventry familiar to the people in the Lady Godiva story is almost entirely gone. The Warwickshire city was damaged more than most other British cities in the bombing raids of WWII, and many traces of the old place have been entirely built over, although the scraps of medieval Coventry are definitely worth a visit. That's not to say that the city doesn't still celebrate the memory of kind Godiva, though — there is even a Godiva festival every summer! Whether clothes are optional or not, we cannot say.

visitcoventryandwarwickshire.co.uk

34. MACBETH AND
THE WITCHES

Moray, Highlands

History tells us that Macbeth was a very good and religious King of Alba – otherwise known as Scotland – who rightly took the throne from a useless usurper and ruled wisely for many years. He was known as 'The Red King' – not because of a bloody reign, but because he had long flowing ginger hair.

Stories, however, tell us something very different, and stories are often far more interesting.

According to the old fireside tales, Macbeth was first given the idea of stealing the crown of Scotland when he had the great misfortune of meeting three hideous witches on a thunder-and-lightning-blasted heath.

Before the Normans invaded England, Scotland was divided between Lords known as 'Thanes', and Macbeth was Thane of Glamis. One day he was returning from success in the war with bloodthirsty Norwegians, when there before him appeared this trio of mischievous creatures. Some say they were fairies, but they have become known as the 'weird sisters' – a gang of crones who were dancing and cackling around a fire as Macbeth approached through the mist.

'A drum, a drum! Macbeth has come!' they laughed. 'All hail Macbeth, Thane of Glamis!'

'What are YOU?' Macbeth cried.

34. MACBETH AND THE WITCHES

'All hail Macbeth, Thane of Cawdor!'

'The Thane of Cawdor lives!' Macbeth bellowed back. But they just grinned greasy smiles, and continued:

'All hail Macbeth, who shall be KING OF SCOTLAND hereafter!'

The ruler of Scotland at this time was actually called Duncan, and like a good servant of the crown, Macbeth demanded: 'I am King Duncan's loyal soldier! Leave me be, you foul midnight hags!'

The strange toothless and bearded witches made it clear to the brave warrior that he was fated to wear the Scottish crown whether he liked it or not, and in one fell swoop, they sowed the seeds of an ambition which would turn the noble Macbeth into a power-hungry tyrant.

With their wicked work done, the witches vanished into the air, like popped bubbles. Only then did a messenger arrive with news for Macbeth... that he had been made Thane of Cawdor.

When Macbeth returned to his castle in Dunsinane, he told his wife Gruoch, the Lady Macbeth, all about the prophetic way the ugly sisters had hailed him as King, and that he had just been made Thane of Cawdor, as they had predicted. Being a very ambitious woman, Gruoch allowed this news to blacken her heart, and she aided her husband in forming a dastardly plan.

When King Duncan visited their castle with his whole family, all were plied with strong booze until everyone was fast asleep. Then, the power-hungry couple crept into the King's chamber and Macbeth plunged two daggers deep into the poor old man's chest, while Gruoch smeared the drunken guards with gore so they would be thought guilty of the murder.

Drenched in blood as they were, Macbeth and Gruoch were crowned King and Queen at the ancient Scottish royal seat of Scone (pronounced to rhyme with 'spoon'), while Duncan's son Malcolm fled south, to the English court. The witches, it seemed, had been proven right.

'To be King,' Macbeth said, 'is easy enough, but to stay King is much harder.' Bloody deeds became everyday business for Macbeth, and Gruoch soon felt haunted by the crimes they had carried out together, and would wash her hands all day as if she could never wash away the old King's blood. But although he too was haunted by the grizzled ghosts of the friends he had slain to wear the crown, Macbeth could not undo what he had done.

The tyrant's rule was grey, miserable and bloody, so the tale runs, and he slaughtered many innocent folk to keep his throne safe from murderers like himself. What worried Macbeth most was that Malcolm had drummed up support down in England, and was planning to invade and reclaim the throne.

So fearful did King Macbeth become that he set out once again to find those three weird sisters. Eventually, he came across them all prancing around their cauldron, singing a tuneless song as they threw nasty ingredients into the pot:

> 'Double double, toil and trouble! Fire burn and cauldron bubble!'
> 'Eye of newt and toe of frog, wool of bat and tongue of dog!'
> 'By the pricking of my thumbs, something wicked this way comes!'

Macbeth demanded: 'You foul bearded hags, tell me if I will continue to rule as King!' and one by one they danced around him, each singing:

> 'Macbeth shall never vanquished be until Birnam Wood marches to Dunsinane!'
> 'No man born of woman shall ever kill Macbeth in battle!'
> 'But the children of Macbeth shall never rule as Kings!'

Macbeth laughed at this last prophecy. 'How can my rule ever fail, if I am safe from being beaten by anyone born from a woman? Everybody in the world is born of woman! And I am also safe as long as Birnam wood stays where it is, many miles from my castle. Trees do not march!'

And so the witches popped into the air with a cackle once again, and Macbeth returned home, content that the crown was secure on his head.

Nonetheless, word soon came that the English forces had set foot in Scotland, and were baying for Macbeth's head. Many of his Thanes and subjects ran away to join them, but even left all on his own, and even with the worst news, that Queen Gruoch's anguished sleepwalking had led to her falling from the highest battlements of the castle, still Macbeth did not shake with fear.

34. MACBETH AND THE WITCHES

It was only as he took to those battlements and gazed out to the horizon that he saw what looked for all the world like a moving forest. Young Malcolm had ordered his soldiers to cut down trees from Birnam Wood and camouflage themselves in the branches as they moved in for the attack – and his plan had worked! Birnam Wood was marching to Dunsinane!

Macbeth fled from Dunsinane to do battle with Malcolm in a village called Lumphanan, and when the carnage was in full swing, it seemed nobody could get anywhere near Macbeth, whose sword dripped with blood as he swung it to and fro, an untouchable warrior.

Then arose Malcolm's finest soldier, Macduff, whose whole family, wife and children, had already been put to the sword by Macbeth. Macduff appeared before the bloody King and challenged him to a duel.

'Lay on, Macduff!' Macbeth laughed, 'Nobody born of woman can beat me!'

Then it was Macduff's turn to laugh: 'I entered the world before my time, Macbeth. The doctor had to cut me from my mother's belly – and so I was never born of woman!'

Only then did Macbeth realise the trick that had been played on him by the three witches – he had been their toy all along! Oh, what cackling they must be doing, he thought, now his fate was sealed. But be that as it may, brave at the last, Macbeth fought Macduff until he was exhausted. At the very end, as the sun began to set, the King's head was sliced clean off, and his cruel rule was over.

King Malcolm was crowned at Scone, and nobody heard from the three cackling witches ever again. But if you do happen upon a trio of bearded old ladies singing tuneless songs around a bubbling cauldron, remember Macbeth, and be sure never to fall for a single word they say.

THE END

MORAY, HIGHLANDS

The legend of Macbeth mingles so confusingly with real history of the 11th-century ruler MacBheatha that anyone looking to walk in the King's steps will have a lot of criss-crossing of Scotland to do! His home was the northern region of Moray — a larger expanse in his day than the county

---

you can now visit — though his seat of power seems to have been the top of Cluny Hill in Grant Park, Forres. He was also said to have built a grand castle on Dunsinane hill, beyond Birnam and further to the south, before losing to Malcolm in battle at Lumphanan, a village 25 miles from Aberdeen. Folklore even suggests that you can visit the very site of the witches' blasted heath, near Brodie Castle, Forres. Bring an eye of newt, if you can find one without hurting any newts.

thisismoray.com

35. THE KINGDOM
OF THE SEALS

John O'Groats, Caithness

T here once was a time when it seemed folk could turn into almost any sort of animal. You always had your werewolves, of course, then your bears, cats, swans, hedgehogs, eagles, lions, dragons, budgies, you name it. And yet, the folk of Britain always seemed to come back to the same beasts: horses or kelpies, and in the far freezing North, there was the Kingdom of the Seals.

The human of our story was not a terribly pleasant example of the animal. He was called Old Ben, and he was a fisherman far out on the crumbliest patch of coast off John O'Groats, as far north as you can run without drowning.

Folk demanded their fish, herring and mackerel, for their slap-up kipper breakfasts, and Old Ben had lived his whole life sailing out on the choppy waters collecting them in his vast net. But what he also liked to do was catch the occasional chubby little grey seal, kill it, and slice off its oily pelt to sell in the market. Not a thought was given to the poor seals' feelings, when they were quite happy in their own skin, and Old Ben always threw the rest of the poor mammals down into the icy depths of the North Sea.

One grey Thursday a particularly glossy and fat seal was unfortunate enough to get tangled up in Old Ben's net, and the next thing he knew, the poor animal was goggling up at the glinting steel of Pointy Myrtle – the fisherman's jagged harpoon-like hunting knife, as sharp as sharp can be.

'Keep still, ye stupid little wriggler!' Old Ben shouted, and plunged Pointy Myrtle deep into the seal's behind – 'AWOOOOOYOW!'

The seal honked and howled so loudly, it nearly deafened Old Ben, and with a wallop of a flipper to the chin, the fisherman was knocked back; and the seal splashed into the sea and under the waves, Pointy Myrtle still jammed in his back-end.

Old Ben was annoyed to have lost his knife, but he had plenty more, and he wasn't going to lose any sleep over it. But that night, what did keep him from sleep was a loud banging at the door of his smelly old cottage.

'Who can this be keeping an old fisherman from his well-deserved kip of a Thursday night?' he wondered aloud to himself. He was a terribly boring old man.

There on Old Ben's doorstep was a dashing Knight in oily armour, astride a glossy grey stallion.

'Old Ben MacFishery?' the impressive stranger boomed.

'If ye call 63 old, then yes, that's me.'

'Get on the horse.'

'Why would I want to get on yon horse at this time of night with the rain whipping down like this?' Old Ben demanded. 'It's a totally stupid idea that I'm going to go along with.'

And with that, the old man climbed up behind the Knight, and they galloped away. This is how humans always behave around huge magical horse riders who come to their doors. They're so gullible.

Though lost in a haze, even Old Ben could not deny a shuddering thump of terror as he realised the horse was galloping at top speed right off the seafront, under the roaring waves, and into the gloomy enveloping cold of the North Sea. He was just beginning to build up the gumption to insist that he could not breathe underwater, when he suddenly realised that he could.

He looked down, and saw in the place of gnarled old pink hands, gnarled old grey flippers, and he could just make out that where his bushy beard once sprouted, long whiskers now splayed out. He could not talk, but only honk – 'HONK!'

The horse was the biggest seahorse you've ever seen, and her companion the Knight was also a seal, and all he could do was honk, too – and yet Old Ben could understand every honk.

35. THE KINGDOM OF THE SEALS

'Follow me, you old murderer!' the seal ordered, and Old Ben could do nothing but obey, swimming along in the wake of his kidnapper.

Soon they arrived in a marvellously beautiful area of seabed, sculpted with coloured sands and impressive rocky towers, decorated with shells and pearls – and in the centre, on a raised throne, lay a very poorly looking large seal. All seals are grey, but this one was the greyest of all. Out of this seal's hind quarters, Old Ben could make out the unmistakably ugly shape of Pointy Myrtle. All around this ailing seal flapped other seals, each looking worried, and crying, but none of them able to do anything.

'Be this my murderer?' croaked the large seal.

'It is, your majesty,' replied the seal who had brought Old Ben. 'You see, old man? You stuck your knife into none other than the King of Seals himself.'

'And what a place to stick it!' groaned the bleeding King.

'Ach, I'm sorry, I didn't know you were a King!'

'What does it matter whether he was a King or not?' replied the Knight Seal. 'None of us seals have ever tried to kill you. We do not harm you. And we all deserve to keep our own skins!'

'Well, what can I do?' begged Old Ben, knitting his front flippers together in anguish.

Then one especially tall and serious looking seal replied, 'Only he who thrust Pointy Myrtle into the King's royal behind can retrieve it. Then we may be able to save his poor Royal Highness.'

'Of course, of course, I will, and I'll never do anything like it again!' stammered the old whiskery seal, and he flapped forward to pull Pointy Myrtle out of the King of Seals' private area. He gripped with his teeth and tugged with his front flippers, and then with an almighty squelch, at last the knife was free, and the King gasped with relief – a loud, bubbly gasp that grew louder and louder and bubblier and bubblier until the Old Ben seal could not see a thing…

And then… this is always a very disappointing end to a story, but it actually happened this way, so what can I do? Old Ben woke up in his bed as the morning sun shone through his grimy windows. He was soaked from head to foot, and a quick taste told him that what soaked him was salty. Was it sweat, from a nightmare, or water from the sea? He was just beginning to think it was the first one, when he felt something cold and jagged in his grip. It was Pointy Myrtle, that razor-sharp harpoon knife. Old Ben gazed at it, blood still visible on the blade, and gulped with guilt.

He took Pointy Myrtle, and from that day forward used it for nothing except digging holes in his garden to plant geraniums. Never again did he kill or skin a seal, and indeed he took everything he owned made from seals, and mournfully buried it all in his garden. He even made sure, every time he brought in his net bursting with fish, to throw one or two back into the water to any seals he saw happily honking in the vicinity.

He never stopped feeling guilty, but he hoped, any time one of his seal friends caught one of the fish he threw, that it was the King of Seals himself, and that he was forgiven for his years of selfishness and greed. And any time he saw someone else selling sealskins at the market, he made a point of telling them: 'Everything needs its own skin. You let them keep theirs, and you keep your own.'

THE END

JOHN O'GROATS

Everybody has heard of John O'Groats — the northernmost 'End of the World' on the British mainland. For years many folk have faced the challenge of making their way there from Land's End, right down in Cornwall. Of course, you can always stand on the shore and watch the seals, puffins and the rest of the wildlife of the area, but the village itself is only small, so don't go expecting a big theme park!

visitjohnogroats.com

36. ELIDOR AND THE GOLDEN BALL

St. David's

The best part of a thousand years ago, this bloke called Gerald was wandering the Welsh hills of Pembrokeshire when he got lost on the far coast of Wales around Dewisland, and had to bang on the door of St. David's chapel to be safe from the rain and the wind for the night. Within the chapel he met a very strange monk called Brother Elidor.

This monk was old, and bald, and welcomed Gerald into the monastery for a night's bed and board very kindly. He showed him where he was to sleep, and where they were to break bread, and the best way to go in the morning to see even more Welsh hills. But what was strange was that all the time that the monk was showing Gerald round, great big tears continually splashed down his wrinkled cheeks.

That evening, after a couple of roasted birds, Gerald could not resist asking the monk what it was that made him so sad. And this is what the monk told him.

I was always intended for the brotherhood, since I was a tiny lad. 'Elidor!' my Dad would say to me, 'It's no life, this turnip-picking, boy! We will send you to the monks of St. David's, and they will teach you all sorts of things that we never knew, and you will be a monk.'

I was happy to avoid a life of turnip-picking, and so when the time came, aged twelve years old, I happily trooped up to the monks' Scriptorium to learn how to read and write.

But these monks were not the good men they were said to be, and as a boy I was a very poor student. I kept getting my P's mixed up with my Q's, and when I read the Bible, I did all the voices in such a silly way that the teachers announced 'Spare the rod and spoil the child!' and began to beat me horribly to try and make me knuckle down.

'So that's how monks behave?' I wondered to myself, and determined to stay away from my lessons for fear of being black and blue and achy all over.

Within sight of St. David's one day, I turned and ran to the forest, preferring to live off hawthorns and rosehips rather than face the monks' cane yet again.

Two days I shivered in the forest – but I didn't like the taste of rosehips at all. Just as I determined to head back to my Mum and Dad and beg for a life of picking turnips, two strange little men appeared before me, full of concern, for I must have looked a real sight after two days in the forest. They introduced themselves as Oddie and Acky, and bowed low before me.

'Come with us, young fellow,' said the pygmy men, 'and you will be allowed to join in all our delights and sports.'

'What kind of sport?' I asked, not really being much of a sporty type. 'It's not tennis is it? I can't stand tennis.'

'We do not know this "tennis",' returned one of the small folk. 'The sport we play is… well, there's this ball, right, and… Anyway, do you want to come with us or not?'

Well, anything was better than my current predicament, so I dutifully followed the curious men through the forest to a hidden cave. They lighted our way through the cave until we arrived at an enormous landscape, bedazzling to behold, beneath the earth. Rich green meadows and tinkling rivers criss-crossed the view, but all was in a golden murk, with no bright sun to light the land.

Shortly, the men brought me to the court of their leader, Good King Polly. Like all the little people, King Polly could not have been more than two feet high, with long golden hair, and he sat perched on a thoroughbred greyhound in his castle. He took one look at my torn and muddied clothes and announced, 'Ydor Ydorum!'

This, I learned, was their sign for water, and a hot shower instantly fell to clean me up. As 'Ydor Ydorum' sounds very much like Greek,

36. ELIDOR AND THE GOLDEN BALL

I have since realised that these underground people must have come to Britain from Troy with Brutus the Great, and made their homes under the ground.

'We have avoided your people for centuries!' boomed the little King, as I was draped in a velvety tunic very like those worn by the other men – it must have been made for one of their 'giants'.

'But why?' I asked.

'Because you tall people are stupid!' laughed the King. 'You have all that sun to bask in, and yet you worry, and moan, and break your fellow man's back to grow your turnips. Whereas down here, we all work together to make life a delight. And you, if you wish, may work with us. But the main reason that we keep ourselves to ourselves is that we, above all, believe in Truth. You humans lie and steal – don't deny it! – just as you lied to us when you said that we would share in Britain's glories all those years ago. You worship and you pray, but you seldom practise what you preach. But for one as young as you, I give one chance. You shall attend on my boy, Prince Pam, and join in our sport.'

Well no matter how I felt about the sport, I was glad to join these little people, under that murky sky. We rode around on greyhounds, and lived on custard and blancmange, and my dear Gerald, I was never so happy.

I was even happy to play their sport, a kind of football in which a golden ball...

(At these words the sad monk gave out a little whimper.)

... A golden ball had to be carried through a golden goal to score a try. Being twice the size of many of the players, I had an unfair advantage, of course; and where in human sport I was always the last to be picked, in this land I was a hero!

In time the King allowed me to travel back to my house to tell my Mum and Dad all about the wonderful life I was leading. They marvelled at my description of the land, the people, and the custard. But when I came to tell them about the football, they moved on from marvelling to positively goggling.

'Young Elidor bach,' my Mum said at last, 'look you. We don't like picking turnips any more than you do, son. If you bring us that wondrous golden ball, we will be rich, like, and live like the little people all the time! Apart from the bit about riding around on dogs maybe.'

I did not know what was right or wrong, but remember, I was a hero in that land! The golden ball seemed mine by right, for all the games that I had won. And so, the next time that my dear friend Prince Pam and I took to the golden field and played a game, I seized my chance. The Prince passed me the ball with skill, and the golden goal lay there before me, an easy win. But once through those golden arches I did not stop to celebrate, I just ran and ran back through the cave, speedily through the forest and did not stop until I came to the front gate of my home.

Only then did a speeding greyhound cross my tracks and send me flailing to the ground. As my Mum and Dad stared agape from the doorway, the golden ball spilled from my grasp and rolled into the turnip patch.

The two little men, Oddie and Acky, raced up and took the ball with a look of disgust on their little faces.

'Yes, you are like all the rest! You take, and you lie, and you will stay here to think about what you have done!' they sneered at me as I lay in the dirt, and then took it in turns to pass wind in my tearful face, before saddling up their dogs and racing away to their land beneath the earth.

Well, I yelled my apologies and my regret to their fleeing backs, I raced after them, but they had gone. I searched every cranny of the forest, trying to find the cave again, but it was no good. My murky golden land was lost to me forever more.

As time went by I determined to be unlike the humans that they so despised, hoping to one day win their favour once more. I worked hard at school, to become the monk you see before you now, and I never spoke a word of a lie or stole so much as a look. I also made sure to break the schoolmaster's cane and never again allowed a student to be beaten for not knowing his P's and Q's.

But the little men, and my good friend Pam, maybe by now the Great King Pam, have never found me again. And they have never allowed me to say...

(At this point sad Brother Elidor sighed and sniffed up a copious bogey of regret.)

... how very, very sorry I was. But maybe. One day. They will.

Gerald patted the poor monk's shoulder, and went off to bed.

When the visitor awoke the next morning, however, Brother Elidor was gone. There on the table, for his breakfast before setting out on his travels through Pembrokeshire, Gerald found a steaming bowl of delicious custard, unlike any other custard he had ever tasted before. And he ate up every drop.

THE END

ST. DAVID'S

Although you should not have to look far to find a good reason to visit Pembrokeshire, a trip to St. David's, the smallest city in the UK, offers a particularly fine added motivation. Pilgrims have flocked to the Cathedral for centuries, and today you can see where Brother Elidor could well have lived, at the now ruined Bishop's Palace, which is open to visitors. Sadly, it's proven impossible to work out precise directions to Elidor's underground world, but as the entire area surrounding St. David's is part of the Pembrokeshire Coast National Park, there's a great deal of fun and immense swathes of soulful scenery to enjoy while you do search for it — just follow the smell of custard.

visitpembrokeshire.com

---

37. LONG MEG
AND HER
DAUGHTERS

The Lake District

You probably know the phrase 'DANCE LIKE NOBODY IS WATCHING.' I love a bit of a dance myself, when I'm in the mood, but if I'm honest, if nobody was watching me I might not bother with all my best moves! That's how you can tell if someone is a real dancer – they love to prance and pirouette and pas de deux, whether they are on a stage before a thousand spectators, or totally alone, just doing what comes naturally.

One woman who always did what came naturally was Long Meg, a wonderfully tall and graceful wise woman of the Lake District, the craggy beauty spot in the north of England. Meg was a dancer, and her mother was a dancer before her, and so on, stretching back to the crack of Britain's dawn, if not further! She and her sisters had been taught to dance to the sound of nature in the same spot for thousands of years, and when Meg's time came to lead this ancient dance, she had a whole troupe of fine and graceful daughters to follow her steps.

Each and every dusk, the talented family warmed up and took their places in a sacred spot, to jump and twirl, swoop and sway to the sound of life on Earth itself, as the sun went down and the stars came out. Their lissom bodies chimed and bent with the wind, and a prettier sight you have never seen.

By the time of this tale, however, beliefs had changed, and a new religion had taken hold throughout the land. In these hard times, dancing and nature took second, if not third, place in people's priorities, in favour of prayer, suffering, and a fear of being struck down by lightning! All too often worries about what was to come in the next life spoiled any joy in the one life everyone could be fairly sure they really did have. Eventually the people began to fear life itself, and hardly ever lived it to the full.

Many of these frightened people called Long Meg and her daughters 'witches', and they could never understand the beautiful dances they performed every sundown.

One particular leader of these religious folk was determined to stop the dancing, which he insisted was 'the most shameful behaviour!' when everyone should be on their knees thinking about miserable stuff. History books record his name as Michael Scot, a famous clergyman of the 13th century. This grey rector warned Meg and her daughters that to dance their dances on his Lord's day, Sunday, would be taken as the foulest sin – which, he taught them, meant it went against his God's rules. And his God, he had to stress, was not the easy-going, jolly sort of god at all. Scot hounded Long Meg and her daughters for years, warning them to be done with their dancing by midnight, or else!

'Why, what would your god do?' Meg chuckled, as she stretched and limbered up for that evening's dance, on the eve of one Lord's day.

'Um… Well, he would… He would turn you all into stone!' Michael Scot squeaked. 'And you would be damned for all eternity!'

'For dancing?' Meg laughed.

'On a Sunday, yes!' returned the nervous preacher.

'This god bloke you worship sounds a bit of a fussy one to me, Michael,' returned Meg, 'but you must worship who you like. Come on, girls, dusk is near, twilight comes and stars appear…'

And with that, the tall graceful dancer took her place, with her many talented daughters in a ring before her, and dance they did, as dusk descended.

Despite his piety, Michael Scot could not resist the sight of the pretty dancers moving in the twilight that hot summer's night, and as he hid himself behind a bush to spy on Long Meg, the sun seemed to take forever to sink behind the Penrith crags…

Indeed, before he knew it, it must have been almost midnight – the witching hour, as folk had started to call it…

But of course, what Scot failed to realise was that Meg had her own plan all along. She and her daughters had suffered for too long, being spat at for so-called 'witchcraft' by the brainwashed villagers, and they had had enough. Meg knew the times were wrong for her and her dancing troupe, but one day the world would change once again, and their freedom to dance as they pleased would return.

Until then, she cried, as the day turned with the rising of the moon: 'Daughters of dusk, dance like nobody is watching!'

And at once, where Long Meg and her daughters had been dancing, there was nothing for Michael Scot to see but a large ring of frozen stones, and one enormous rock which once had been the remarkable Long Meg.

It was all his doing, the lying preacher told all the credulous villagers – 'That's what the power of prayer can do, see!' – and henceforth the people were more afraid than ever before, and especially careful never to move so much as a little finger rhythmically on a Sunday.

These silly villagers would never know that it was all Long Meg's scheme from the start: that what they saw as dead and silent rocks was just a disguise to fool the weak of mind. But as soon as every mortal eye was off the stones, the dance of Long Meg and her daughters was continuing, that night and every night, until such a day that the people of the island would truly be free from that fear of infernal judgement, which marred the only lives they had to lead.

And even on that day, all ten graceful women agreed, they would still be dancing.

THE END

THE LAKE DISTRICT

Britain's largest National Park needs no big tourist talk-up, being blessed with natural wonders, places to go and things to do, be it windsurfing on Lake Windermere or sampling any of the gastronomic delights in the region's many pubs, hotels and restaurants. The Bronze Age stone circle known as Long Meg and Her Daughters, however, is just a few miles north of the national park, not far from the market town of Penrith. It is said that it is impossible to count how many 'Daughters' there are, but

---

this may well be because as soon as your back is turned, each one returns to its graceful human form, and dances around to a different spot.

english-lakes.com

38. POOR OLD GELERT

Beddgelert, Gwynedd

I'm afraid that this is one of the saddest stories in the British treasury, but also such a famous one that there's nothing for it but to attempt a stiff upper lip and let the legend unfold. If you prefer something more jolly about naughty fairies or brave knights, then do try another tale.

The story concerns one of the last of the Welsh Princes to lose his kingdom to the English Kings – he was known as Llywelyn the Great, and as a politician, peacemaker and war-wager, he is remembered as one of the greatest rulers of Wales. He knew the wisdom of keeping bad old King John on his side – he married John's daughter Joan, and they had a boy called Dafydd, who would be the first ever 'Prince of Wales'. On the other gauntlet, he also knew when to show his father-in-law who was boss, and was one of the many powerful men who made the King sign the Magna Carta – a famous document which taught English Kings that they couldn't just do whatever they wanted. And yet now, Llywelyn is best known for the biggest mistake he ever made.

Besides his family and Wales itself, there was one important love in Llywelyn's life – his big friendly dog, Gelert. This hound had been a present from King John, but despite that, he was absolutely lovely. He was large and quite capable of serving as a powerful watchdog, but in his heart Gelert was just a great big hairy puppy, always happiest when giving his master licks and playing ball, and cuddling up in front of a roaring fire.

Gelert was the best friend Prince Llywelyn ever had, and his most trusted servant. Shortly after Llewelyn's son Dafydd was born, the proud father was compelled to travel to England on important royal business, but he knew that everything would be well with Gelert in charge, protecting his son and heir from any number of dangers.

'Who's a good boy, Gelert?' Prince Llywelyn said on his way out of the portcullis, 'You're a good boy, that's right!' Gelert wagged his tail and licked his master's face. 'Now, you be the man of the house, and protect young Dafydd while I'm away in England, and I shall be home before you know it!' And with that, Llywelyn mounted his horse and galloped away.

What the Prince discovered when he returned home to his castle broke his heart.

The first thing Llywelyn saw at the end of his long journey from London was Gelert, who bounded up more pleased than ever to see him, barking with rapture as his tail wagged away to the dozen and more. But the dog was not looking quite his old self – Gelert was dishevelled, and smeared with crimson.

'What's happened, boy?' Prince Llywelyn asked, as he dismounted. 'Have you been hurt?'

With a brave bark, Gelert made it clear that he hadn't been harmed at all. And so… why did he have red on him?

Llywelyn marched quickly into the castle and looked around for his son, calling desperately for help. There was the royal cradle, in pieces and flipped onto its side, the bedclothes also smeared in hot red blood, and no sign of young Prince Dafydd could be seen. Llywelyn's own blood was pounding in his head as he tried to put it all together. His trusty hound was badged with hot gore, as were the cradle's bedclothes. And the baby was gone.

'You damned CUR!' yelled Llywelyn, reaching the worst conclusion he could possibly come to. It seemed so obvious to him, in a flash, that his trusted dog had become feral and attacked his baby boy, tearing him to pieces like the wild animal he obviously was! So utterly confounded with blind anger was the royal Prince that he drew his sword there and then, and as the trusted Gelert bounded up to his master, Llywelyn ran the poor dog through with his sword.

Gelert let out a wounded, haunting howl, and died in the blink of an eye, laying still on the hearth where he had so happily cuddled up with his master.

It was only then that Llywelyn heard the baby's cry. He followed the sound, and found the little Prince safely wrapped up in his swaddling clothes, hidden in the corner of the room behind an old curtain. And there, not far from the safe, healthy baby, was the body of a wild wolf, in a growing pool of crimson. The wolf was covered in dog bites which could only have been Gelert's.

Now it all became clear. The wolf had stolen into the castle, and tried to attack little Prince Dafydd in his cradle. But dear, brave, noble Gelert had been there to protect him. He had fought with the wolf, and managed to triumph in what must have been a vicious fight. He had killed the beast, and saved the heir to the crown of Wales. And his master had repaid him with death.

The brave hound Gelert was buried in a place where all could pay their respects, and the story of how unfairly his life ended was written on his gravestone in English and Welsh, so that everyone would know what an honest, valiant dog he was.

Llywelyn's story does not end there. He lived a long life filled with deeds and tales long forgotten. And he was always known as 'Llywellyn the Great'. But it is said that from that heartbreaking day, when he returned home and made his greatest mistake, Llywelyn the Great never managed to crack another smile, ever again.

THE END

BEDDGELERT

There is some bad news to be imparted right from the start here — it seems likely that the grave of Llywelyn's trusty hound in the North Welsh town of Beddgelert was created only a few hundred years ago by a pub landlord trying to attract tourists. The 'Gelert' of the town name actually comes from an old Christian saint. That's not to say that the story isn't true, or that it didn't happen here — but the truth of the tale will have to come down to the power of your imagination if you ever visit the poor dog's graveside. Don't be disappointed, though — it's nestled in a wonderful corner of North Wales at its most rugged and naturally

---

38. POOR OLD GELERT

breathtaking, with three other story locations (at least!) within short
distance, so you'll have plenty to do and see.

beddgelerttourism.co.uk

39. THOMAS THE RHYMER

Eildon Hill, Roxburghshire

N ostradamus is a famed name the world over: he was a French man who claimed to have predicted the end of the world, among many other events. But he was not the only medieval fellow who boasted of seeing the future, and in Scotland, the most famous prophet of all was called Thomas the Rhymer. Some people insist to this day that Thomas was a shrewder sage than Merlin himself!

In his time, 'True Thomas' was said to have predicted the outcome of all sorts of battles – and William Wallace and Robert the Bruce were fighting the English back in his day. But he also foretold the arrival of King James to unite the island of Britain, and all sorts of things that haven't even happened yet. Although it's hard to be sure: like Nostradamus, Thomas only made his predictions in mysterious rhymes, which could really mean anything:

'The kestrel dances with the worm, And thus do all the planets turn!'

This could, for instance, predict the establishment of the first international space station, or a skirmish in Glasgow in 1363. It's very much up to how you read the rhymes.

At least the extraordinary way in which Thomas gained his powers of prediction were very clearly related on many occasions by the man himself. When he was still a lad of around 18, Thomas liked to live his life idling under an old hawthorn tree on the banks of the Huntly

39. THOMAS THE RHYMER

Burn, a stretch of water trickling off the river Tweed near his home in Earlston. There he would strum his lute, making up silly songs and dreaming of being rich.

One warm afternoon in May, Thomas was doing just this when a figure rode by, intrigued by his singing. Thomas gasped and goggled at this rider, who was without question the most desirable person he had ever laid eyes on. Some people just seem to glow with beauty, and this tall elegant lady, clad all in green velvet, red hair cascading down to her knees, seemed to shine with glamorous gorgeousness. She was perched on a grey dappled mare with 59 jingling bells threaded on its mane, and Thomas didn't need to look into her eyes to know they were green. That kind of fantastically beautiful woman always has green eyes.

Thomas was never a shy laddie, and when the lady drew near, he arose, and bowed.

'My dearest lady, I am Thomas the Rhymer and can only speak the truth: you must surely be the Queen of Heaven? No other place could provide such a flaming torch of beauty!'

The Queen gave a small giggle, but did not blush. 'Thomas the Rhymer, your truth is wonky!' she replied. 'For I am the Queen of Elfland, which is a much more jolly place.'

'I wish I was not cursed to always speak the truth, your highness, because then I could deny that the only thing I wish to do before I die is kiss your lips.'

There was still no blushing from the Elf Queen. She dismounted from her horse. 'Well, I shall not lie either, Thomas. Anyone who kisses me has to remain in my thrall for seven years.'

'It looks like a very nice thrall to me. Seven years would be cheap! Come here, under my hawthorn tree, your majesty, and kiss me, do.'

And so the Queen pressed her powerful lips on Thomas' own, and folded him in a fond embrace. Then she rode on, and Thomas trotted along behind her with a smile on his face which stretched right up to his eyebrows.

Soon they arrived at the grand Eildon hill, which folk to this day insist is completely hollow. There was a horn hung on the horse's saddle, which the Elf Queen lifted to her lips and played a short but pretty tune. At this sound, the side of the hill opened up like a gigantic flower, and Thomas could see through the entrance a road which split three ways.

196

'The first road is paved with thorns and nettles, and they say it leads to paradise,' the Elf Queen said. 'The last road is festooned with roses and lilies and may well lead to the darkest pit of Hell. The middle road leads to my home. Which shall it be, Thomas the Rhymer?'

The lad needed no thinking time. 'I'm always happy to take the middle road, Your Majesty!' He grinned, and so their journey continued down a green and winding path for many miles.

Deep underground they travelled, and to Thomas's surprise, they had to wade through a river of blood. The Queen explained that all the blood shed on earth trickled down into the Middle Earth, and ran in rivers. Fortunately, they were then bathed clean by a splashing waterfall, and eventually arrived in a green and pleasant pasture, with the Queen's silver castle just in sight on the horizon.

Trees loaded with the juiciest, ruddiest apples and pears filled the pasture. Thomas was weak with hunger, but as he lifted his hand to the fruit, the Queen of Elfland stopped him.

'Not yet, Thomas,' she warned. 'You are not yet ready for the knowledge this fruit brings.'

Luckily, she had brought some sandwiches with her, so they shared those and were soon on their way again to the Elfland Castle, Thomas happily plucking on his lute as they journeyed.

All was pleasure and playtime at the Castle when they arrived, with pink wine flowing and bountiful buffets of rich berries and fantastic toast all being enjoyed by a glorious array of nymphs, elves, fauns and knights, all laughing and dancing to the sound of the sweetest faerie band.

Thomas was welcomed with open limbs and in such a place it's hardly surprising that seven years felt like one long-ish pleasant weekend to the young laddie. Soon it was time for him to return.

The Queen of Elfland walked Thomas back to the fruit trees and twisted off a particularly ripe and luscious pear. 'Before you eat, and before you go,' she said, 'which shall you choose? To be the greatest lute player in the world, or the greatest prophet? There can be no going back once the selection is made.'

Thomas already considered himself rather gifted with the lute, so there was no doubt in his mind as he took the biggest, sweetest bite out of the fruit, and chewed it with mouth-watering delight. The delicious taste was only crowned by the delivery of one final kiss from the Queen of Elfland. Thomas only dared glance back once as he set off, but all he saw beneath the tree was a white hart, chewing on a pear.

The return journey to the old hawthorn tree seemed a lot quicker than the journey outwards had been, and soon Thomas was back with his astonished family and friends, who had presumed that the poor poet had been swept away by the river and was a goner.

He only told his very nearest and dearest what had actually happened, but most folk guessed, due to his new and wondrous ability to see into men and women's minds and foretell not just their future, but the whole future of the Scottish, the British, and indeed all the people of the world, perhaps until the crack of doom. (This was always depending, of course, on how you interpreted his curious rhymes.)

Nonetheless, his poetic powers made True Thomas the Rhymer rich and fat, and he built himself a tower atop a hill where he would feast with friends and regale them with poems and lute performances.

Until, one day, when his hair was as festooned with silver as his treasury, a friend of Thomas' arrived at one of his parties and reported that a handsome white hart had been seen in the village nearby, seemingly seeking something. 'Ah, that is the sign for me,' Thomas stood and announced with a big smile that stretched up to his eyebrows. 'Enjoy the rest of the feast, everybody. And mind how you go.'

From that time forth, nobody saw Thomas the Rhymer again – although many say he's somewhere beneath the hollow hill of Eildon, strumming his lute and preparing for his comeback tour.

THE END

EILDON HILL

A special stone marks the very spot where Thomas and the Queen of Elfland were said to have plunged into Eildon Hill — and at the top of the hill is a monument to writer Sir William Scott, who was himself inspired by Thomas' legend. Thomas was certainly real: the storyteller and seer Thomas Learmouth, Rymour de Ercildoun lived in Earlston, Berwickshire, in the 13th century: the remains of his ivy-clad tower still stand, and the

---

writings attributed to him were taken extremely seriously as foretellings of the future all the way up to the Jacobean rebellion, if not later. Why not pop to the borderlands of Roxburghshire to visit Eildon hill, put your ear to the ground, and see if you can hear a lute playing?

melrose.bordernet.co.uk

40. THE WISE FOLK
OF GOTHAM

Gotham, Notts

T he Nottinghamshire village of Gotham first came to fame for being full of extremely silly people... or were they? Just like those tales of big black ghost dogs, lonely grey spectres, and the endless hosts of Christian saints who had their heads chopped off near some sacred spring, Britain is very well stocked with stories about 'stupid villagers'. For as long as humans have been living in tribes, laughing at the stupidity of neighbours has always been a very common tradition. There's the old gossip about the fools in the next village who married their sheep, or executed a monkey believing it to be French – and the least said about the stupid dairy farmer who tried to milk a bull and tugged on quite the wrong part, the better. Every county is well stocked with these hoary old gags.

But this story is a little different, and well worth the telling. Because 'The Wise Folk of Gotham' may not be as sarcastic a title as it sounds...

Like many of the best medieval British yarns, this one features Bad King John, whose very name will always trigger boos and hisses wherever it is uttered. This thoroughly unlikable King announced one day that he was making an official procession to his northern lands – perhaps to deal with some unrest caused by Merry Men – and it was the law in those days that such a procession required an official public highway to be built for the journey, which would be paid for with extra taxes from the towns and villages he passed through.

One of these villages was Gotham – and word reached the good people of Gotham in advance that the King's Men would soon arrive in the village to check that all was going to plan for the King's journey. There was much whispering and plotting in the inns of Gotham that night...

The day arrived for the royal investigation, and when the King's Men marched up to Gotham's gates, they were wide open in welcome. King John's advance party strode the streets of the village, and wherever they looked, they were bamboozled.

'Hello there, King's Men!' chorused one gaggle of villagers. 'Isn't it a lovely night?'

The King's Captain gazed at the clear blue sky, and sneered. 'It is the brightest day, you simple northern folk! What are you up to there?'

The villagers were all gathered around a bush, and the tallest of them spoke up: 'Ah, see, sir, here we have a cuckoo's nest. And as there's nothing tastier than a cuckoo, we have all gathered to capture one in its nest. See, we built a fence all the way around it so there's no way it can possibly escape!'

At this, the cuckoo, who had been hitherto comfortably nestled in its nest, flapped its wings, and flew away. Everyone watched it disappear into the sky.

'You stupid villagers!' the Captain snarled.

'How embarrassing!' the tall villager replied. 'Lads, we really should have built a MUCH higher fence!'

And the King's Men rode on, shaking their heads in disbelief.

Next they came across a baker's wife riding along on a donkey so weighed down with bags of flour that it could barely hobble one step.

'You, stupid woman!' cried the Captain, rudely. 'Can you not see you have weighed that ass down so much it will surely collapse before you get home?'

'How very kind and thoughtful of you to notice!' cried the baker's wife in reply, and after a moment's visibly painful thought, she picked up two of the heavy bags of flour, and heaved them onto her back.

'That should solve the problem, ducks. Trot on, donkey, your burden will be much lighter now!'

And with that, the donkey hobbled another couple of steps, and toppled over sideways into a ditch with the baker's wife still on his back, giggling for all she was worth.

And the King's Men rode on, shaking their heads in dismay.

Wherever the royal messengers rode that day, they found villagers all employed in the silliest pursuits. Here they saw the local vicar trying to drown an eel in a pond. There, they saw a gang of farmhands trying to erect special umbrellas over a small wood to protect the trees from sunburn. Just around the block, they saw children rolling cheeses down the hill, just as they still do in Gloucester, to get them home without getting their dirty hands all over it. Out on a lake, they spied a butcher, a baker and a candlestick maker trying to sail across in a bowl! Well, it was more of a bathtub – with the plug removed, of course. They didn't get far.

And finally, as the sun went down, came the last straw – the Mayor and all the gentry of Gotham gathered around a puddle, doing their very best to sieve out the moon, which they insisted was in grave danger of drowning.

The King's Men did not just shake their heads. Their whole bodies shook with fear at the realisation that…

'EVERYBODY IN THIS VILLAGE IS ABSOLUTELY, TOTALLY HATSTAND-BANANAS-CRAZY-MAD! Men, we CANNOT let his Majesty ride through this village! What if the madness should be catching?'

And with that fear planted in their heads, the King's Men dug their spurs into their horses' hinds, and galloped out of Gotham and back down south as fast as the nags' legs could carry them.

No royal procession ever bothered the Wise Folk of Gotham ever again. And as the whole village gathered at the gates and watched the terrified King's Men flee, the Mayor turned to everyone, and smiled.

'It seems to me, my friends, that there are far more fools that pass through Gotham than remain in it!' he said.

And he closed the gate behind him.

THE END

GOTHAM, NOTTS

The tales and rhymes of 'The Wise Men of Gotham' were already widely known and loved throughout Britain by Tudor times, and the place soon became famed for its mad people — so much so that superhero Batman's home of Gotham was named after it. These days, a visit to Gotham will hopefully prove that nobody foolish lives there today — but maybe one of the locals will show you the actual thicket where the villagers were said to have built the fence around the cuckoo's nest. And then you can pop into the Cuckoo Bush Inn for a drink afterwards.

gothamvillage.org.uk

41. THE GIFT HORSE

Bonne Nuit, Jersey

Britain is a famously seafaring nation, surrounded as it is by deep blue drink; and thanks to inventive sailors, there are endless maritime yarns of sea sprites, mermaids, kelpies, and generally very soggy supernatural tricksters waiting offshore to lead humans to their doom.

This is a tale of Jersey, the sunniest and furthest away of all the Channel Islands. These pretty isles aren't technically part of Great Britain, but have always clung to their Englishness.

The story stars a sea sprite with no name at all. Perhaps we can give it one. How about 'John'? That's a lovely name for a sea sprite. After all, it was Bad King John who lost his lands in Normandy, northern France, but refused to give up these sun-hugged islands, which is why they remain British.

It may well have been some sunny weekend around the time of King John that Jersey's northern port of Bonne Nuit set the scene for a very strange occurrence. A shapely figure ran down to the beach, and began to play and paddle in the sea. Anne-Marie was a young woman of singular, glowing beauty often remarked upon by the men and women of her small village:

'That Anne-Marie's smile always brightens up my day, Jean-Luc!'

'You're right there, Juliette, what a smasher she has turned out, and no mistake, and very pleasant with it!'

'And she knows a surprising amount about gannets as well, you know.'

'Mais oui!'

– And so on. But it was an unfortunate pain to Anne-Marie that people tended to fall for her without the slightest encouragement, whether she liked it or not – and she never did. She had happily given her heart away to her childhood sweetheart, the stable boy, Guillaume – who she called her Little Willy. He did try and ask her to call him something else, but the name stuck.

On this hot sunny lunchtime Anne-Marie was singing an old Jersey song:

Jèrri, man paradis, pus belle taque souos l'solé,
Qué j'aime la paix dé chu Jèrri...'

And as her lusty voice echoed around the bay, she began skimming stones, which she did with an impressive heft to every throw. Unfortunately, one stone happened to skim off a frothy wave, and ping right into the belly button of a creepy sea sprite – John, if you like – who was paddling on the tips of the waves.

'Youch!' the sprite squawked, but then he caught sight of the person who threw the stone. And, like so many others before him, he was gone. Down, down, down-de-down in love he tumbled – and as he was not a human and knew he could never truly make the young woman happy, it was instantly a kind of twisted love, as much hate as love in every way.

'But she must be mine! That human will be mine!' he hissed. But how? The bitter sprite frothed his way onto the shore, hiding between falling raindrops and inside horse troughs, wherever there was water to conceal himself, and he watched poor Anne-Marie from afar.

It was not long before he started snooping on Anne-Marie and Willy as they kissed in the hay, and poor John the sprite almost evaporated with jealousy and anger! And he quickly cooked up a despicable plan. 'If I cannot enjoy the beauty of Anne-Marie, I swear on every drop of my being that nobody can! And especially not this handsome, honest young man, this Little Willy! PAH!'

Guillaume was indeed a humble workman, whose life largely consisted of mucking out barns and stables for his elderly grandfather, a wise-bearded old owl of a man known as Drew. The family did not have a lot to boast about, and the stables Willy cleaned out every day only boasted a skinny old grey mare which had seen better days.

That was until that Sunday morning, when he opened the stable door to find a huge, strong, beautiful white stallion, huffing and puffing in the morning mist – clearly worth more gold than the entire tumbledown farm!

'Hullo, my fine fellow!' gasped Willy, 'Where on earth did you come from? Grandfather, come quick, and look at this amazing good fortune!'

The dear old man hobbled his way over to the stable, and ran his fingers through his silvery beard in astonishment. 'It's a fine horse, young Guillaume, there's no denying, but I cannot guess how it came to be here.'

'Well, I say we just cheer our good fortune, and enjoy it while we can!' replied Willy. 'What is that old saying about looking gift horses in the mouth?'

'Oui, oui, there is an old saying along those lines,' Drew replied. 'It means you shouldn't get too suspicious about good fortune, lest you find out something you don't like. But if you ask me, my boy, many of these old time sayings are nothing but a bucket of old sheep dugs. Be very careful...'

'But surely I can at least take this wonderful horse on a ride to show Anne-Marie, Grandfather?' the stable lad complained, patting the fine steed's nose. Guillaume was a skilled rider, and knew he could gallop up a storm on this beast's strong back. 'What shall we call him?'

'I'm not sure you should go calling him anything, my boy—'

'What about John? John's a good name for a horse?'

'John is a very stupid name for a horse, but it doesn't matter,' replied Grandfather Drew, and he gazed long and hard into the horse's round shiny dark eyes. Then he had an idea. 'Tell you what, young 'un,' he said to Willy, 'I know you're a fine horseman, so of course you should take the horse for a ride, but...' at these words, the old man climbed the ladder which stood nearby against the old apple tree. As Willy waited, a snip was heard, and down fell a bushel of mistletoe, the white-berried plant which grew in clumps all over the trees in that area. 'Take this sprig of mistletoe with you,' the old man said, 'and if what I fear turns out to be true, you will know what to do.'

This seemed an incredibly vague warning to young Guillaume, but the young seldom pay enough attention to what their elders say;

besides, he was so keen to saddle up the horse and ride to Anne-Marie, he did not care.

'Thank you, Grandfather!' he smiled, and leapt onto the horse's back, the mistletoe in his hand. 'I shall be back before teatime! Hi-ho, hooray and away!'

And with a slap on the horse's rump, off down to the beach he rode at top gallop.

At first, the thrill of such a speedy steed thundering away beneath him, after years of clip-clopping about on the old grey mare, was so great that Willy could do nothing but whoop and holler with joy. The air was fresh, the wind was rushing through his hair, and the horse was galloping and steaming away fit to burst! Galloping and steaming away… right towards the sea!

'Woah there, John, woah, boy!' Willy cried, but all to no avail. Suddenly, John the horse turned his head around until he was facing his rider, and roared back at poor Willy:

'WOAH YOURSELF, YOU HIDEOUSLY ATTRACTIVE YOUNG DUNG-SHOVELLER! HOW DARE YOU DIG YOUR HEELS INTO MY SIDES AND RIDE ME LIKE A COMMON DONKEY! YOU SHALL BE DROWNED IN THE DEEP DEEP OCEAN, AND ANNE-MARIE SHALL BE MINE! MINE, FOREVER! MWAHAHAHA!'

Of course, Guillaume had only one thing to hand, startled as he was at the sight of this terrifying shape-shifter between his thighs. And so, as rider and horse splashed into the sea, heading into perilous waters, the young stable lad took the mistletoe and beat the horse sprite desperately all around the head with it, as hard as he could. Eyes shut tight, yelling for all his might, Willy screamed and thrashed and swiped with the green bough of berries, and was finally thrown, bruised and dazed, back onto the beach. He heard a loud whinny, and a crash, and then just the sound of the lapping sea.

As he looked across, no fine white stallion could he see. And no vicious water sprite, either. Instead, there was a dark grey jagged rock, poking out of the waves, in the shape of a horse called John.

'MY LITTLE WILLY!' Anne-Marie cried, as she rushed down to the coast and took her wounded lover in her arms, quieting his babbled cries about horses and mistletoe and drowning him with big sloppy kisses. She took him home, made him better, married him, and

41. THE GIFT HORSE

they barely gave poor old John another thought throughout their long and happy lives together.

Except sometimes, as they played with their children on the beach at Bonne Nuit, when Willy spied a rock very like a horse's head poking out from the frothy waves of the English channel, and he shivered.

THE END

BONNE NUIT, JERSEY

The seaside settlement of Bonne Nuit is centrally located on the north coast of Jersey — an island so close to France that it was once still part of the country, even while Britain had been flooded away from the continent. For all its turbulent history, Jersey has been a popular holiday destination for generations, and Anne-Marie's home of Bonne Nuit Bay is as sun-kissed a seaside as you could wish to visit. And of course, you can go down to the beach and try and spot which of the rocks is John the horsey sea sprite… Just make sure none of the surviving sea sprites take a fancy to you.

jersey.com

42. ROBERT THE BRUCE AND THE SPIDER

Craigruie, Stirling

B ritain has always seemed a very desirable jewel up in the cold North Sea, so it's no wonder so many generations of immigrants have come over to try and make the place their own – Iberians, Celts, Romans, Saxons... but since their first triumph over the Saxons in Hastings in 1066, no people have been quite so vicious in their desire to own the whole island of Britain than the Normans.

Once William the Conqueror announced his success at Hastings (and changed his name from the less marvellous sounding 'Billy Bastard'), his French-speaking descendants were set to rule over England for centuries to come, and Wales, and... well, Scotland was another story altogether.

Moving forward a couple of centuries, the Norman King Edward Longshanks waged war against the Scots for years, stamping his big size thirteen boot down on any sign of rebellion from the hairy northerners. For a while, the country celebrated the successes of a man they called Braveheart, William Wallace, who had triumphed in battle at Stirling Bridge; but his triumph was short lived. As soon as King Edward had Wallace in his clutches, he decided to make an example of the troublemaking Scot by pulling out all his innards and burning them in front of a jeering crowd. Wallace's dying cries of

42. ROBERT THE BRUCE AND THE SPIDER

'FREEDOM!' echoed around the country for many years after that, and yet the English remained masters of all Britain.

One soldier who tried to keep the spirit of Braveheart alive had crowned himself 'King of Scotland' – and yet he was full of Norman blood himself. His name was Robert the Bruce, Earl of Carrick, and he had once been an ally of William Wallace. As the Norman Powers That Be continued to trample all over Scotland, Robert took it upon himself to lead the resistance fight against the English and French invaders.

He was not very successful. The Scots were passionate warriors, many dyed blue with woad, as British soldiers had presented themselves for battle since before the Roman invasion. But for all that they believed to their last dying breath in protecting their ancient British ways from the Normans, Edward Longshanks and his army had more men, more money, and far more great big spiky things for slicing up ginger people. Robert the Bruce had lost many battles – at Strathfillan in 1306, and at a place called Methven that cold winter. He had been declared an outlaw by the Normans, and as the King of Scotland, he had to flee and find safety on each occasion. But he never gave up.

Or rather, he came very close to giving up. It was probably after his defeat at Methven that Robert the Bruce was at his lowest ebb. Even the fact that Edward Longshanks had died, and been followed as King by his weedy son Edward II, was no comfort – it was the same old English armies taking to the field every time a fight kicked off.

Robert was hiding in a cave, protected by loyal Scottish nobility. Nobody knows exactly where the cave was; it may have been in Ireland, or somewhere in Scotland, but wherever it was, King Robert was sick and tired of it. He was used to the good things in life, and scratching out a cold and soggy existence in caves was not fitting for a King.

All the battling had worn Robert down, and he was tempted to finally accept that he would never win, and settle for a quiet life somewhere far away, or perhaps even kneel to the new King Edward and accept him as King, just for a quiet life.

And then he gazed towards the opening of the cave, and saw a wee spider going about its business, spinning a web in one corner of the entrance. This spider was such a committed little weaver, knitting away from dusk till dawn to construct a home for all its tiny spider babies, full of big fat flies to feed upon. It was all just survival to this little eight-legged mother.

Robert watched as the spider tried to swing its way from one side of the web to another. It tried once, and missed its target terribly, dangling for a while on a single thread, before scrabbling back to where it started from. Twice Robert saw the spider do this, and fail. Three times, the spider attempted to leap across to the other side, and again it dangled there in failure. Four times. Five. Then Robert stopped counting.

And it was only just after he stopped counting the number of attempts the spider made to leap across the cave's mouth that he saw the tiny stubborn bug land just where it needed to be. And all of a sudden, all of that fighting Scottish spirit that had been beaten out of Robert the Bruce fired up once again in his gut. He would not be beaten by some English bully! He was the King of Scotland! And he would not waste any more time hiding away in caves. 'If at first you don't succeed,' Robert proclaimed, 'Try, try again!'

On that very day, Robert left the cave (being very careful not to disturb the spider's web as he left, of course), and began a new campaign, reuniting what remained of his armies and urging the country of Scotland once again to 'FREEDOM!' Just a few months later, in June 1314, once of Scotland's greatest military triumphs took place near Stirling Castle, at the Battle of Bannockburn. The English had seized the castle, but although Edward's forces numbered at least 20,000, and Robert had at most 5,000 men, they took Stirling back, and won perhaps the most impressive victory in Scottish history. Before Robert the Bruce breathed his last, a treaty was signed with the English that proclaimed Scotland an independent country, with Robert the Bruce as its rightful King.

And on that very day of independence, Robert the Bruce remembered that industrious little spider, and whispered a tiny thank you. Who says spiders are always scary?

THE END

CRAIGRUIE, STIRLING

Although the name of 'Craigruie', a tiny hamlet not far from the impressive historic town of Stirling (site of the Scottish victory of Stirling

---

42. ROBERT THE BRUCE AND THE SPIDER

Bridge in 1297), does literally mean 'King's Cave', there is no solid reason to believe that this was where Robert the Bruce spied his diligent spider. In fact, a whole host of caves lay claim to being the real spider's cave, including two on Rathlin Island, over in Ireland, one at Drumadoon, on the Scottish isle of Arran, and another near the English border, at Kirkpatrick Fleming. For this tale, however, we have plumped for a cave called Uamh-an-Righ, just above Craigruie on the road north of Stirling. You can visit the cave to look for the descendants of the spider, but also pay tribute to another famous Scottish hero on the same day trip — the nearby village of Balquhidder is the birthplace of legendary rebel Rob Roy.

undiscoveredscotland.co.uk

43. THE FAIRY INVASION

Vazon Bay, Guernsey

Everyone in Britain has washed up on these shores due to a whole host of highly unlikely events and circumstances, and yet there has always been a curious relationship between the mainlanders and the people of Britain's many isles which dot the foaming seas around the Great bit. To this day, there remains some idea that the islanders are a breed all of their own.

This is an especially strong tradition on Guernsey, the nearest of the two main Channel Islands, which are actually much closer to France than Britain – the other island being Jersey, with the tiny island of Sark peeping out between them. From coast to nearby coast, Guernsey is awash with fairy stories – and a mixed bunch the fairies seem to have been, as well! In some areas, it's said that ploughmen once dug up a broken kettle, and when begged to fix it by a fairy creature, they were finely rewarded with gold. Others who were not so kind when the fairies requested a favour received much nastier gifts...

But there are so many different kinds of 'faeries', or 'fairies', however you like to spell it. When the first blue-eyed settlers came to Britain, they thought of the short swarthy natives they found there as 'fairies', living in little more than holes in the ground. There are short fairies, tall fairies, and perhaps even tiny green ones with sparkly gossamer wings and magic wands. It's so hard to tell with fairies.

If the people of Guernsey have a special understanding of the fairy

213

people, it may be because many of them claim to actually be descended from fairy invaders. One fine morning, way back in the Middle Ages, a saucy young milkmaid of Vazon Bay called Michelle discovered a queer little green man sleeping under a hedge.

'Alive or dead?' the milkmaid asked, and when the small fellow opened his eyes, she got her answer. In fact, she got a lot more than she really expected.

'Not just alive, my dear, but more alive than I have ever been before!' cried the green man. 'Allow me to accost you properly. I am the King of the Fairies, you know?'

'Yeah, pull the other one, mate, it's got a bucket on it.'

'No, my dear udder-tugger, it is true! And yet nowhere, throughout the entirety of fairyland, is there a single sight as beautiful as you.'

'Don't you think you can get round me with all that nonsense neither,' Michelle returned – but he did, and he could, and he did. Fairies are notoriously convincing forms of life, so the wisdom runs, and the dizzying flow of words of love which wrapped around the unsuspecting milkmaid's heart was enough to make her drop her milk pails right where she stood, and run away from her island home to start a family with the King of the Fairies. Rumour suggested that the name of this Fairy Kingdom sounded very like 'Far-Away-Over-There-Land'.

All of this would be strange but harmless enough, perhaps even a happy ending, for a humble milkmaid to become Queen of the Fairies… but regrettably the tale goes on.

In the shadowy realm of the Fairy King, the beauty of his tall blonde Queen Michelle had made jaws drop throughout the population. If there are such beauties to be found on this 'Guernsey', the fairy boys decided, why shouldn't they all go off and find themselves wives there?

And so, the fairy fleet shimmered over the sea and landed back at Vazon Bay one warm dawn. The invaders hid themselves in the hollow now known as Creux ès Faies, and in the morning, they poured out of the caves like swarms of bees.

However, there was a welcome party there on Guernsey to greet them – and to make it clear that invaders of any kind were not at all welcome. The island's enraged menfolk stood there, swords, longbows, maces and pitchforks at the ready, roaring with macho indignation at the fairy feet tramping across their land.

When the milkmaid had disappeared, it had not taken the locals long to work out what had happened. 'FAIRIES!' cried one butcher from Pleinmont, and everyone quickly agreed: 'FAIRIES!' Thousands of blokes, big and small, all armed and dangerous, amassed and faced the fairies in battle – well, except a couple of clever fellows in St. Andrews, who weren't at all interested in fairies and decided to hide themselves in an oven until the all-clear had been given.

'Now look here,' bellowed the self-styled King of Guernsey, a big, grubby, stubbly man brandishing a club studded through with rusty nails. 'We don't take kindly to weird little fellas in green coming over here, stealing our women! They're OURS, you hear? Our mothers, wives, girlfriends, sisters and daughters.'

'And nieces!' added one small cowherd who was largely zits.

'Well, nieces, yeah, them too, obviously,' the King snapped back, before returning to fix the fairy hoard with his fiery, kingly gaze. 'You leave our women alone. You move your fairy feet that way, you get back on those fairy boats of yours, and you go back to fairy land, or we'll clobber and spifflicate every last fairy one of you into fairy dust! Our women is OURS!'

If you're wondering what the women of Guernsey thought about all this, it seems fair to say that none of them were at all happy to be spoken of as if they were horses, or sheep, or mouldy old turnips. That morning, though, they did what they always tended to do: they got on with all the important stuff while their meat-headed menfolk were off measuring their manhoods.

The King of the Fairies was also tired of the other King's bellowing, and so before more human spittle could be launched in their direction, the invaders attacked, and battle commenced. Well, it wasn't much of a battle, as the fairies were small and nimble, and able to simply POP each sluggish islander with a click of their magical fingers.

As the Guernsey army was forced back to the east, to their last stand at St. Peter Port Hill, the fairies' spells locked onto the bloodlust which was raging in each of the Guernsey men's veins, and in a split second, all that anger and rage and toxic masculinity was magically turned into explosives! So each time they tried to attack the invaders, every angry islander simply burst, very messily. It was said that the red pulpy mess left behind all washed down to the shore, in an area still known as La Rue Rouge.

43. THE FAIRY INVASION

As we have seen, these fairies were supernaturally persuasive types, and so with big smiles they worked their way around the women of Guernsey, and before sundown, they held one huge mass fairy wedding, and settled into the lives of the men they had just ruthlessly popped – all except for that one wily pair of fellows from St. Andrews, but thankfully the King of the Fairies was perfectly happy to let them live.

The womenfolk of Guernsey were quite pleased to have attentive, thoughtful companions for once, and the fairies worked hard farming the land, and doing their fair share of all the housework, and soon new generations of half-fairy folk were thriving across the island. To this day, they say that any native Guernsey people who are tall and blonde must be descended from the two chaps from St. Andrews, while the shorter, slighter, darker majority are all descended from those invading fairies.

This sounds far-fetched, but if anyone from Guernsey brags to you about their fairy blood, it's probably not a good idea to get angry and tell them they're talking rubbish. After all, you can't be entirely sure what they might do to you with a quick click of their magic fingers.

THE END

VAZON BAY, GUERNSEY

One of the larger of the sunny Channel Isles between England and France, the 'Bailiwick' of Guernsey is so packed with tourist attractions, it's lucky that this story pretty much covers the entire landmass, from Creux ès Faies to La Rue Rouge. There are many ways to get to Guernsey — and to Sark, and other islands, from there. But if you do fly in, you will land in the south, whereas only a boat to the north coast at Vazon will do to recreate the invasion of the fairies. In truth, the story seems to stem from a very bloody invasion of mercenaries from Wales in 1372 — but that version of events is not quite so magical.

visitguernsey.com

---

44. ROBIN AND THE CURTAL FRIAR

Fountains Abbey, Yorkshire

We all think of Robin Hood, that famous outlaw of the North Country, as a Nottingham hero, riding through the forest of Sherwood. But what many people forget is that centuries ago, Britain was stuffed to bursting point with rambling forestland. They say that a particularly daring and agile squirrel could bound across branches from John O'Groats all the way down to Land's End, without ever setting paw on the ground.

Back in Robin's day, Sherwood's trees flourished further in every possible direction, including up north to Yorkshire and the outwoods of Wakefield and Barnsdale. In these lands, the folk rhyme 'Robin Hood in Barnsdale stood' was used to mean something that was undeniably true – so it's fair to say that the Merry Men knew those hills and villages well.

Once outlawed into the dangerous brush of the greenwood, the dashing rebel Robin gathered quite a motley crew of jocund ruffians around him. There was the mighty Little John, crafty Will Scarlet, faithful Much the Miller's son, and Alan-a-Dale, the balladeer. Alan would idle back and strum the lute, while his merry cohorts looted from the rich Norman nobles and selfish clergy of the counties. The Merry Men would then share the wealth and bread among the over-taxed and desperate folk.

44. ROBIN AND THE CURTAL FRIAR

Robin Hood was often heard to cry 'The more the merrier', however, and while the wicked Sheriff of Nottingham was viciously squashing the people of the North Midlands under his heel, the outlaw wanted his band of freedom fighters to grow and grow until they were so strong, there would simply have to be changes, from Nottingham to York and throughout England. The rich would see that they were no better than the rest of us, and everyone could find their own happiness.

When it came to forming his band, Robin had many a challenge to face. Little John was a tall, strong, hairy Derbyshire man, from Hathersage. Robin had encountered the giant blocking his way across a rickety bridge, and the two had fought with quarterstaffs until both were sent sprawling into the water below. Will Scarlet, or Scathlock, was a wily crook of Blidworth. He had a kind heart and slashed a fine sword, and Robin had barely bested him in a swordfight many years earlier.

Each of the brave band had their story to tell, and most of them involved some form of scuffle with Robin, the Lord of the Greenwood. But they had all become firm friends and comrades in the end.

It was witty Will who first mentioned the Friar: 'There's this gluttonous chaplain of Fountains Abbey,' he said one evening, mouth full of roast venison, 'A fat man of the church, all wobbly bits and booziness, but I tell you, Robin, that friar seems to be sheer metal underneath the flab. I have the word of my kinsman, who once tried to wrestle a chicken wing from his greasy grasp, and barely lived to tell the story!'

Robin was no friend of the greedy church. In those days, abbots and bishops were among the richest men in the land, covetous and powerful, and happy to take what few pennies the poor folk had, in return for the cleansing of their souls, and similar holy favours which they swore were compulsory.

But there had to be some good folk among them – they could not all be like that, surely? Robin knew that the learning of a man of the Abbey, sure to be able to read, write – and perhaps even make sweet honey mead – would be a worthy addition to his army of outlaws.

And so out the Merry Men rode to find this greedy monk.

On arriving at Fountains Abbey, Robin told his friends to hide themselves away in the leafy undergrowth before setting forth on his own on foot. It only took him a few steps to spy a very round fellow in a brown habit, who was merrily fishing on the banks of the River Skell.

This monk had been called many things in his life, as of course have many big people throughout history. 'Chubby', 'well upholstered', 'rotund', or 'big boned' were just the nicer ones. But Robin did not mess around.

'Hello, fatso!' he cried, with a laugh in both syllables.

'Hello, stupid!' fired back the Friar at once, proffering barely a glance Robin's way.

'Come now, brother,' returned Robin, 'It is a sin to prejudge, surely? How can you be certain that I am stupid when you have only just become aware of me? That you are a big and fat friar nobody can deny with even the quickest sight of you!'

'And I know full well that only a foul fool would wander around being so loudly rude to strangers, so your stupidity is there for all to know in half a second. So hello, stupid!' the Friar laughed back.

That said, only then did the holy man fully turn and take in his ill-mannered companion, standing behind him on the banks of the rushing river. This loud fool was an outlaw, he could see – though he could also tell somehow that this was no common man, not least thanks to his well-groomed beard and flashing white smile.

This Friar was wily. He knew who was who. Robin laughed, and prodded him in his ample belly. 'You're a holy man, then?' he said.

'I wear the tonsure,' came the indignant reply. The tonsure was a small round bald spot all monks had to have shaved into their hair. For this Friar, it just hid the fact that he was going bald anyway.

'Not too humble, for a Bible reader!' the outlaw sneered. 'Too many chicken drumsticks, too much claret! Why, we must get you some exercise, Tuck!'

'You know my name?' demanded the Friar.

'Aye, and if you do as I say, maybe you will know mine. As you are a man of the church, you surely know the tale of St. Christopher, who took the Lord Jesus upon his back and carried him across a rushing ford without getting the soles of his feet wet?'

'I know the story...' Tuck admitted, suspiciously.

'Well, as a Christian brother, you may carry me across this river on your back. I need to get over to yon shore on my journey, and as the Bible tells you to help your fellow man, let's see how much of a believer you are!'

With barely another sound besides a 'Hi-ho!' Robin quickly and

219

nimbly leapt up onto the stout monk's shoulders, and began whooping like a wild huntsman riding his horse: 'Get along now, Tuck, take me across the stream!'

Now, Friar Tuck was a very big and strong man. He could carry Robin Hood without getting a crick in his back – or equally, he could easily throw him off and squash him in the river. But Tuck was also game for a laugh, and he thought he would play this game to the end, and see where it got him. So, without a word of complaint, Tuck tucked his robes up under his arms and made his way across the rushing river, with Robin perched on his back chuckling away like a giddy toddler, until they got to the other side.

'There, now leave me in peace!' Tuck thundered, once he had set Robin down on the other side of the river.

'Do you know, I've completely forgotten why I wanted to come over here now,' Robin said with a twinkle, 'Sorry, you'll have to take me back now, Tuck! Can't be getting wet toes, you know!'

The look on Tuck's face made Robin hoot with laughter more than ever. Nonetheless, soon the outlaw was back on the monk's shoulders, goading him on like a donkey at the seaside.

'You can surely go faster than this, tubby!' the loutish Robin crowed when they were halfway across the second time. 'All the fine meats and wine you enjoy should give you a bit more vim! Come on, speed up or I'll never tell you my name!'

'Oh, I know your name well enough, ROBIN HOOD!' thundered Tuck, suddenly shaking the silly merry man off his shoulders and into the chilly water with an almighty 'SPLA-LOOSH!'

Within less than half a moment, the two of them had drawn their swords, and set-to! Robin, the greatest archer in the land, was also in the running for one of the best swordsmen alive, but he could tell with a few dazzling flourishes that with this ferocious friar, he had met someone quite capable of giving him a thrashing.

Robin smiled as he saw how Tuck parried his every blow, and came within an ace of puncturing his defence. Eventually the two of them raced back up onto the far bank of the river, both soaked from head to foot, but neither ready to call a truce just yet.

'You fight well, Friar Tuck, but I wouldn't be too sure of victory today if I were you!' panted Robin, giving a mighty blow on his hunting horn.

Actually, at first the horn only squirted out a jet of dirty river water, but then it sounded a musical blast that carried on the wind. The sound alerted all the waiting Merry Men, who rushed out of the nearby brushwood to lend their comrade a hand. Dozens of arrows pointed directly at Tuck from the far side of the river, and any one of them could effortlessly have hit such an easy target.

Tuck was taken aback. Was it to be him alone, against a whole army of vagabonds? But the wily Friar was not finished either.

This time it was the churchman's turn to laugh as he pulled out a tin whistle and played a few piercing notes, barely audible to anybody standing on that soggy riverbank. At the sound, a full fifty ravenous forest dogs ran barking from the grounds of Fountains Abbey, and Tuck held them back with a commanding glance. He had raised every dog from a puppy, and they were each ready to pounce on the first Merry Man to make a move towards their friend the Friar.

For once, Robin did not laugh his lusty laugh, but merely applauded. 'My dear Tuck, you are more than a match for me, the celebrated Robin Hood! I am, so everybody says, and sings, the greatest longbowman in the land – but I am nothing without my friends. We have a fierce and burning battle to fight against the injustices of the Powers That Be, and all my men are soberly sworn to work together until the likes of the King's taxmen and the Sheriff of Nottingham are turfed out of their golden chairs, no longer to profit from this wonderful land of ours. Until all the people have enough to eat, and a roof over their heads! But we need a man like you, Tuck. Will you join us... fatso?'

Tuck, who had been just about to say 'Yes', gave Robin a boot up the hindquarters that everyone watching felt for a fortnight. As laughter broke out, he crowed:

'I'll join your cause, Hood, you giggling buffoon, but don't you ever – EVER – 'fat', 'fatty' or 'fatso' Friar Tuck, or anybody else who may be a bit on the big side, ever again! In fact,' Tuck continued, 'one thing you will do for me in return! Just to make sure you keep your promise...'

And so, stranded as they were on the far side of the river, Friar Tuck jumped on Robin Hood's back and forced the staggering outlaw to carry him across to where he had been happily fishing.

The Merry Men hooted with delight at this spectacle, every last pound of big round Friar Tuck perched atop Robin's shoulders as he painfully forded the rushing waters. Soon the whole band, Friar Tuck included, made their way back to the green secrecy of the forest, their home from Barnsdale down to Sherwood.

Robin was strong, but his back was bent double for a whole week after that! And good thing too: he certainly never called anyone 'fatty' – or anything like it – ever again.

THE END

FOUNTAINS ABBEY, YORKS

Yorkshire is so packed with famous sites and astonishing natural beauties, despite its fame as an industrial county, that the proud place has little need to 'poach' one of Britain's greatest icons, Robin Hood. The fact remains that the very earliest ballads from which we have come to know Robin place the outlaw in Barnsdale, in a forest which very probably merged into Sherwood in medieval times. Tuck's legendary home of Fountains Abbey is in North Yorkshire — a 12th century Cistercian monastery, more intact and impressive than any other in the country, right now in the 21st century. As a busy cultural centre packed with things to do, a drive to Fountains Abbey from Nottingham (perhaps taking in the real Robin's stamping grounds, Barnsdale and Wakefield) would be a must for anyone wanting to walk in the footsteps of the real Merry Men.

fountainsabbey.org.uk

45. THE SILVER ARROW

Nottingham

Robin Hood is one of the most inspiring heroes ever to emerge from the mists of British history and gain fans all around the world. However, if you've been reading stories about him and his antics with the Merry Men, you may have got the impression that he was something of a bighead, swinging about and enjoying being the boss of a gang of bad boys out in the greenwoods of the North Country.

And of course, he was! But that was only when he was out on his own. What only a handful of his closest allies knew at the time was that Robin had a wife, and nothing – not even helping the poor by stealing from the rich – mattered more to the great outlaw than this love of his life. Everything he did, he did it for her.

Robin's wife was called Matilda, and she was the daughter of a poor knight known as Richard of the Lees. This made her rather posh, and surely far from likely to get involved with a ruffian like Robin. Some people who never even met Robin Hood have since claimed that he was also a very well-to-do chap, the Earl of Huntingdon, hiding out in Sherwood Forest in the hope of retrieving his lands from the crown – but this was made up to try and please the toffs and make them buy more copies of the Robin Hood adventure stories, or 'Gests'. Robin was a good yeoman, an honest man turned to crime against the Norman nobility because of the cruelty shown by the Powers That Be against the English poor.

45. THE SILVER ARROW

It was this distrust of nobles which first caused Robin to hold up Sir Richard as he tried to make his way through Sherwood. Robin, Little John, Will Scarlet, Much the Miller's Son, Friar Tuck, Alan-a-Dale and all the Merry Men knew a knight when they saw one hurrying through their forest home, and the grey-haired Sir Richard did not provide much of a challenge; they saw their chance to kidnap him, and take him back to their well-hidden hideout.

However, they soon learned that this was not one of the wealthy landed gentry holding the peasants under his yoke, but a penniless, desperate man who had to give every coin he had to the Sheriff of Nottingham as repayment for his son triumphing over another nobleman in a jousting battle. Even worse, he had tried to find the money he needed by taking a loan from an abbot in York, a supposedly holy man who was a corrupt friend of the Sheriff's, and who gave the poor trusting knight one week to repay the amount with interest – or otherwise, Sir Richard's lands would be handed over to the authorities. And not just the lands, but his fair daughter Matilda, whose beauty had caught the Sheriff's roving eye.

Robin had a kind heart and a keen nose for those deserving of his help, and without hesitation – but to the astonishment of his fellow Merry Men – he dug into the ground and pulled out a leather purse containing all the money Sir Richard needed to make his repayments. Then they all shared some freshly roasted boar and Friar Tuck's best mead, and the poor knight was led back to the safety of his home.

But how safe was it? Not very, as the Merry Men soon found out when a new outlaw was discovered in their territory. This young stripling was masked with a muffler, and well-armed, and asked of the gathered Merry Men: 'Which of you is known as Robin Hood?'

'Why, who asks of him?' replied Little John.

'Is it you?' the mysterious lad replied.

'There are many who would wish to find the bandit Robin Hood,' replied Robin, 'but there is only one way you will know him, my lad – you will have to fight.'

This was the way Robin began most of his conversations – with an enormous fight. It wasn't the easiest way to make friends, but it had always worked for him. And so Robin and the lad faced each other with their swords drawn. At first, Robin fought with only half a mind on victory, giving the youngster a chance to show what he could do, but as this lithe newcomer parried and slashed like a fine warrior, and could twist and leap out of danger with every bit as much agility as Robin himself, soon the fight was for real.

Eventually, Robin managed to whisk the youngster's sword out of their grasp, and it clanged to the floor. He carefully faced the stranger with his own sword, and laughed, 'Now, let me know who it is I have the pleasure of beating?'

But before he could get the last word out, the youngster performed an astonishingly agile standing scissor kick, turning a backwards somersault that knocked Robin's own sword out of his hand before bounding forwards and pinning the surprised outlaw to the ground.

'You have had the pleasure of being beaten,' replied the stranger, removing the muffler and letting her long hair fall, 'by the Lady Matilda, daughter of Sir Richard of the Lees – though you may call me Marian.'

The Merry Men laughed fit to burst at this, as if a woman triumphing over a man was a great joke. But Robin never laughed at all. He was too instantly bedazzled by this new arrival. Unusually for him, there were no jokes, and there was no swaggering. He and his band of brothers led Marian to their hideout, and soon they were sitting around the fire sharing venison stew, and the newcomer was explaining why she had dared to come to the forest.

'The Sheriff is a swindler and a devil!' she announced.

'Tell us something that is NEWS!' laughed Friar Tuck.

'When my father proved that he could pay off his debts, the Sheriff announced that he would charge DOUBLE interest, and now he's dumped Daddy in prison for not paying up, and will split all of our lands with the church! And worse, he made it clear he wants me to be his bride! Well, there could be no worse fate, so I disguised myself as a boy, and here I fled. If you are the Sheriff's enemy, you are my friend.'

'To Hell with that Sheriff of Nottingham!' cursed Robin, his cheeks red with anger at yet another injustice against the people of England. He stood and raised his sword, and swore an oath alongside the rest of the band of outlaws that they would save Sir Richard and deal with the wicked Sheriff.

An opportunity to do this came sooner than any of them were expecting. The Sheriff had long been seething at the outlaw Hood's daring antics, robbing from his rich Norman friends and sharing the loot with all the poor people of the surrounding villages, and the

45. THE SILVER ARROW

Sheriff had been warned by his superiors that if Robin Hood wasn't stopped, it would be his head on the block!

'And so,' the Sheriff announced to the loyal brutes that made up the Nottingham Castle guard, 'what we shall do, men, is have a GRAND COMPETITION! Everybody, from Worksop down to Derby, says that this Robin Hood is the finest archer in the land! But we also know he is the biggest BIGHEAD in the land, don't we, men? And so what better than to announce a contest to find the greatest bowman in the whole of England? A swaggerer like Hood will not be able to resist, and then all we have to do is arrest the winner! Then he can tell me where the Lady Matilda hides, and she shall be my wife whether she likes it or not!' And he let out an evil laugh. No, really, nobody had a more evil evil laugh than this Sheriff. 'Mwahahahaaa!' he chortled, rubbing his hands with glee before the fire. The guards, and the Sheriff's aide Guy of Gisbourne, simply rolled their eyes, and set about arranging the contest.

Thus it was that Robin and his Merry Men found a poster pinned to the trees on the outskirts of Sherwood Forest, announcing:

The ALL-BRITAIN SILVER ARROW COMPETITION

A grand tournament shall be held at NOTTINGHAM CASTLE on SATURDAY the 6TH day of JUNE to decide which MAN in the whole of the LAND shall be named the greatest ARCHER of all, presented with an ARROW made of purest SILVER. Report to the Castle Gates by NINE of the clock to claim your entry.

GOD SAVE THE KING.

The Merry Men all turned to their dashing leader.

'You'll be entering then, Robin?' Little John asked, gruffly.

'I'll be WINNING, John!' Robin laughed.

'Even though it's painfully obvious that it's a trap designed to put your neck under an axe?' grinned Will Scarlet.

Robin mused. 'Well, of course, the magnificent swashbuckling hero known as Robin Hood can't possibly take part. But maybe if I combed my beard differently, stuck on an eyepatch, walked with a limp, nobody would guess it was me...?'

In fact, all of the Merry Men arrived bright and early at Nottingham

Castle on the allotted day, well disguised, with their weapons carefully hidden from the guards, who were so swamped with entrants for the archery contest they just waved the whole gang in through the gates.

And 'the whole gang' of Merry Men of course included Marian herself, still dressed as a man. Robin had tried to argue until he was blue in the face that being an outlaw was no life for a woman, but Marian had blocked and parried his every declaration just as masterfully as she had blocked and parried his attacks with a sword, and she would not stand for the slightest attempt by this swaggering man to tell her what to do.

'Besides, Robin,' she concluded once the argument was won, 'the Friar and I have been cooking up some plans of our own.' Tuck had long been a family friend of Sir Richard's, and was a sometime tutor of young Marian, teaching her all sorts of secrets he had gleaned, of alchemy and natural science, which she assured Robin would be key to saving her father.

Back in those distant days, it was the law of the land that all men had to practice archery, in case of another invasion – like the one the Normans themselves had succeeded in carrying out many years earlier. And so it was a very long and tiresome contest with hundreds of entrants, and long past noon by the time it was the turn of the Merry Men to draw back their longbows and aim their arrows at the bullseye of the Sheriff's archery board.

They all sported themselves admirably, and Little John had racked up by far the highest score of all the entrants, which made the Sheriff suspicious that he might be this pesky Robin Hood – that is, if Robin was known to be nearly seven feet tall and as hairy as a bear. He let the moment pass.

And then Robin took his place.

'This limping, one-eyed peasant is only going to waste everyone's time,' the Sheriff sneered to Guy of Gisbourne. 'This is useless,' he continued, 'We're never going to find Robin Hooooo....'

The Sheriff trailed off in this embarrassing way because the limping one-eyed peasant had let loose his arrow, and it had cracked into the dead centre of the archery board with a thundering force.

'TWANG!' 'SHHHHHOOOOM!' 'KER-THUNK!'

The whole crowd exploded with applause, and the mysterious archer prepared his second of three arrows.

'TWANG!' 'SHHHHHOOOOM!' 'KER-THUNK-THUNK!'

The second arrow zoomed right into the first one, splitting it in two and landing perfectly dead centre once again. But could he do the same thing again with his third arrow? Of course he could – he was Robin Hood. When all saw that third arrow thunk into the bullseye, splitting the second –

'TWANG!' 'SHHHHHOOOOM!' 'KER-THUNK-THUNK-THUNK!'

– a colossal cheer rang around the courtyard of Nottingham Castle; those whose turn was yet to come dashed their longbows to the ground, and the winner was quickly announced, to widespread approval...

But the greatest approval was the Sheriff's. He knew he had the outlaw Robin Hood in his clutches at last. He took to the field, applauding loudly, and approached the one-eyed limping peasant.

'I say, that man, what skilled archery! What a sure shot! What is your name, Saxon?'

Robin paused. 'It is, I mean, I am, er... Dave! Of, um... Hull!'

'Dave of Hull, eh?' the Sheriff grinned, and Guy of Gisbourne approached bearing the silver arrow as Robin's prize. 'Well, we must get your name engraved into this silver arrow for you, Dave of Hull. Or how about another name? Something more suitable, like – ROBIN HOOD OF SHERWOOD?'

And at these words, Guy dashed forward and held the sharp silver arrow to Robin's neck. The Merry Men did not dare to make any move, as they knew Guy of Gisbourne to be a bloodthirsty psychopath even worse than the Sheriff himself.

'And these seedy riff-raff would be your so-called Merry Men?' sniggered the Sheriff as his guards closed in. 'Well we'll see how merry you all are when your heads are bouncing across the grass. Men! Seize—'

But the Sheriff got no further than that when a huge sound unknown to any ears present rattled all around the castle walls, and a plume of white smoke and debris shot up into the air. KA-BOOOOM!

This was the clever plan of Maid Marian's. She and Tuck had all the ingredients required to make gunpowder – sulphur, saltpetre, and charcoal. This recipe was still known to very few on the island of Britain, but had been sneaked through to the clever Friar thanks to some friends who had fought in the Crusades out in the Middle East. It was hard to come by saltpetre, which was either mined from underground caves or made from a very long process involving wee, but Tuck had saved just enough to create a powder with plenty of kick – and Marian had insisted on being the one to use it.

'Matilda, is that you, my dear?' asked Sir Richard as the clever pair approached his cell.

'Yes, father, now don't say a word, just stand well back and cover your ears!' And with that, she poured the gunpowder into a small heap at the window of Sir Richard's cell, leaving a trail which she could ignite with a handy burning torch. There was a bright sparking light, a fizzling sound, and then, as already mentioned – KA-BOOOOM! – the iron bars of the cell were blown clean away, allowing the old man to escape.

Of course, to everyone at the archery contest, this seemed like the thunder-spewing finger of God himself at work, and there was pandemonium! And certainly just enough confusion for Little John to lunge forward and run Guy of Gisbourne through with his sword, freeing Robin to throw his disguise aside, place the silver arrow firmly into his longbow, draw back, and aim directly at the terrified Sheriff.

'No! Guards! Look, keep the arrow and...'

'Robin Hood I am,' said the Merry Man, hotly mindful that this man planned to ravish Marian, 'and I will show you how I like to share my riches, Sheriff!'

Robin Hood let loose the silver arrow and it thunked right through the Sheriff of Nottingham's cold heart.

Robin, Marian, Sir Richard and all the Merry Men made their escape back to the safety of the greenwood, where they knew every branch and dell, and the castle guards had no idea where to search for them. There in the wood they were safe, and free, and able to contend with anything the Normans threw at them.

Sir Richard needed little encouragement to make his home with them all, and he was overjoyed to give his daughter Matilda – who even he now knew as Marian – away in marriage to brave Robin Hood.

'Do you promise to love, honour and obey?' Friar Tuck asked Maid Marian.

'I will if he will,' she replied.

'I will!' grinned Robin.

'You may now kiss the bride!' laughed Friar Tuck.

And so Robin did. They lived happily together in the wood for many years, and with each passing year, their legend, and that of all the Merry Men, who fought for justice, robbing the rich and giving to the poor, grew stronger and more famous. Which is why we remember them all to this day.

THE END

NOTTINGHAM

The fight over which county owns the rights to the Robin Hood legend has raged for centuries, and won't be settled any time soon. But the original 'Gest' telling of Robin's exploits at the Silver Arrow contest held by the Sheriff of Nottingham leaves no room for doubt — it takes place at Nottingham Castle. Admittedly, the castle you will find in the North Midlands town today is largely modern, with only a few crumbly corners dating from Robin's time — but just a quick look around Nottingham on your arrival will reveal no shortage of places that celebrate the site's connections with one of Britain's greatest heroes. So fans of the Merry Men will surely have a very merry time!

experiencenottinghamshire.com
robinhoodtourism.co.uk
nottinghamcastle.org.uk

---

46. BABES IN THE WOOD

Wayland Wood, Norfolk

A t night, when the shadows rise and dark noises fill every dell and hollow trunk, Wayland Wood in Norfolk is a spooky place to be indeed. Imagine how much spookier it would be for little lost children wandering the wood alone. This is just what tragically happened to two wee tots, a brother and sister, four or five centuries ago.

It's rare that any story requires a warning in advance, but this tale is sadly all too true to life, and because of that very reason, it is not as happy a story as any of us would like. Now read on...

Tiny Tommy and his sister Tilly were barely out of their cradles when their mother and father were taken away from them. Their parents were struck down by an illness which would be cured by a single pill these days, but the plague of the Black Death cut through the people of Britain like a scythe back in those dark times.

Before he died, their loving father, the master of Griston Hall, Thomas de Grey, summoned his younger brother Robert and urged him to take care of the children as if they were his own. In return the brother, who had led an idle and murky life so far, could be master of Griston until Tommy was a man and ready to take over. Robert promised with all his heart that nothing bad would ever befall the two babes, and so the kind father passed away, happy that his children would be safe.

The babes' uncle was as good as his word... for a while. But before a year had come and gone, the selfish man began to feel hard done by. 'Why should I look after two noisy, nappy-smelling children, only to be shown the door when they grow up, when I could be master of Griston Hall right away?' asked the uncle of his reflection in the mirror – by far his favourite person to talk to. 'This place, by every right of blood, should be mine. And all I need to do is… rid myself of these unwanted babes!'

This bad uncle knew a lot of even worse men whom he could get to do his dirty work. He gave silver to a pair of villainous villagers, and told them to take the two babes far off into Wayland Wood, and simply make sure that they never came back. He would tell his wife and everyone around that the babes were being sent to London to be taught in a posh school. With that done, he could eventually announce that the plague had got them, and take over the running of the Hall and all its estates – and nobody would suspect his evil plotting.

When the two swarthy villagers arrived early the next morning to spirit away the children, Tommy and Tilly were so excited! Riding on a cockhorse to the greatest city in the world! London was going to be such an adventure, they agreed to each other.

But their excitement turned to bewilderment when the men dismounted and led them into the dark and chilly wood. London did not look anything like they expected – where were the palaces and people? But they were such little children they could not ask the men what was happening. And so they trusted them, following along in the shadowy strangers' wake, hand in hand.

Soon the babes were so tired that they flopped down together on a grassy knoll and fell fast asleep. This was the moment the two men had been waiting for. However, although one of the two villagers, Jim, was certainly a rascal and a criminal, he simply could not bring himself to carry out bad Uncle Robert's orders and leave two such sweet and innocent babes to their fate. His mind made up, he demanded that his partner give up the job right away, and find a safe place for the children.

'I just can't go through with it, Frank,' he told his accomplice.

But there really was no end to his partner's villainy. Robert de Grey had paid him so handsomely that he was determined to do away with poor little Tommy and Tilly there and then. 'Now look here, Jim, this is a job and I intend to do it, and nothing's gonna stop me,' Frank growled. Nothing, that is, except the more kindly villager. Jim was not a murderer; he did not want to kill anyone – but, with a quick and deadly flash of a dagger, he was more content to stop his horrible partner Frank than he could be to hurt those two poor babes.

'Sorry, Frank,' Jim said as he drew out his bloody knife. 'I couldn't let you hurt 'em.' He pushed the lifeless Frank down into a deep ditch, where he was forgotten by all. Nonetheless, the kindly criminal knew that he was now in trouble! He had to act fast if he didn't want to be caught by the new master of Griston and punished for disobeying orders. It was getting darker, and colder, and Jim knew he had to spirit away the babes somehow. He decided to ride off on his horse to find food and blankets for them. He would consider where to take them in the morning. As the babes slept, Jim mounted his horse and galloped off.

What happened to the kindly Jim nobody ever knew, but when Tommy and Tilly awoke, they found themselves all alone in the deepest, darkest part of the forest. They missed their home, and did not know how to get there. But bravely, Tommy took Tilly by the hand and they set off to try and find it.

After much travelling, hand in hand through the roots and undergrowth of Wayland Wood, the babes found some blackberries that were good to eat. But there were not many of them, and so they were both hungry when they once again lay down together to sleep.

Even the woodland creatures could not bear to see two such tiny tots lost in the wood together, and so that night they all flocked to the babes, to do what they could to keep them safe. Robin Redbreast brought them leaves for blankets, red squirrels dragged moss across to use as pillows, and a pair of kindly badgers sat on their feet to warm them...

And that was the last that was seen of the two Babes in the Wood. What really happened to them can never be known, but you can make your own choice of the many rumours.

Some say that angels carried them up to eternal paradise. Some say that the kindly birds of the forest joined together to lift the babes high up into the air and fly with them to somewhere else, a foreign country where bad Uncle Robert would never find them. Some say that Robin Hood and his Merry Men were travelling from Sherwood and happened upon the poor sleeping babes, and Tommy and Tilly joined his band of outlaws and grew big and strong in the forest, helping to fight the wicked rulers of Norman England...

46. BABES IN THE WOOD

But most say that the poor babes never woke up from that sleep in Wayland Wood, and still their little ghosts wander the site, wailing on every chilly, dark evening, trying to find their way home. However, if you do go to the wood, and you do see the ghostly babes, remember that Tommy and Tilly are kindly ghosts, and will always lead lost children out to the safety of the wood's edge before disappearing.

One thing we do know for sure is that bad uncle Robert de Grey did not thrive. Being so very bad, he was not deserving of the riches he inherited by doing away with his nephew and niece, and just a few short months after sending them off, he'd gambled away all of the family riches and was kicked out of Griston Hall. The despicable uncle went mad, often swearing to anyone who would listen that two tiny ghosts were haunting him to his grave. Everybody jeered at him for this, so he wandered, broken and alone through the Norfolk countryside, until death stopped him in his tracks.

Nobody missed him at all, but even hundreds of years later, people still remember the two Babes in the Wood, and come to Wayland Wood to pay tribute to their memory. By doing this, we can all make sure that the innocent little brother and sister will never really die, but live on forever – in stories like this one.

THE END

WAYLAND WOOD, NORFOLK

Both Wayland Wood and Griston Hall are real places, not far from the market town of Watton in South Norfolk — which has an image of the two Babes in the Wood as the town emblem. The Tudor Griston Hall is now a privately owned farmhouse, but tourists can still explore the beauties of the ancient Wayland Wood, which dates back to the last Ice Age — its name was originally 'waneland': a Viking place of worship. The wood is filled with rare wildlife and plants, and as pretty on a sunny day as it is scary on a cold dark night. As long as you make sure that you don't visit the wood all on your own, you will be all right.

norfolkwildlifetrust.org.uk

---

47. ROBIN'S END

Kirklees, West Yorkshire

R obin Hood will live forever – an eternity of swinging through the greenwood of medieval England, blowing his horn and fighting Normans. But the wisdom goes that 'Robin Hood in Barnsdale stood', so if this brave yeoman really lived, he must have met his end at some point.

The conclusion of Robin's story creates as many mysteries as it dispels, but one thing is clear – it is a sad story from the start. Having vanquished the Sheriff of Nottingham and returned to the forest with all his Merry Men and wife Marian, it seems that one day Robin accosted no less than the King himself travelling through Sherwood, and thanks to his fame and bravery, he was commanded to serve the King out in the Middle East, in the Crusades. These wars were bloody and pointless, but Robin had no choice but to say yes, and leave his home, his wife, and his friends to fight a meaningless fight. You could say this was the biggest sell-out of all time.

Nonetheless, the swashbuckling hero of course survived the worst that the Crusades could throw at him, and eventually, he did return to his homeland, and the wooded North Country he loved so much. But he was very ill after so long out in the hot desert, and of course, the Merry Men's hideout was abandoned; his friends had returned to their normal lives without him to blow his horn and lead them to adventure. Worst of all, his beloved wife, Marian, was not there to welcome him back. He travelled here and there, trying to find some news of what happened to her, but when he reached the home of his old friend Little John in Hathersage, he was so ill, his giant comrade feared that day would be his last.

'Do not fear, John,' Robin coughed, 'My cousin is the Abbess at

Kirklees Abbey, to the north, and she will be able to help me.' And so the two of them travelled to a grey nunnery in Yorkshire, on a grey day, and Little John hammered at the door.

'Who waits without?' a voice came from a slot in the door.

'I have here Robin of Wakefield, a cousin to the Abbess, and he will die unless she can save him!'

The door was unlocked, but John himself was told to wait in the courtyard as his old friend was carried up into a room in the gatehouse, where the Abbess soon joined him.

'My poor cousin Robin,' she said, mopping his fevered brow with a wet cloth. 'There is nothing else for it – you must be bled.'

Now, the idea seems monstrous today, but in medieval times one of the cure-alls for so many problems was bleeding – which meant exactly what it sounds like; patients were cut and their blood drawn out, in the belief that too much of it was the cause of the illness. And so the Abbess opened a vein on Robin's arm, letting the blood drip into a large pot, and left the ailing adventurer, pale-faced, propped up on a pillow and gazing out of the window at the grey clouds...

She should have returned within half an hour to check on Robin's progress, but instead, she was accosted by her lover, the nobleman Red Roger of Doncaster.

'Is it really him?' he asked.

'Most certainly my cousin. He who left poor Matilda and followed the King.'

'And he who waged war on the Holy Men of Yorkshire for years. Well, now his assault on the church will be over. Come, my darling, we will drink a toast, to the death of Robin Hood.'

And so this wicked couple cheered, as Robin's lifeblood drip-drip-dripped away...

Suddenly Robin sensed he was in peril. He must have dozed off, but when he came to, time had passed, and he felt weaker than he had ever felt in his life. Treachery! How long had he been bled? He just had the strength to find his hunting horn, and blow one long blast as loud as he could.

Little John, whom no door could stop, came running up the stairs into the small room where Robin lay, and one glance told him that his friend was done for.

'Robin! What have they done?'

'They have killed me, John, as so many have tried to do for so long. I think I am to join with my Marian once again.'

'I will not let them get away with this, Robin!' John thundered, his eyes wet with grief already. 'This wicked priory will be burned to ashes, and every last nun will feel my revenge, as I...'

But as the huge warrior Little John broke down into tears, his friend put his finger to his lips. 'No, John,' Robin said. 'That would be senseless violence, and I have had enough of that in my life, old friend. You must promise me there will be no revenge, and do me one more favour...'

This Little John did, by helping Robin to his longbow, and lifting his weak shoulders until he was facing the open window. Robin placed an arrow into the bow one final time, and with a last effort, he drew back the shaft, and said, 'Bury me where the arrow falls, John. And remember me.'

And with one final resounding 'TWANG-SHOOM', the arrow soared through the window, and Robin Hood breathed his last.

Little John obeyed his friend's final wishes. He left Kirklees standing that grey day and went home, but not before digging a grave for brave Robin, and leaving a marker there for all to see. But he needed no encouragement to remember Robin Hood. All of England, Britain, the world, would remember his bravery, kindness, and downright swaggering skill, forever more.

THE END

KIRKLESS, W YORKS

Kirklees Priory was demolished many centuries ago, but mercifully what still stands of it is the guardhouse, which is precisely where Robin's legend ends. A Hood-themed visit to Yorkshire should take you to the village of Brighouse in the west; just to the east of there, near a place called Clifton, is Kirklees Park — sadly not open to the public. There is a grave here reputed to be the grave of Robin Hood, but archaeological studies have suggested no body lies beneath the gravestone, which has all the hallmarks of being a later fabrication — it even mentions him being 'Earl of Huntingdon'. However, a body was said to have been found nearby in the 18th century, within an arrow's shot of the gatehouse. Also,

---

47. ROBIN'S END

when a grave said to be that of Little John in Hathersage, Derbyshire, was excavated, the remains of a man nearly seven feet tall were found there...

visitcalderdale.com

48. THE SAFFRON COCKATRICE

Saffron Walden, Essex

I t's sometimes hard to avoid the suspicion that people in the olden days were very, very silly. Saffron Walden, the ancient town in the East Anglian county of Essex, was packed with silliness a few hundred years ago, when it was still known on all the maps as Chipping Walden.

The 'Saffron' bit of its name came from the saffron crocus, a precious flower which the Mayor of Chipping Walden one day decreed should be planted in every field, paddock, garden and windowbox throughout the town. This wasn't just because the crocus is nice to look at or smell – its secret lies in its bright red pollen-like parts, which protrude from the blue petals. These can be dried and crushed to create the most desired spice in the world: saffron. The golden yellow delicacy had a thousand uses, from medicine and dye to cooking – especially cakes!

So there was nothing that silly about turning the town over to growing saffron crops at all. Soon everywhere you looked in 'Saffron' Walden, the bright blue blooms carpeted the place, filling the air with exotic scents.

Some of the folk of Saffron Walden, however, were a few rungs higher on the silly ladder than the Mayor. One particular gang fancied themselves as Knights Of Yore, and they regularly met in the marketplace to annoy everyone, dressed in rusty buckled old suits of armour they had slung together. Among their number were Sir Baz,

48. THE SAFFRON COCKATRICE

Sir Del, Sir Jeff, and Sir Billie. Well, Sir Billie wasn't one of the gang, but they had all been to school together and she never could escape the bone-headed bullies, who all insisted 'GIRLS CAN'T BE KNIGHTS!' The boys often held what they called 'jousts', but what anybody else watching would more correctly describe as 'idiots running at each other, helmets down, banging their brainless skulls together at top speed.' The so-called Knights loudly assured everyone that this was a 'top laugh'.

Every day, Sir Baz or one of his cohorts would chide Sir Billie, 'Oi, Sir Belinda, my lady, do ye feel ready for a good joustin' then?' and the others would all cackle snidely.

Sir Billie was a fair bit smaller than the rest of the gang, with weedy limbs, a big nose and a curly shock of ginger hair. To them, she was usually known as 'Sir Cowardly Clown', 'Sir Knock-Kneed Nelly' or 'Sir Gingery-Wets-Herself-A-Lot'.

'Oi, Sir Big Nose,' Sir Jeff would also snarl, 'I lay down my gauntlet, and challenge ye to a joust. Come on then, let's have ya.'

'A joust for what?' Sir Billie dared to ask.

'Well, for a top laugh!' belched Sir Del.

Sir Billie had never really cared what the others called her. She knew that they were barely one step up from walking slabs of meat. She also knew the laws of chivalry better than any of them, and as 'a top laugh' is never a good reason for potentially killing anyone, she would reply: 'You must forgive me the battle, Sirs, I am washing my armour.' And she would pass on her way, the hooting jeers of her non-friends ringing in her ears.

This wasn't just an excuse, either. Sir Billie worked hard on shining, straightening and buffing her own suit of armour like any good real Knight of Yore. Nobody saw her as she scrubbed away at it night after night, until it shimmered like crystal. The last thing she was going to do was spoil it by being crushed by those rusty nincompoops.

The problem with having fields of luscious saffron everywhere you look is that the exotic flowers can attract exotic pests. Saffron Walden attracted one particularly silly but nonetheless terrifying creature.

It used to be said that Britain was once packed with snakes, serpents and deadly reptiles of all sorts, and of course, we know of a number of notably hideous dragons that plagued the land here and there. But the Cockatrice was surely one of the strangest beasts of all. Some say that Cockatrices were made when a toad sat on, and hatched, a chicken's egg. This is of course another case of extreme silliness. Even if a toad could or would manage such an impossible task, that doesn't explain the monster which was then said to emerge from the egg – the scaly body and tail of a vicious poisonous black and yellow serpent, strutting around on chicken legs, and with a cockerel's bright red comb atop its head. Worst of all, the Cockatrice was a basilisk – which means it was able to kill anyone with a single look; and the Cockatrice that emerged out of a crocus patch in Saffron Walden one sunny summer's day had the reddest, most angry eyes. The ugly monster had been enticed by the sumptuous saffron, and nobody was going to stand in the way of it gobbling up the entire year's crop.

Pity the poor fool who was the first to discover the horrifying powers of the Cockatrice – even though it was Sir Baz. Thinking it was just an ordinary chicken, he was about to launch it into the air with a hefty kick, like he did with all the chickens he came across, when the Cockatrice turned its head and shot him a flashing, evil glance.

With that one look, Sir Baz was frozen to the spot, transformed from head to foot into cake. Warm, perfectly baked, saffron-yellow sponge cake.

'He's… cake?' squealed Sir Del in horror.

'Some kind of sponge cake!' replied Sir Jeff, picking off a piece and shoving it in his mouth.

'OI, YOU DON'T EAT BAZ!' Sir Del roared back, pushing his fellow 'Knight' to the ground.

'Yuck, you're not wrong,' replied Sir Jeff. 'He tastes ruddy 'orrible.'

By now the citizens of Saffron Walden were screaming and heading for the hills. All around the town the cry went out, 'Cockatrice! Cockatrice! Run far away! It kills with a look! Cockatrice! – Well, it's a sort of chicken dragon thing, you see, and… ARGH! Cockatrieeeece!' And so on.

If anyone could save the town from such a hideous beast, then surely it should be the brave 'Knights of Yore'? Sir Del and Sir Jeff drew their wonky swords out of their grimy scabbards and stood there where the Cockatrice had been, both shaking in their rusty, dirty (and by now very wet) armour. They looked over at their poor cakey friend. They looked back at the ominous rustle in the saffron crocuses. Then they turned around and fled as fast as their hearts could pump, screaming little baby screams as their knackered old armour clattered off in the hurry.

Then, the town was silent... But if I tell you that there was a sudden clanking noise, and something glinted in the sun, you will probably have already worked out that Sir Billie did not run away.

Wearing her shining crystal armour for the very first time, the brave ginger knight strode into the town square. There was no denying she was petrified with fear – she did not want to be cake! And admittedly the visor on her helmet wasn't going to be a lot of help in shielding her from attack, as her nose did stick out quite a bit and left her freckly face exposed.

But still, she would prove to the people of Saffron Walden that she was worthy of the name of 'Sir Billie', girl or boy. And so she drew her sword...

'Nooo! Don't do it!' cried the Mayor from his hiding place in a nearby water butt. 'The Cockatrice can turn people into cake even just by touching it with a sword or a spear!'

'Oh, what?' complained Sir Billie. 'That's hardly fair now, is it? Talk about uneven battles...'

But before she could go on there was an ear-curdling screech, and the Cockatrice revealed itself once again. Who was disturbing its saffron scoffing? They had better get ready to face a horribly cakey fate!

Sir Billie swallowed hard. She knew she could not look around, but then who knows where the Cockatrice could be strutting to next? One look and she would be a beautifully baked goner!

The terrifying serpent had Sir Billie in its sights. Its murderous red eyes flashed.

With another terrifying screech that was heard throughout the whole of East Anglia, the Cockatrice's evil glare bounced straight back off Sir Billie's shining crystal armour, and rebounded at the beast itself, which frazzled in the hot sun and toppled forward. There was a hot, golden yellow cake steaming on the ground. It was shaped like a cross between a lizard and a chicken.

You shouldn't really eat anything you pick up off the ground of course, but Sir Billie was happy to share the Cockatrice cake with as many of the townsfolk as it would stretch to, as they cheered and patted her shiny back. What dazzling armour! What clever chivalry!

'Hooray for Sir Billie!' the cry went up. And for many years afterwards similar Cockatrice-shaped cakes were baked in Sir Billie's honour – the bravest and shiniest Knight in the whole of Essex!

THE END

SAFFRON WALDEN

Much of Essex has become something of an East London overspill, but if you reach perhaps its most idyllic town, Saffron Walden, you'll get a very different flavour of the county. After countless millennia of occupation, there's history written through every layer in the town's soil, with Walden Castle's turf maze a definite lure. Admittedly, they don't grow saffron crops there in abundance like in Sir Billie's day, but that may be because it attracted too many Cockatrices. If you're travelling in the area, sixteen miles north is lovely crumbly old Cambridge, where a visit to the Folk Museum is a must for all lovers of folklore!

visitsaffronwalden.gov.uk
museumofcambridge.org.uk

243

49. THE BUGGANE
OF ST. TRINIAN'S

Isle of Man

The Isle of Man is its own Kingdom, plonked in the cold grey sea between north-western England, south-western Scotland, and Ireland. On this small rugged Manx island is a hill called Mount Greeba, and at the foot of this hill, you will find the ruins of a church several centuries old – if not much older. These are the ruins of St. Trinian's.

There are many tales in Britain of churches which were difficult or impossible to build, usually because of the meddling of 'faerie folk'; but the Isle of Man often has its own way of doing things, and it seems the building of St. Trinian's was a particularly tricky task, thanks to a creature known as the Buggane.

This unspeakable monster from the lost reaches of time lived within Mount Greeba itself, which may have been why he was less than pleased about a load of strangers coming along and building a church there. Like the giants, the Buggane had been around a lot longer than these tiny idiots, who never left anyone in peace with their building and industry and noise.

The Buggane was not at all as large as a giant, but he could easily have scooped up two or three grown gorillas in his huge sharp claws and chewed them up with his blood-red jagged teeth. With the hooves of a billy goat and the shaggy hair of a black yak, eyes like flaming torches and mighty tusks protruding from his wide red mouth, the

Buggane also possessed strength beyond human imagining, to make up for his galumphing, awkward body.

When buildings began to be constructed just outside his front door, and the first completed St. Trinian's church started to cling-clang-clong-clang its bells loudly every Sunday morning, of course the Buggane was somewhat annoyed. The creature responded as any decent Buggane would – by tearing the roof off the church, hurling the bells into the sea, and eating anyone who had a problem with his response.

A second St. Trinian's church fared little better than the first – the roof ripped off, bells thrown, choirboys for Buggane breakfast and so on. But even the Buggane had to goggle at the human invaders' sheer gall, to have a third crack at trying to complete the church by his mountain.

This third time, there was someone else in the church who would get up the Buggane's nose – he was known as Timothy the Tailor. Where many of the men of Man were hairy, rugged types, all judging their manhoods on fights, and arm-wrestles, and how many pints of mead they could drink without passing out, Timothy was one of the few who was just happy to be himself. Fair-featured and slight of build, Timothy was always the butt of the other blokes' jokes, and this only increased when he showed great skill as a tailor and clothes designer. But Timothy never cared a jot, because he knew it was only men who were insecure about their own 'manliness' who felt the need to mock others.

Timothy was a wily chap, but also rather poor. One day, he fell madly in love with the local cake baker, and though the two of them wished to set up home together, they had no money at all. And so Timothy had an idea. He placed a wager with all his hairy friends that he would be able to survive the whole first night in St. Trinian's, where the last few slates were being placed on the roof for the third time. Not only that, but he would return with the Buggane's head, no less! And on top of it all, he would even tailor a snazzy new pair of trousers before he left.

That night, Timothy lit a large candle under the new roof of St. Trinian's church, and set to, cutting up a stretchy, slinky material, and stitching away with needle and thread as fast as he could go. After an hour of industrious tailoring, Timothy did something undeniably brave – he popped over to the belfry, and gave St. Trinian's bell a quick clanging, before racing back to his needlework.

Before long, the ground began to shake, and right on cue, a huge chunk of the roof disappeared just above Timothy's head. There, leering down through the hole he had made, was the Buggane.

'You, tiny tailor!' he stormed, 'What are you doing here?'

'Making some trousers!' answered Timothy, without looking up from his work. His hands were a blur as he long-stitched and double-long-stitched the cloth together.

'Stop doing that, and look at me, and be terrified!' boomed the Buggane. 'Do you not see my huge sharp tusks?'

Timothy glanced up, murmured a quick 'Yeah!', and went on with his sewing.

The Buggane ripped off another huge chunk of roof. 'And do you not see my mighty claws?' he demanded, brandishing his fists in Timothy's face, which was a mask of concentration.

Timothy barely looked up. 'Claws, yes indeed,' he said, and carried on making the trousers.

Finally, the Buggane wrenched off what remained of the new St. Trinian's roof, and was revealed in all his hideousness. 'And do you not see my astonishingly hairy legs?' he cried.

Finally, Timothy completed the very last stitch in the trousers. Only now, as he stood up, was it revealed that he actually had no trousers on himself. He slipped the new shiny pair on immediately, and they fit as snug as can be.

'Yes, I see them,' Timothy replied, 'and it looks to me like you need a decent pair of trousers. Do you like these ones of mine? They're specially made for RUNNING!'

And with that, Timothy the Tailor jumped right out of the window, landing in the grass outside with the poise of a particularly agile cat, and set off at incredible speed towards the nearby church at Marown, where he hoped to be safe. He could hear the cackling, roaring Buggane flolopping after him as fast as he could, but was sure he could outrun the monster in his special trousers. At top speed, he jumped with all his might through a small window in the big thick wall which encircled Marown church, and was just in time! Half a second later, the Buggane crashed into the wall, and his big shaggy black head smashed into the window. His neck stretched out through the hole like well-chewed chewing gum before his huge shaggy head snapped back. The Buggane may have got away with nothing more than a sore neck, had his mighty tusks not got caught in the window frame, snapping the head clear off with a stomach-churning 'SQUISH-PLOP!'

And there, at the tailor's feet, was the Buggane's ugly head. Timothy was almost tempted to kick it all the way back to the pub where his friends were waiting to give him his winnings – but he felt that would be a bit too macho for him. So he dragged the head home, and made a fortune for himself and his new cake-baking partner – not just from winning his bet, but from making special run-fast trousers for anyone who could afford a pair.

Nobody ever saw any more Bugganes again, but the Manx folk never bothered with a fourth roof for St. Trinian's – to this day, all you'll find there on the Isle of Man is four lonely grey walls, and nothing more.

THE END

THE ISLE OF MAN

You can fly to the Isle of Man from a whole host of British airports, as well as get there by boat — but compared to many of Britain's isles, it's a sizeable landmass with far too many places worth a visit to mention. The island even has its own tail-less breed of cat — the Manx cat. However, if you do want to soak up the atmosphere of the ruins of St. Trinian's, you'll find it within the central county of Marown itself, halfway along the main road between the town of Douglas and Peel Castle. Bring your own trousers.

visitisleofman.com

---

50. THE LAMBTON WORM

Tyne and Wear

Whisht lads, haad yer gobs, an' aa'll tell yez all an aaful story aboot THE WORM!

Now. There are quite a few things that run in families – noses, aristocratic titles, and of course, curses. Many of Britain's most ancient aristocratic lines do not feel they're worth a pinch of salt unless they have some kind of dark and deadly curse placed on their genes, and no curse was whispered of with more terror than that of the Lambton dynasty. And all because of The Lambton Worm.

Not that this was a typical wiggly worm, you understand. Not the kind of pink harmless worm that fishing fans skewer onto their hooks when they cast their rods. Once upon a time in the north, there was a young lad fishing with fistfuls of these normal worms on the banks of the river Wear, which winds through the county of Durham. This freckle-faced fisher was called John Lambton, and although he was only ten years old, he was heir to all the estate for miles around, which was owned by his father, Sir John.

This white and wistful morning he had only caught a few tiddlers, but was happily idling away waiting for a bite when a strange and wizened old woman hallooed him from the nearby bridge. 'Why aye, bonny lad!' the woman cried, 'What are you doing, like, murdering fishes on a grim morning when you should be in school, growing your brain?'

'Haddaway and shut it, old woman!' the careless young truant hooted back, 'My brains are fine as they are, I'll own all this land one day! And when I do, all I'll want to do is fish!' and he chortled merrily... until suddenly, a mighty pull on his fishing line nearly tugged him into the foaming Wear!

Young John grunted and heaved, but whatever was wriggling on the end of his hook seemed to easily be a match for a ten-year-old boy. His feet skidded down the bank, and he would have gone in, had the old lady not hurried down and caught hold of his tunic. With this extra ballast behind him, John just managed to reel in the catch and haul it out of the river onto soggy land.

Both boy and wise woman gasped and goggled at the horrific creature which flailed on the hook, dangling in mid-air and letting out a high-pitched gargle which sounded disturbingly like a pig passing wind in a bath full of beans. Despite John's exhausting struggle, the catch could have been no bigger than a thumb, and was a sickening shade of white. It wriggled its slimy worm-like body, and nine black holes streaked across each side of its terrifying head, from which a whirring mouthful of jagged razor-like teeth gnashed at the air.

'It is a worm! The deadliest demon you ever could have caught!' cried the old woman, but the young lad gave a snort.

'What are you saying, like? That's no worm. I know what worms look like. This, this is more like a sort of... THING!'

'If you'd gone to school when you should have, you'd know to believe your elders and wisers!' the woman shot back. 'That there is a vicious white worm, no earthworm because it is not of this earth, and unless it's put out of its misery right away, it will spell doom for you and all who come gannin' after ye!'

'Well I'm certainly not having it for my supper!' John replied, staring at the squealing monster with disgust. 'But I'll do with it what I will, old woman, and you'll be getting off my fatha's land!'

But by the time he'd said these rude words, the old wise woman had already disappeared. He looked around to see how she had dashed off so quickly, then gave a shrug and stomped off towards school with the white worm wiggling on his hook. It was football practice all afternoon anyway, and he didn't mind that.

On the way, he came across an old wishing well which stood near the village of Fatfield. He took one last look at the hideous worm, which seemed more intent than ever on swinging round and chewing his nose off, and he threw worm, line and fishing rod down into the bottom of the well. Then he walked away, rubbing his hands at a job well done, and disaster averted, just in time for dinner break.

John Lambton never really listened very much at school, but when he came of age, as it was harder to find a job as a football player in those days, he decided to join the Crusades to the Holy Lands, fighting anyone he could get his hands on who wasn't Christian, and loving every minute of it. In fact, it rather ruined his planned day of heretic-bashing when he received a message from home, telling him that his father, Old John Lambton, needed him to gallop back to his ancestral lands at the earliest possible moment.

Jerusalem to Tyne and Wear was quite a journey, and when John finally made it, he was a very tired and haggard Crusader indeed. However, he was not as tired and haggard-looking as his dear old father, who greeted him in front of the great hall's roaring fire with tears and hugs. There on the hearth lay his old dog Jim, who was little more than a bag of bones, though he had been but a puppy when last John stood in his family home.

'My boy, my John, my returning hero!' Old John's voice wavered, 'Thank the heavens you've finally arrived.'

'What is it, fatha?' John asked, as he collapsed into a cosy chair. 'I've had to come all the way from Jerusalem, y'knaa?'

'Aye,' his father replied, 'But your fighting fists are of far more use to us here at home than out in some desert somewhere, bonny lad. John, our land, it's INFESTED!'

'Infested in what way?' John asked.

'First they noticed the cattle were thinning out. Our poor coos! A heifer here, and a heifer there. It was only when the brewer disappeared that anybody really took notice – suddenly there was no beer!'

'NO BEER?' thundered John, who liked a pint, more often than not. 'Who's killed our brewer, then?'

'Oh, John, it was THE WORM!' Old John croaked. 'The Lambton Worm, they're already calling it, and I wouldn't have believed in it myself if I hadn't had to rely on my own eyes! It's got to be half a mile long! Scaly, white and hideous, with nine black holes streaking along its head, and, my lad, the hugest, sharpest fangs you've ever seen!'

At this description, John had turned an unattractive whiter shade of pale himself. That school morning from so many years before, which he had barely thought upon for a minute since, came crashing back into his mind.

'Now it all comes back to you, young Lambton!' came a creaky voice from the doorway, and there stood the old wise woman. 'I warned you to destroy that worm, and here it comes gannin' back to bite you in the behind!'

'Haddaway, old woman,' John retorted, 'Where the hell did you come from?'

'Watch your gob, son,' Old John replied, 'This is my girlfriend Ethel from next door. Don't you remember Ethel?'

'Oh I remember you,' John went on, looking at the old woman, who seemed not one day older than on the day she had saved his life. 'Busybody.'

'Thank you, I do my best to keep busy,' she replied. 'But though you never listened then, you'll listen now, John Lambton,' and with a kind word to the ailing Old John, she led his son out of Lambton Hall and through the terrorised countryside. 'That well you dropped the worm into was a wishing well, as well you know,' she explained, 'and there's nothing a worm like that enjoys better than wishes – bitter wishes, that is. Every time anyone dropped a penny into that well and wished anyone harm, or wished for dastardly reasons, that worm fed itself on their wickedness. It grew fat, and huge, and snaked its way out of that well through an old underground tunnel, coming out into the Wear, from where it has galumphed around for miles, scoffing whatever it can kill. Sometimes it curls itself around yon Hill, sometimes around another hill at Penshaw, and it acts as if it owns this land which you call yours.'

'Why, I'll wring its ruddy neck if I can find the slimy piece of dog-todd!' John growled.

'Your fatha and I have attempted to keep the Worm sated up until now with the milk from nine cows every day, which we leave out in a vast stone dish for him. But it will never be enough. And there is only one person who can stop it in its tracks.'

'Say no more, Ethel,' John said, 'Stand back and watch me pummel that worm into a kind of pâté that nobody in their right minds would ever spread on toast.'

John was more keen for a scrap than he had ever been, but Ethel had to prepare him properly for battle. Dozens of local would-be heroes had tried to take on the Worm, and all had been shredded by its vicious fangs in half no time. But Ethel had an idea, and presented John with a new set of armour, fresh from the village smithy.

50. THE LAMBTON WORM

'Now this armour suits me down to the ground!' John beamed, as he marvelled at the shining, spiky bodywork. Each sheet was razor-sharp and covered in jagged metal spikes and edges, like an enormous cheese grater.

'But it won't be enough just to stab him, you see!' Ethel warned. 'Every time someone's ever managed to have a hack at the Worm's body, whatever they have managed to cut off has just reattached itself!'

'Gah, well that's hardly fair, is it?'

'That's worms for you!' replied Ethel. 'But here's what you do – you stop old Wormy in the Wear, and I'll tell you why…'

The next day, shortly before the time the Worm was expected to slither its way out of the river for its daily milk, John was back on the banks of the river Wear, armed and ready. But there was another catch – Ethel and Old John had explained that when he was finally victorious, the worm slayer had to let out three loud blasts on his hunting horn to let them know, and they would release Old Jim to meet him. But why was the dog such an important part of the plan?

'Because,' Ethel explained, 'of the CURSE of course! When you slay an evil demon of the like of the Worm, there is a price that must be paid. The first living creature you see will have to be sacrificed, or the curse will doom you and the next nine generations of Lambtons!'

Though John was not the kind of man to pay heed to curses, his father was, and so he agreed to the plan. It would be a kindness to poor old Jim, anyway.

But there was no time to feel sorry for the poor old dog, as the whole countryside reverberated to a colossal slurpy noise and a kind of ominous tummy-rattling gargle which sounded horrifyingly like a tyrannosaurus passing wind in an ocean full of beans. This told the soldier that the fight was on!

As he waded into the Wear, John Lambton faced the Worm, which seemed to know what was expected of it, and had no interest in anything but whirring its razor-like fangs through John's body like he was made of butter. It looked no different all those years later, except that now it was easily five feet wide, and as long as a traffic jam on Bank Holiday Monday. John actually smiled to see the magnitude of his foe, and greeted him like an old enemy: 'HOWAY, WORM!' he yelled, 'Do ye want some o' this, like, do ye? Gan on!'

And in a trice, they were upon each other. The Worm roared, and chomped and gnashed and whirred its fangs, but every time it got near John's armour, another bit of it was quickly sliced off, helped along by John slashing away with his sword with a wild, frenetic abandon! Soon it was clear why the fight needed to be in the fast-flowing river Wear – whenever John cut another bit of the Worm off, it washed downstream before there was any chance of it reattaching itself to the Worm's body and renewing its attack!

With a lamenting howl, the last living piece of the Lambton Worm – the head – was finally skewered, and the land was safe once again. John was sweaty and exhausted, but victorious, and he waded out of the Wear to the bridge, and blew his hunting horn three times.

Tragically, unbeknownst to anyone, poor old Jim the dog had raced off into the mist when the horn was blown, but only got about ten steps before conking out dead on the spot and falling in the Wear himself. Poor Jim! But even poorer Old John Lambton, as he happily shuffled over the bridge, and appeared out of the mist to congratulate his brave son.

'Well done, my bonny lad!' he chuckled, and then saw his son's face.

'Fatha! Where's the dog?'

'I sent him across, did he not...? Oh dear!' Old John cried, and eyed his son with fear.

'Howay, fatha, I'm hardly gonna slice you in two, now am I?' said young John, and the two embraced. So they, and at least nine generations of Lambtons after them, were now cursed, the final sting in the tale of the Lambton Worm.

But after all – curses were becoming terribly fashionable in aristocratic families by this time, and 'the Lambton curse' sounded horrifying, but all it actually amounted to was that every third daughter born to the family had shockingly hairy toes.

And so, they all lived cursedly ever after.

THE END

TYNE & WEAR

There are two hills associated with the Lambton Worm — Penshaw Hill in Sunderland, where you will now find the Penshaw monument; and near the village of Fatfield, also in Sunderland, the very obviously named

---

50. THE LAMBTON WORM

Worm Hill, where the big old pale demon himself was said to curl his slimy long body. Lambton Castle, which the river Wear runs past, is in Chester-le-Street to the south-west, in County Durham, and is only available for event bookings. The building was established in the 18th century, long after the events of the tale, but it was the descendants of John Lambton who commissioned it; and the family has lived on the land for centuries. The curse continues.

visitcountydurham.com

51. THE WIZARD
OF ALDERLEY
EDGE

Cheshire

It's impossible to say when, but on the first really crisp day of autumn one year – far more than twelve years ago, but fewer than a thousand – a farmer known only as Farmer set off across the sandstone crags of Alderley Edge in the county of Cheshire, on his way from his smallholding in Mobberley to the market in the town of Macclesfield.

With him, this Farmer had the most dashing milk white stallion, bequeathed to him by a careless relative, which he hoped would fetch him a pretty penny – if not a gorgeous guinea, seeing as his latest crop of marrows was too tiny to make him very rich that harvest.

This Farmer was not exactly the shiniest pebble on the beach, but he knew a twinkly-eyed old gentleman with flowing green robes and a long white beard when he saw one, and that was exactly what he saw as he turned a corner and came upon the Thieves' Hole – a dingly dell, with its own tinkling well. The well tinkled as the old man twinkled.

'Ahaha-ha!' beamed the beardy man, 'Farmer at last, isn't it?'

Farmer eyed the strange man askance. 'That's for me to know and for you to…'

'… Have a pretty good idea about too,' chimed back the beardy man. 'But what year is it?' he continued.

Farmer told him with a snort – what he said, of course, we do not know, but he told him. Farmer had never been called clever, but at least he knew what year it was, and the month – though he often had a bit of trouble with the days of the week.

'Well, no matter, no matter,' sniffed the strange stranger, 'I thought you may have come along a year or two earlier, but heigh-ho. And speaking of hay, you know, I'd really love to buy that fine snow-white steed from you, if I may…'

'Oh, ahh? And what would you offer me, beardy?' grinned Farmer. 'You can see he's a real smasher.'

'So he smashes, too? Oh, then I think I could run to a reasonable price…'

'Ah, save your breath, old man,' returned Farmer. 'Whatever you can offer, I could double at Macclesfield market – they'd pay top whack for a white stallion like this 'un.'

'Well, if so you say,' smiled the beardy man, 'I'll stop holding you up and let you continue on to market. But take my promise, Farmer: no man will buy that horse from you today.'

'Well, cheers for that, mate,' barked Farmer through gritted teeth, and set off down the sandy path to Macclesfield.

The Macclesfield market dealers came out in force to admire Farmer's white stallion that afternoon. They measured him, and brushed him, and looked him in the mouth, and found that he was the finest specimen they had ever had at market.

'But, erm…' one particularly impressed coachman scratched his chin just as Farmer was moved to start the pleasant job of haggling, quoting prices, and planning a big mutton steak for supper.

'But erm what?' he moaned. People had been saying that to him all day.

'Dunno, Farmer,' replied the coachman, 'Something ain't quite…' and the coachman's face took on a glassy look as he wandered off into the hubbub of the market.

'They're all mad! Or drunk!' roared Farmer. 'Come on, horse, we'll try the ostlers in Wilmslow instead.' So off Farmer trekked once again.

It was with a groan that he espied the old beardy man, still perched on a sandstone rock on Alderley Edge, twinkling as ever by his well, and patiently awaiting him.

'How did you get on then, friend?' he chortled.

'I reckon you know well enough, hairy chin,' shot back Farmer as he dismounted. 'Go on then, clever clogs, what are you offering for him? Mind, he's the best thing on four legs you'll find in Cheshire, if not all of Britain!'

'I'm sure you're completely right,' replied the beardy man, with an admiring pat of the by now visibly blushing horse's nose, 'He will fit the bill perfectly. Follow me. But first, wash your face in this well.'

'You trying to say I've got a dirty face?' Farmer bridled.

'Just do it please, Farmer. I may have centuries to spare, but there's no time like the present.'

Once Farmer had taken a handful of water and rubbed his grimy fizzog, the Wizard gave the well a kick and suddenly it wasn't there.

'Never mind that,' chirped the beardy man. 'I've returned it to its home at Castle Rock! Now, chop chop, after me, Farmer!'

And so the man with the flowing robes and even more flowing white beard held aloft his stick, which suddenly glowed an eerie green in the twilight, and led Farmer past Seven Firs and the Golden Stone and Stormy Point and finally Saddlebole. Eventually the three of them reached a mighty rock face, with a crack right down the middle.

'Would you be so kind as to put your fingers in your ears?' the beardy man asked Farmer.

'Daft old loon, mad or drunk!' grumbled Farmer, but did as he was told with a grunt. Only then, with much goggling, did Farmer see the crack in the rock face glow with the same eerie green light as the man's stick. Shudderingly but undeniably, the hill seemed to creak open, like an old wardrobe draped in thick cobwebs.

Without another word, a whistle, or even a gasp, Farmer followed the old beardy man inside. Just within was a mighty set of iron gates, which the Wizard (because, let's face it, that's exactly what this twinkly, beardy old man obviously was) carefully pushed open, and invited the gobsmacked Farmer to take a look around. Over on one side, standing silently asleep, were six white stallions, bridled and readied for battle. Shining in armour opposite them, and equally deep in sleep, seven mighty warriors dozed, their faces hidden behind dazzling visors, but their weapons sharp and ready. Farmer's first thought was that it was an ambush.

'Be calmed!' the beardy Wizard said, 'Leave this fine horse with me, and you can take with you all the jewels you can fit in your pockets, as fit and fair payment.'

A mound of gold and precious stones formed a throne in the centre of the cave, and with a shriek of delight, Farmer fell to, stuffing opals and rubies and emeralds in every fold of his jerkin, even filling the brim of his battered old hat with handfuls of sapphires.

'Yeees, that's probably enough now, I think,' laughed the beardy Wizard, 'You should be sent on your way... I would demand that you speak not a word about this to anybody, but let's be honest, Farmer, no one's ever going to think you're anything but mad or drunk if you do, so say what you like, friend. Just don't expect to see us again. Not until the reign of George son of George will anybody see me or my army again.'

'George son of George?' asked the puzzled mortal, trying to find a cranny of his clothes where he could fit in another fistful of diamonds.

'Yes, I'm sure it was George...' ruminated the Wizard with a frown. 'Maybe it was Ralph son of Ralph. Or Terry? Anyway, it's not this century, certainly. Goodbye for all time, Farmer, and thank'ee!'

And, with a thunk, Farmer found himself weighed down on the edgiest part of Alderley Edge, out in the open, and alone.

That's the story as told by most, but there are some who say that the pig-headed Farmer couldn't leave well alone. He swore to folk that a fortune beyond imagining lay hidden in Alderley Edge, that he had seen the Wizard's Well from Castle Rock in the Thieves' Hole, and that a strange old man and an army of seven warriors... actually, that was as far as he ever got before people stopped listening.

Farmer scoured the whole of Alderley Edge, and was sure he found the cracked rock. He spent his riches on a team of strong oxen to pull at it until it cracked open, but they were exhausted before the stone had shifted an inch.

Eventually he spent his last penny on a barrel of gunpowder, took it into the woods to find the Wizard's cave, and was never seen again. Though one little girl called Ellen did say that she heard the most almighty bang coming from somewhere near the Saddlebole hill.

'That will be old Farmer,' returned her mother, 'but don't mind him. Since he became rich, he acts as if he's either mad or drunk.'

THE END

ALDERLEY EDGE, CHESHIRE

For a tiny village sited only a dozen miles or so from the urban sprawl of Manchester, Alderley Edge, in east Cheshire, has to be one of the most mystical sites in Britain, particularly for fans of Alan Garner's timeless book series, beginning with *The Weirdstone of Brisingamen*. The posh area may not be bursting with tourist information booths and gift shops, but that makes exploration all the more exciting. Every landmark featured in the Wizard's tale can be found if you look hard enough, and there are few better ways of spending a bank holiday afternoon than trying to find the doorway to the Wizard's cave. But you're not allowed to use dynamite!

alderleyedge.org

52. THE VERRIES
OF PENNARD
CASTLE

Gower

Pennard Castle is just a ruin these days, sinking into the Gower sands. Travel down to the south coast of Wales, and you will find the crumbling red sandstone remains, and will surely agree that it's not a place you would want to spend the night! But although ruined castles can be wonderful places, they were usually only ever built for one reason – to fight battles, and to wage war. This is why a ruined castle is probably the best kind.

The last owner of Pennard Castle was a mighty general whose name was Mowbray, and he became the master of the place due to his own prowess in war – which means, he killed everyone who stood in his way until the castle was his. Not only that, but he was given the hand of a Welsh Princess in marriage, simply because of his ability to spill his enemies' blood. The Princess was not at all happy about this, but sadly in those days, Princesses were usually treated as if they were trophies, or book tokens.

Mowbray and his band of bloodthirsty knights stormed home to Pennard Castle one summer's evening, victorious and bathed in the blood of their foes.

'Hooray for Mowbray!' yelled one particularly creepy-crawly knight, 'Nobody killed as many men as him!'

'True!' boomed Mowbray, 'I think today was my personal best! I must have slit a thousand throats before teatime!'

'So many pints of blood, my lord!' replied the knight. 'What a man you are!'

'Oh yes, I'm a man all right!' came the lusty reply, 'For what could be more manly than swishing your trusty sharp blade through the guts of some other nutter? It's kill or be killed out there, and I've NEVER been killed!'

'Nor me!'

'Well no, but you've not been killed in a far less manly way than I've not been killed...'

And as Mowbray had by far the sharpest sword, they all agreed that he was the manliest man of all the men, and toasts were drunk. Many toasts, in fact, and roast oxen were eaten and really manly songs played by a travelling band of musicians, and a party the like of which Pennard Castle had never seen got into full swing. There were endless arm-wrestling contests (Mowbray always won, of course), head-butting competitions and shouting tournaments, while ale and mead flowed out of barrels and down manly gullets, and a great time was being had by all...

Until, that is, one of Mowbray's lookout men announced, 'Sir! Weird lights coming along the sands of Three Cliffs Bay, sir! Seem to be heading this way. Maybe an enemy attack party! Advise please!'

'Advise?' Mowbray replied in a beery drawl, 'I advise that we all arm up and march down there to find out what's going on. We'll soon sort these gatecrashers out, right, lads?'

And the colossal drunken roar that greeted this suggestion made it clear – Mowbray was right.

And so, Mowbray and his men marched down towards the sands, where they could see the strange lights flickering away, and getting ever closer.

Suddenly, Mowbray called a silent halt. They could see these gatecrashers now – a party of grinning, singing faerie folk, all tripping along on the beams of the shining moon, some on their heads, some hovering with a dizzying flap of their wing-like ears, some zooming about in UFOs, and all clearly having the most wonderful time.

'Come no further!' demanded Mowbray, 'What do you mean by marching on Pennard Castle?'

'Woah, hey, are you, like, the boss of this fancy joint then?' asked one grinning faerie with a turquoise face and a hat which seemed to be singing a song about tulips. 'That's faaaaar out! We heard there was a party on, man, so we thought we'd come and join in the fun! We're the Verries, this is like, our place, but it's totally cool if you want to build a castle here, so let's party! We've brought some nectar and...'

'Get ye back to the hellish underworld where ye came from!' ordered Mowbray, his sharp sword glinting in the moonlight.

'Heeeey, there's no need to, like, bring us down, man!' the faerie replied. 'Why can't we all have some fun? It's a beautiful night.'

But Mowbray and his men had no more time for words – they charged at the curious faerie folk as one, all chopping and hacking with their swords, spears and axes and roaring for all they were worth... Until they realised they were attacking clean air. The faerie folk were gone.

But the voice of the funny faerie remained: 'You need to stop your warring ways, you men do, man! You think you can spoil our party with your silly metal swords and spears? You think you can break our faerie spirit? Your silly metal spiky things are nothing compared to what one song from us can do, you dig? And you will have to dig, now you've spoiled our innocent little party. NAMASTE!'

And all of a sudden, the loudest musical wailing filled the bay, and with it came a whirlwind which instantly blew Mowbray and all of his men into a panic, whisking the weapons from their hands and throwing them far out into the sea.

But worst of all was to come, as the men retreated to Pennard Castle, and looked back to see a tidal wave of...

'SAAAAAND!' yelled Mowbray, before getting a face full of the stuff. Grainy sand filled his eyes and mouth and got stuck between his teeth, and the same was happening to all of his men.

'HELP!' they cried, and ran as hard as their legs could manage – not just to Pennard Castle, which was quickly sinking beneath the pelting storms of sand, but through the drawbridge at the other end, and off into the night, all squealing like tired toddlers, and all never to return.

Pennard Castle was never reclaimed from the sandstorms, and just about stands, empty to this day. It just goes to show that it's far better to approach verries, or faeries – or in fact, anyone, human or magical – with smiles and peace and love, than with snarls and war and weapons.

THE END

GOWER

As the story says, what remains of Pennard Castle is indeed still visible
down on the South Wales coast, swamped as it is in sand — because,
verries or no verries, the place was abandoned around the year 1400
precisely because of the sand encroachment. People think of South Wales
as rather an industrial area, due to the closeness of Swansea, but a coastal
region so studded with history of war and bloodshed is also going to be
filled with areas of historical interest, and a craggy, sandy beauty all of its
own.

enjoygower.com

53. DICK
WHITTINGTON
AND THE CAT

The City of London

For the lion's share of two thousand years, people throughout this island have seen the mighty City of London as the centre of the whole wide world. The broad River Thames snakes so strongly through the country here it could easily be taken for the sea, and from this river armadas of grand ships and weighty clippers have set out to sail the world, bringing back the richest spices, jewels and goods which made Britain such a powerful island for so long.

So prosperous did the City become that in the Middle Ages poor folk all over Britain told each other that the streets there were paved with gold! Imagine that! Any time you fancied a sandwich, you could just scrape off a piece of pavement and pay for it.

Of course, this wasn't actually true. What these poor people found, if they made the brave journey to the pulsing heart of England, was that the streets of London were actually paved mainly with poo. Gold and poo have always been very different things, and this often disappointed ambitious travellers.

It certainly disappointed one young stranger in town, Richard – Dick – Whittington. He had travelled on foot all the way from the Forest of Dean, far out west in the county of Gloucestershire, hoping, like so many who entered London's imposing gates, to make his fortune.

Dick was not from a poor family, but as the youngest son, he was expected to make his life in the church, or some lowly occupation – but he could not ignore the call of adventure whistling in his ears. And so one day, with nothing but a hunk of bread and a change of pants knotted into a spotted handkerchief hurled over his shoulder on a long stick, he set out east...

And this is what he found. Streets crawling with poverty, and crime, and of course, all that smelly poo. All around him, Dick saw beggars scratching out a living, and though his heart ached for these poor folk, he decided that while he had strength in his limbs, he would do all he could to find work, and make his own living, if not fortune!

'Good idea!' said a fine glossy tortoiseshell cat who nimbly jumped up onto a stone pillar right next to Dick. Well, she didn't exactly say that, but as the lad gazed into the Cat's large green eyes, the two seemed to reach an instant agreement.

'Hello there, puss!' Dick chirruped. 'Whose cat are you, then?'

The look the Cat returned left no room for confusion: 'I am my own cat, thank you very much,' it said, 'but come with me and we will soon see who makes your fortune.'

And with that, the Cat sashayed ahead of young Dick, and he dutifully followed through the bustling streets of London.

Soon, hungry and tired from picking their way through the smelly alleyways, they arrived at a relatively clean stone neighbourhood, by the riverbank. The Cat mewed, and found a patch of sunlight on the fine marble steps to lie back on and purr happily. Dick was just about to explain that this area was far too posh for them both, when a hearty female voice was heard from the window: 'Is she your cat, then?'

'Um... sort of,' Dick replied, and then he goggled at the most wonderful person he had ever seen, a young lady perched on the sill of a nearby window. 'We're friends, really. My name's Dick, and I call her Puss.'

'I am Alice,' the young lady replied. 'My father is Mr. Fitzwarren, the famous trader, and you look like you need a good meal and a lie down!'

Dick could not deny that he had travelled far, and the Cat and he had shared the last crumbs of his hunk of bread. So Alice asked her father to let the lad into the kitchens, where he quickly offered his services to the family as a scullion, or kitchen servant.

The hard-working lad scrubbed the floors, cleaned the coppers until they sparkled and did everything he was told, while the Cat revealed herself to be an excellent mouser, with a deadly fast skill at rounding up all the rats which infested the house, and – shall we say – convincing the ravenous rodents that they would be better off elsewhere.

It was a hard life for Dick Whittington. The servants' hall was ruled over by a grumpy old cook who regularly let poor Dick feel the rough edge of her broom, and told him 'You'll never amount to anything! Not like my boy Jack!' This lad, Idle Jack, never did a speck of work, but Dick didn't dare say so. Besides, it wasn't all the hard work that blighted Dick's life, so much as the knowledge that he would never be rich or powerful or clever enough to win the heart of Alice Fitzwarren.

Still, the Cat curled up beside Dick in the straw at the end of every day's hard work, and let him know that she, at least, was there for him.

One day, Mr. Fitzwarren excitedly gathered the entire household together and announced, 'I have built the largest trading ship the river Thames has ever known – the *Saucy Unicorn*! We are ready to set sail, bound for the spice islands and anywhere we can find precious booty to bring back to Britain. This is a fine opportunity to INVEST!' he told the whole staff. 'If you send even a few pennies off with this boat, you will be rewarded with... well, more than a few pennies, for sure! How about you, young Richard?'

Dick was the lowliest in the whole house – even Idle Jack had invested two ha'pennies and a pair of socks in Fitzwarren's venture, but Dick had nothing but the rags he stood up in. Nothing, except...

'What about that cat who's always meowing around your feet, that's something to send, surely?'

'Well she's not exactly mine to give,' young Dick stammered. 'We're more sort of friends, really, and I don't think...'

'Nonsense!' Mr. Fitzwarren boomed. 'She'll do nicely. Come over here, Puss!'

And although Dick wanted to explain how much the Cat meant to him, his furry friend hopped onto his shoulder, nuzzled his nose, and he knew at once that she had already decided to make the journey for him. 'I'll be back,' she purred.

The Cat zipped down from Dick's shoulder, gave him one last wise wink, and left with the swarthy ship's crew to Who Knows Where.

At first Dick was tempted to go with her – excitement, exotic islands, adventure! But the crew of the *Saucy Unicorn* was already fully in place, and as he looked around at the grey crumbling towers of Old London Town, he knew that although he was already far from home, it was simply not in his belly to go much further.

It was a glum Richard Whittington who lay in the straw that night, and it seemed his luck was not going to improve. No matter how hard he worked, still he stayed a scullion, and the Cook still buffeted him with her broom as Jack lay around yawning and eating peanuts. Worst of all, although Alice and he exchanged the odd smile and kind word, she seemed further away from him than ever.

After what must have been months of this slog, assured that he had lost all he had gained from his London adventure – the best cat a fellow had ever befriended – Dick decided he would just have to make his way back to the Whittington home out west.

And so once again, he strung his spotted handkerchief on a stick over his shoulder and left the Fitzwarren home in the deadest of dark night, determined to walk home. A tiny tear plopped from the end of his nose as he closed the door behind him.

By the break of dawn, he'd trekked quite far north from the small square mile that was the old City of London, to the top of tall Highgate Hill. Dick rested his feet for two minutes and gazed back, glowering at the glowing pink-streaked sunrise which silhouetted the crumbling London skyline. Ships were clearly visible sailing in the breeze along the Thames, and Dick began to dream of what might have been.

Whether it was part of his daydream or not he could never recall, but just then it seemed to Dick as if the Bow Bells of the church of St. Mary's were singing to him as he sighed, pealing out an insistent and tinkling cry:

'Turn again, Whittington! Thrice Mayor of London!'

'Mayor of London?' Dick wondered aloud to himself. 'What a preposterous idea!'

But Dick also had to admit to himself that he quite liked preposterous ideas, and there and then, as the sun rose in the sky, he turned around, and declared that he would not be beaten by the City, but he would triumph, come what may!

So saying, Dick trudged back towards the Fitzwarren house.

53. DICK WHITTINGTON AND THE CAT

When he finally arrived, expecting a thrashing from the Cook and even maybe losing his lowly position altogether, Dick was stunned to hear Idle Jack yell 'He's here at last!' All the servants turned smilingly to him and said as one, 'Good morning, Mr. Whittington!'

'Mister?' Dick puzzled, but before he could ask any questions he was thrust into a warm soapy bath, clothed in a velvet gown and ushered into the grand Fitzwarren front parlour.

There was Fitzwarren, and the whole crew of the *Saucy Unicorn*, all laden with the most opulent gifts of the Mystic East! The beaming trader explained, 'The *Unicorn* was blown off course to the Barbary Coast, where we were welcomed by the Sultan, who told us all that he was beside himself with horror – his Palace was overridden with rats! Hordes of the greedy little beasts were always gnawing their way into the corn sacks and scurrying over the royal breakfast table, and even nipping at the Sultan and Sultana's feet in bed every night! One of them was as big as a spaniel, I swear! And so,' Fitzwarren continued, 'it was especially fortunate that our lads had with them...'

At these words, from somewhere behind a gigantic sack of gold and jewels unimagined in any of Dick's most preposterous dreams... out leapt the Cat, and Dick could swear that she was actually grinning.

'PUSS!' Dick cheered as his old friend settled on his shoulder. 'Clever Puss, I knew you wouldn't ever let me down!'

The Cat nuzzled his human friend's nose, and gave Dick a look with those beautiful big green eyes that clearly said, 'Well, obviously.'

'Was it rough out there, Puss?' asked Dick.

'Well, the King Rat was a bit of a nasty piece of work, but I got him in the end!' the Cat purred.

'... So your investment naturally had to be rewarded above all others,' Fitzwarren concluded, 'not least as it turns out that your feline friend here was filled to bursting with hungry little kittens as she boarded the boat, who are all equally gifted mousers! Puss's children now stand sentry in the Sultan's Barbary Palace, and as I am an honest trader – would that all were so in this City! – the Sultan presents you with these copious, sagging sacks of barely imaginable riches! My dear Mr. Whittington!' laughed Mr. Fitzwarren.

Having finally found the gold so clearly absent from the pavements of London, Dick Whittington vowed never to forget his lowly beginnings, nor those he had seen begging in the streets. The Barbary Sultan had given him such riches he could afford to share them out, among the servants – yes, even the Cook and Idle Jack – and the people of London. He built public toilets and founded hospitals and important buildings, and as a result, yes, Richard Whittington did become Mayor of London three separate times – or thrice – at the turn of the 15th century. He was friends with Kings Richard II, Henry IV and young Henry V, and respected by all, from monarch to lowliest scullion.

And there always beside him, through all these good deeds, was not only his clever Cat, and her equally clever children and grandchildren, but his Lady Mayoress – Alice Fitzwarren.

Unusually for those times, it was Alice who asked Dick to marry her one fine summer day. He told her, 'But I was afraid, I was sure you would never want someone like me! I am not grand enough!

At this, Alice scoffed.

'And because I am not brave enough!' Dick went on, 'I have never travelled afar to the Barbary Coast and seen the world!'

At this, Alice laughed. She kissed her husband and told him, 'Dick, I was never interested in money, wealth or power, nor exotic, reckless adventures. All I ever dreamed of was someone who showed true kindness.'

And not for the first time in his life, Dick Whittington felt very lucky indeed.

THE END

LONDON

There's no question of the true historical inspiration for the popular pantomime plot. There certainly was a charitable benefactor from Pauntley in Gloucestershire called Richard Whittington, who was indeed thrice Mayor of London in the late 14th and early 15th centuries, and moneylender to three Kings of England. Barely an atom of the City of London as it was in Whittington's day remains in place, but the city still bears his mark, and amid the endless crowds of attractions for tourists in the capital's heart, perhaps you can make time to visit the statue in Holloway marking the legendary spot where Dick heard the sound of

---

53. DICK WHITTINGTON AND THE CAT

Bow Bells (impossible, given how far away they are, but then bells seldom talk anyway), or even keep an eye out for the Whittington Hospital in Islington, one of the still successful remnants of Dick's charitable legacies. The hospital is easily identifiable from its logo: a cat.

visitlondon.com

54. THE
CANTERBURY
TALES

Canterbury, Kent

When April, with its showers sweet, comes to quench the grey drudgery of March, it was once very popular among God-fearing folk of the Middle Ages to go on a pilgrimage to some holy site, where they hoped their sins would be forgiven. Nowhere in the British Isles was more popular for this than Canterbury, in the eastern county of Kent. The city was selected as the seat of British religion to convince the Anglo-Saxon pagans who conquered the area to convert to Christianity, but it didn't take off as a red-hot pilgrimage spot for another 500 years, when one Archbishop of Canterbury, a powerful man called Thomas Becket, was killed.

Thomas and his old friend King Henry II began to have vicious arguments about the kind of things Kings and Archbishops argue about – land, money and so on. One day, after a particularly annoying spat with his ex-pal, Henry roared to his court, 'What kind of servants are you, if you allow your King to be treated like this?' And so a few drunken knights dutifully rode off to Canterbury and sliced up the Archbishop for him. Despite everything, Henry was extremely miffed when he heard the news, and before long, folk began to insist that miracles were happening right where Thomas was murdered. In very little time at all, Becket was called a saint, and his church became a much-sought-after pilgrimage site for Christians all over the country. The visitors thought touching his grave and saying prayers would rid them of all sorts of ailments, from rheumatism to painful verrucas, and that the visit would move them one step closer to getting into Heaven when they died. It was also a bit of a holiday.

A very clever beardy fellow called Geoffrey Chaucer once went on one of these pilgrimages to Canterbury, as part of a rowdy group, and wrote down everything that happened. As it took many days to travel to Kent on horseback, this strange assortment of holy tourists had plenty of time to tell each other stories en route. There was a Knight, a Miller, a Cook, a Sheriff, a woman from Bath called Alison who described herself simply as a 'Wife', and a whole host of priests, monks, pardoners and other religious clerics. And each of them had a tale to tell!

'Let's have a competition!' roared Harry Bailey, the landlord of the London inn where the gang all stopped to refresh themselves. 'We'll see who has the best story, before reaching the holy church! Winner gets a slap-up feed on the house when they get back. Who shall start?'

The Knight was the first to leap in and take up the challenge, of course. The pushy battler told a predictably courtly tale of two knights: 'These fine, vicious fighters were called Palamon and Arcite,' he began, 'and they were the best of friends until they both fell in love with one poor girl called Emily, and were ultimately called upon by the Greek hero King Theseus to fight to the death for her. The brave Arcite eventually won the battle, but was then thrown from his horse and died, leaving his old, wounded friend Palamon to mourn him... and marry Emily himself!'

The Knight didn't actually tell the story that quickly, though – it went on for hours...

Having sat through such an old-fashioned and lengthy story, the Miller was the next to barge in, with quite the filthiest tale of the lot! It is hardly the kind of shaggy dog story to be repeated over the tea table, and innocents may want to skip this couple of paragraphs, but the Miller set his yarn...

'In the old city of Oxford, where there was a silly old carpenter who enjoyed a fruity young wife. She was as GORGEOUS as he was doddery, but it was a beggar for her, that gorgeousness made her the target of the passion of two love-hungry students. Well, in no time at all, the carpenter's wife took one of the students to her bed – the sexy one. But while they were closeted together, doing what young people do when their gander be a-throbbin', the second student – who was a greasy little squit, if truth be told – came to the window begging for a kiss! The carpenter's wife came to the window and told this weedy youth to close his eyes, pucker up and waaait... and then she stuck her bum out the window! Hahaha!'

At this revelation, some of the gathered pilgrims laughed, spurting beer, some looked sour-faced, but the Miller had hardly begun, and went on, 'I don't mind mentioning bums, we've all got one! Anyway, this girl shoved hers out the window, and it's enough to say that the poor loser outside gave it a big wet kiss, and never noticed anything was wrong until the wife let rip with a massive bottom-burp right in his face!' At this, the sour faces grew sourer, and the laughter grew louder. 'Anyway, nobody was going to put up with that, even a greasy little student. So, boiling with anger, this fart-faced student dashes away, only to return at the window a few minutes later asking for another kiss! This time, the first student, the sexy one, thought that he would repeat the funny joke, so he shoved his own botty out of the window... only to scream the whole house down when he got a red hot poker right up the hole from his rival! HAHAHA!'

Of course, after the Miller had panted his way to the end of this scandalous story, everyone was rather disgusted – except for those who were still giggling. A Reeve, or Sheriff, jumped in next with a markedly similar tale in which a Miller's wife and daughter ended up in bed with a couple of students, and soon the pilgrims were all topping each other's stories. The Cook told one about a party animal servant, the Lawyer bored everyone with a long legend about a Muslim Sultan, and there were stories about the Devil, and Death, and marriage, and birth, and everything in between.

The Wife of Bath was a woman well ahead of her time, more than happy to share with everyone her own stories, of men she had married, and men she had loved, and the pleasure she had gained from life; and the listeners admired her for her honesty and good wit. Unfortunately, despite earning the admiration of everyone with her life story, the tale that Alison chose to tell was far less popular with the crowd, being a very dodgy Arthurian yarn about a frankly disgusting old sexist knight who was charged with the task of finding out what it is that all women really want. The answer, according to this story – and as approved by Queen Guinevere herself! – is that all women desire total power over all men. This punchline of course triggered another noisy row among the group...

Still, on and on the tales spun, from all quarters and on all themes, from all areas of medieval life, covering everything that plagued

54. THE CANTERBURY TALES

the mind of the 15th century pilgrim, as the travellers inched and stumbled their way along the long and winding road to Canterbury.

Finally, only one of the group had not yet shared a tale – and that was Geoffrey Chaucer himself, the most famous storyteller of them all! 'I know how to win this competition!' the bright spark said, 'I will tell the tale of this whole pilgrimage, including all of the stories you told, and it will be one of the most celebrated and longest remembered pieces of writing in the whole English language!'

And so he did. Thankfully, this is the incredibly short version.

THE END

CANTERBURY

The verdant county of Kent, to the east of London, is more than a place you pass through — or under — on your way to the Continent on the Eurostar, so steeped in ancient English history is the county. Canterbury is the centre of so much of Kent's appeal, and some people still make pilgrimages there to this day to see where Thomas Becket was cut down. Besides Chaucer, another famous storyteller whose footsteps you can walk in while visiting Kent is Charles Dickens — but on the other hand, if literary outings aren't your thing, you can always have an ice cream and a donkey ride at Margate, or one of many traditional seaside towns.

visitkent.co.uk

---

55. HERNE THE
HUNTER

Windsor, Berkshire

What a mysterious figure Herne the Hunter is. If you've never had the terrifying experience of seeing him, he is a colossally tall spirit who haunts the woods of Windsor Castle, west of London. Herne has antlers growing out of his head, and an aura of fire surrounds him whenever he puts in an appearance. But who was this horned phantom originally, and why does he still manifest himself around the hunting grounds of the Queen's home?

Over six hundred years ago, in the reign of the arrogant King Richard II, huge Herne was one of His Majesty's hunting staff. A host of serfs were paid pennies to ride out with the King and his rabble of howling hounds, which flushed out deer, pheasants and other animals unfortunate enough to be bred for the sport of killing.

Everybody wanted to be the head of this hunting pack, and when the job became vacant, most folk favoured Herne for the promotion. Herne himself said very little, but he knew every inch of Windsor Forest, each knotted root and hidden foxhole, and stood a clear foot taller than anyone else, with arms like mighty tree trunks. But one day, as the hunting party rode out among the ancient oaks and copper birches in the darkness of autumn, Herne came a cropper.

The King had expertly wounded a fawn, and had just stepped down from his saddle to strike the killer blow, when a stag charged out of the foliage, antlers aimed directly at the royal rear end!

55. HERNE THE HUNTER

Quick as a flash, Herne hurled himself from his saddle and into the path of the ferocious stag, his head butting the creature's own as they smashed into a rolling mess of legs and horns, only ended by Herne's dispatching of the stag with his trusty hunting knife.

Bloodied and broken, it seemed the victorious Herne was done for. The royal party gathered around the huge body at the foot of the ancient oak tree, where he had just about managed to stagger. In the darkness of the wood, rivulets of blood gushed from his face, and the stag's antlers were still buckled around his head.

This darkness then seemed to grow somehow darker, as a hooded figure appeared from behind the oak tree, and bowed slightly before the imperious Richard.

'I am Urswick, and your friend seems to have been in the wars.' None of the hunting party could speak. 'I can cure him,' Urswick continued – 'For all the good he has done the deer of this forest I should not, but bear up his body and follow me to Bagshot.'

This was a nearby heath, where Urswick's humble hut stood. King Richard, feeling his tummy rumbling and remembering all the tasty venison which was lying mangled in the forest, announced that he would return home.

'But if you should happen to be able to fix old Herne there, that would be awfully good of you, because he's so nifty at all the trapping and the fighting stags and so forth. He was a deffo for the head huntsman job. So do your best, what? Thankee, mysterious peasant!' And off he rode.

Tragically, King Richard left Herne in the charge of his jealous fellow huntsmen, who all wanted the top job for themselves. And so the tallest huntsman begged Urswick:

'Mate, do you really need to bother making this big old tangle of broken bones any better? If it's all the same to you, we'd rather just put him out of his misery and bury him, much quicker. We're as good at strangling deer and slitting up pheasants as he is. And I for one am the best rabbit-smotherer in the whole of Berkshire!'

Urswick flinched. All this talk of violence and destruction seemed to bother him. 'I will cure him whether you like it or not,' he assured the villainous huntsmen, 'but at a cost. One which you will discover anon…'

Within no time at all, Herne was back on his feet and was rewarded with the gold star of head huntsman, for all his colleagues' grumbling.

But as soon as the King set off on his first hunting party since Herne's accident, everyone noted something very different about the mighty hunter – not least the enormous antlers, which had been fused into his head by the clearly magical intervention of Urswick.

Being so big and now encumbered with the antlers, which kept catching on the branches around him, Herne seemed incapable of riding more than a few paces without falling out of his saddle; and when he went to shoot a baby bunny rabbit at the King's command, he fumbled and the arrow simply fell out of his fingers.

The King gave Herne a withering look, and raised a regal eyebrow. He offered to give his new head huntsman two more chances, but after yet another failed hunting party, the spoiled Richard simply tore the gold star from poor Herne's tunic and fired him in front of the whole court. 'Not really working out, is it, big boy?' Richard sneered.

Poor Herne trudged his way out of Windsor Castle and into the wild green forest. There, that night, by the light of the moon, the poor hunter was found by a gamekeeper, hanging from the ancient oak. Some say his antlers caught in a low bough; some say Herne decided to do himself in deliberately. But the strange thing was, when a group was put together to retrieve the brawny body, there was no trace of him to be found anywhere.

A fellow called Will the Willing received Herne's gold star, and another hunting party rode out the very next day. And yet Will proved even worse than Herne, his arrow pinging off a poplar and knocking a carrot out of the King's horse's mouth. This frightened the poor steed so much he nearly shook the monarch off his back as he bucked and whinnied. White and sweaty, the King ordered Will to be hanged before supper.

The next head huntsman was no better, nor the one after that. In fact, soon there were no huntsmen left, and the King's animal-hurting fun was all over. But then, King Richard had other worries by that time anyway – his war-like cousin Henry Bolingbroke was as sick of his rule as all the animals were, and so Richard was just about to have the English crown grabbed off his head once and for all.

However, the crown was still on Richard's head on the very last time he dared to ride out into the Windsor Great Forest. As he approached the ancient oak, his horse bridled at the sight of a great green glow which emanated from the tree's mighty bowers. There in front of the screaming King was Herne the Hunter, sitting astride an enormous black steed and now, it seemed, ten feet tall, if not taller, his grand antlers stretching up and disappearing into the branches. This Herne spirit laughed at the terrified King, surrounded as he was by his undead servants – the other huntsmen Richard had hanged. All of them were enveloped in the same green glow that only a fool would hesitate to describe as 'ghostly'.

'Die and despair, King Richard!' Herne boomed. 'I am Herne the Hunter, and this is now my forest, and all the creatures within it shall be under my protection from this day on!'

Lightning cracked down from the sky, and an almighty BOOM split the ancient oak in two, sending the King's horse into yet another whirlwind of whinnying terror and throwing Richard right onto his royal rear end. The frightened steed galloped back to the safety of Windsor Castle, his muddy and gibbering master hurrying fast behind, crown slipping from his great big head.

There was a thunder of hooves, a flash of green, and nothing left of Herne the Hunter and his spectral hunting party but a deep, booming laughter, which filled the dark and gloom of Windsor Great Forest: 'WAHAHAHAHAAA!'

THE END

WINDSOR, BERKS

Many people take the short journey west out of London to visit the royal grounds of Windsor Castle. When taking the tour there, the tale of Herne is always a feature of every guided walk, and you can ask to be shown the way to the ancient oak where Herne was found, and where, one day, Shakespeare had Sir John Falstaff dress up as the mighty Herne in his comedy *The Merry Wives of Windsor*. Well, all right, the supposed actual tree was felled and cleared away in 1796, but it's said that George III planted an acorn in the exact same spot, so let's not spoil it.

windsor.gov.uk

---

56. BLACK
VAUGHAN

Kington, Herefordshire

S ince the first day that one nomadic hunter took more share of mammoth meat at the feast than their dining companions, there have always been rich people and poor people. It would be very pleasant to think that this will not always be the way things are, but there's little sign of this changing any century soon.

Not that the rich need always be at fault for their position: many people higher up the rung of wealth or society know to see others as fellow passengers to the grave and not some other lowly species. Many share their good fortune, and bring happiness to everyone they meet.

Black Vaughan was not one of them.

Thomas Vaughan was a Lord of Kington, in the Welsh border county of Herefordshire, nearly halfway through the last millennium. He was tall and foxy-faced, with a scrag of raven black hair and beetle brows that earned him his nickname.

He may have lorded over the land, but if thou shalt know a man by his friends, then Black Vaughan was a nobody. He treated his servants like mangy dogs, sneered at anybody with less than a thousand pounds in their treasury, and deliberately flicked earwax at any peasant unfortunate enough to cross his path. He seemed to enjoy ANNOYING people more than anything else in life, and would often trip bakers up on their rounds or relieve himself in the font of the local church if he was passing.

279

56. BLACK VAUGHAN

'WEH-HEH-HEH, you didn't like that very much, did you?' Black Vaughan would hoot to his latest victim.

'No, my lord!' would come the reply.

'But what are you gonna do about it, eh? I'm the LORD Black Vaughan, right?'

'Indeed you are, my lord!'

'So you'll just have to take it, right?'

'Yes, sir, my lord!'

And with one more throaty giggle – 'WEH-HEH-HEH!' – Black Vaughan would kick the nearest peasant in the behind and be on his way.

No wonder nobody had a good word to say about the lord when he was gone. Because, although he loudly confirmed himself to be one of life's winners, one day Black Vaughan was commanded by the King to ride north to help win a battle near Banbury. Well, actually he originally pledged to help the King's enemies, but he changed his mind at the last minute to annoy everyone. At this battle near Banbury, a mere skirmish compared to other epic scraps in the Wars of the Roses, Lord Thomas Vaughan turned out to be a loser. That is to say, the King was perfectly fine, but Black Vaughan lost his head.

The moment Black Vaughan's disembodied black locks hit the blood-soaked grass, the loudest, darkest laugh you ever heard echoed around the whole battlefield – 'WEH-HEH-HEH!' – and a great black hound swooped in to pick the bloody head up in his slavering jaws, and howled off into the night. 'GRRRAWOOO!'

Ordinarily, you'd think, that's the end of the story, good thing too! But when Thomas Vaughan's headless body was brought back to Kington and laid in the church, the story was just beginning. Black Vaughan really was very, very committed to being annoying.

Soon the superstitious folk of Kington were under siege from a whole menagerie of beasts, all of the same Bible-black hue.

Most annoying of all was the great black hound which lolloped through the market, knocking over all the barrows of fruit and veg, nibbling innocent babies and leaving the most horrific steaming great piles of stinky hound mess all over the village on laundry day. Easily six feet tall and terrifying the hound stood, darker than the darkest shadow. Huge black fangs protruded from his hairy muzzle, and blood and drool dribbled down his heaving chest as he barked and howled at the moon throughout every night. 'GRRRAWOOO!'

'Tis that Black Vaughan again!' the people of Kington would cry. 'Why won't he rest in peace? It's starting to become extremely... ANNOYING! Annoying is the word I would use. I'm annoyed, you're annoyed, we're all annoyed.'

Then there was the fly – obviously, flies are always annoying, but this fly seemed indestructible, zooming through the village inns, sipping at every pint of ale and cider it came across, buzzing in folk's ears just when they were about to let loose an arrow at archery practice and so on. 'BZZZZ!'

But the Bull – 'MOOO!' – was the last straw. Halfway through a particularly dull sermon from the local vicar one Sunday...

'And so the Lord did say... well, I can't exactly recall what it was the Lord said, but he was such a wonderful chap, I'm sure it was jolly interesting, like that time he did the thing with the fishes, or rather that should be 'fish', but as we know, the Lord moves in mysterious ways, his wonders to...'

There was an almighty bellow – 'MOOO!' – and a crunching sound. The doors of St. Mary's church were butted and wrenched asunder by the biggest black bull you would ever have set eyes on, had you set your eyes on it. This gigantic steaming longhorn more than filled the doorway, fully nine feet tall and almost as wide, with eyes of deepest ember red, the only part of him not composed of black. Big black horns curled from the bull's black head and within the church, it seemed even a black smell, of death and danger, filled the pews.

One by one, each of the candles in the church snuffed themselves out. The Bull snorted in silhouette, and pawed the ground ready to charge the stammering preacher. It let out another loud 'MOOO!' which seemed to break into a deep throaty giggle – 'WEH-HEH-HEH!' – and it galloped into the church...

Thankfully, the people of Kington had been preparing for just such a moment. A young woman with a newborn baby was seated before the altar, and at the sight of the suckling child, the evil Bull stopped. Seated around the aisles were twelve parsons of the church, all reciting random passages from the Bible in Latin. The Bible was by far Black Vaughan's least favourite book, and he always hated Latin. The Bull seemed to cringe, and growled at the assembled flock of Kington.

'You think you can defy me?' the Bull roared, and sent a beautifully arranged flower display flying with a toss of his horns. 'You didn't like that very much, did you?'

56. BLACK VAUGHAN

'No, O Bull!' chorused the parishioners.

'But what are you gonna do about it, eh? I am the EVIL BULL Black Vaughan, here to annoy you all for all eternity! WEH-HEH-HEH! Right?'

Suddenly, another voice came alone from the doorway.

'You think?' said a funny little man in a brown cassock. It was a drunken monk called Brother Bobby Baulch. He had been off fishing, which he always found far more enjoyable than church, and proudly displayed a silver haddock on the end of his line. He was also clearly already a few ciders up on the day.

Before Black Vaughan could bellow a reply, Brother Bobby went on: '... Because, while a great big black bull is certainly quite impressive, I've heard tell that the really difficult thing for evil undead spirits to do is appear as smaller critters...'

'I can do small!' Black Vaughan cackled, and in a flash of black smoke, there stood the big black slavering hound. 'GRRRAWOOO!'

'Call that small?' squawked Brother Bobby, slightly overbalancing and righting himself with a couple of spins around on one leg. 'That doggy has to be the biggest one I've ever seen! Surely the great Black Vaughan can do better than that?'

'Oh yeah? Oh yeah? I'll show you, you stupid little nobody! GRRRAWOOO!' howled the Hound. He gave a deep guttural growl at Brother Bobby, and in another flash of black smoke, the little black fly was buzzing around just where the dog's head had been. 'BZZZ!'

'Actually, yes, that is pretty impressive. A tiny little fly just like the ones I use for fishing. Well done, Black Vaughan!'

'Thank you! You nobody! BZZZ!' squeaked the fly.

'Mind, this is quite impressive too, if I do say so myself!' replied Brother Bobby. Now, Bobby may have been a bit keen on the booze, but as everyone in Herefordshire knew, there never was a more skilled fisherman, no matter how many drinks he'd drunk. In one swift move, he pulled the haddock off his fishing hook, and cast his line out into the church, where it skewered the tiny fly right where it buzzed: 'BZZZ! BOOF!'

'QUICK!' yelled Brother Bobby as he reeled in the teeny tiny protesting Lord Black Vaughan. Somebody produced a small silver box, and quickly the buzzing fly was put inside it.

'Noooo! You cannot treat me like this! I am BLACK VAUGHAN! BZZZ! Noooo!'

And the lid snapped shut.

'Where will you be laid, little Black Vaughan?' asked Brother Bobby to the tiny silver box.

'Anywhere, anywhere, but not in the Red Sea!' came the tiny muffled reply.

Nobody ever worked out what he meant by this, but the box was quickly tied up with the strongest twine, and then put in the thickest iron safe, and Brother Bobby and the twelve old parsons hurled the safe into the deepest pond they could find, where it plop-plop-plopped to the murky muddy bottom...

And nobody has been even slightly annoyed by Black Vaughan ever since. Which he must find extremely... irritating.

THE END

KINGTON, HEREFORDSHIRE

Nearby Hereford is a historic city whose cathedral contains the Mappa Mundi — the medieval equivalent of Google Maps — and some decent shopping; but those who travel out to Kington itself can enjoy the peace and beauty of a Welsh border market town. What remains of the real Vaughan's own house is now a private dwelling — indeed, Sir Arthur Conan Doyle once stayed there with descendants of Vaughan, and picked up ideas about devil dogs for *The Hound of the Baskervilles*. However, if you go to the church of St. Mary's, where you'll still find poor Thomas Vaughan's effigy (he surely wasn't really as bad as everyone claimed after his head was knocked off), we would advise against dredging any nearby ponds to find a tiny silver box with a length of twine tied around it. Let annoying things lie.

kingtontourist.info

57. THE WHIKEY TREE

Dunfermline, Fife

Not many people remember the name of Robert Henryson, sadly – though once he was the greatest storyteller in the isles of Britain. He lived his life and told his tales up in the Scottish kingdom of Fife, at Dunfermline. Writing in rich Scottish accents, he retold animal fables from Aesop, and even had a go at the old story of Tristan and Isolde.

But this was in medieval times, when it was so easy for folk to die of the slightest things – a cough, a cold, or a particularly nasty look. And, unpleasant though it is to report, the great tale-spinner Robert Henryson died of what they called 'flux' – which is what you and I would call an upset tummy. In fact, Henryson's tummy was more than upset, it was inconsolable. The doctors of the day did all they could, but every time the poor man went to the toilet, he would have to be there for hours, and it was little wonder that he grew weaker by the minute.

He can also be forgiven for the fact that with each passing day leading up to his passing, he grew more tired and had a shorter temper with people who wasted his precious remaining time, when he could have been telling his stories or putting his affairs in order.

It was unfortunate that, on the very last day of his life, Robert Henryson had a most unwelcome visitor.

It was cold and snowy, but the old lady who rapped at his door had travelled far to meet the great storyteller. She fancied herself a bit of a mystical weaver of yarns as well, if she did say so herself.

'Oh by all the gods, I cannot believe it is really you!' she gushed, as the famous rhymer struggled to breathe.

'Believe it, madam, but not for very long!' he replied as best he could.

'I'm your biggest fan!' she cried. 'I have heard all your tales, and told them myself too, with a few refinements, many a time!'

'Well that's... I mean... what can I actually do for you, old dame?' Henryson sighed, losing all pretence of patience with his visitor.

'Ah, 'tis more about what I can do for you!' the old lady returned. 'You see... I am a wise woman!'

'Are you entirely sure about that?' the poorly writer replied.

'Oh, I know many secrets of the world and the way it works!' she went on, 'And if you would like to know the cure for what ails you, I can tell you!'

At this, the exhausted Henryson brightened a little. 'Well, the physicians say there is nothing that can be done for me, so I am happy to try almost anything! What do you suggest, my dear crone? Special herbs? A potion of your own devising?'

'Nothing so complex!' came the reply. 'There is a tree at the bottom of your orchard – I just passed it. It is an old tree, I see, and its name is The Whikey Tree. All you have to do is rise from your bed, go down to it, and walk around it three times, crying: "Whikey tree! Whikey tree! Take this flux away from me!" And you shall see that all shall come right.'

The sick man lay there agape. He could no longer rise from his bed even to go to the toilet, let alone walk down to the orchard. He cleared his throat, pointed to the oak table next to his bed, which was covered in medicines and treatments, and replied to the old woman:

'Good dame, I pray tell me, would it not do quite as well for me if I sat on this table and said: "Oaken board, oaken board, let me shit a decent turd!"?'

And despite everything, at this rhyme, good Robert Henryson laughed. The old woman looked deeply offended, what folk in Scotland call 'black affronted' – but she had no time to protest any offence at what he had said, as this final laugh was also Robert's final breath. The great storyteller's own tale was finally done.

It's just a shame that few people ever care to repeat his final words.

THE END

DUNFERMLINE, FIFE

The work of Robert Henryson received a boost of popularity thanks to his work being translated by the great Irish poet Seamus Heaney, and turned into a cartoon series! But there isn't much in the way of a 'Henryson trail' to visit if you ever do want to walk in his footsteps. He lived and died in Dunfermline, in the rugged kingdom of Fife — so if you're a fan (preferably a less annoying one than the old woman), heading there for the Dunfermline Festival in late summer may be the best time!

welcometofife.com

58. THE BISTERNE DRAGON

Burley, New Forest

D ragon slayers were the superheroes of their day – just look around you and see all the monuments, the carvings, the pub names that celebrate a brave soul's triumph over a bloated reptile of some description, be it a knucker, a cockatrice, a wyrm or one of those great big things with bat wings and fiery breath. Fortunes were demanded by those who vanquished the great beasts, and only when every species of dragon was gone forever did the tradition die out.

The Bisterne Dragon, as he became known, was an absolute textbook example of the animal. He was large, scaly, green, rather lazy, and spent most of his time coiled up at Burley Beacon, a hill a few miles from the villages of Burley and Bisterne, in the heart of what is still known as the New Forest – the King's hunting grounds down in the middle of the south coast. He had big leathery wings, and breathed billowing balls of fire, and was in all respects a 10/10 dragon.

For a long time, this monster had a nice deal going with the folk of nearby Lower Bisterne Farm, whereby they would bring him buckets of creamy milk every day in return for the dragon not eating any of their cows – or indeed, any of *them*. True, the dragon could not live on cream alone, and often disappeared into the forest to find something or someone tasty to eat, and had been seen flapping around as far afield as Crow and Winkton. Nonetheless, many of the usual dragon problems – villages being burned to the ground, princesses taken away to gold-filled lairs and so on – were less of a problem.

But then, swaggering into town came Sir Maurice de Berkley, a knight who had come all the way from Gloucestershire in his best armour to do battle with the dragon, and make himself famous in the process.

'Fear ye not, simple folk of Bisterne!' he boomed as he rattled along. 'At last, you have a real shining knight here to save your cream! That dragon won't know what's hit it! But!' – and here he lowered his voice to just a rather loud volume – 'It will be me, Sir Maurice de Berkley! HOORAY!'

The farmers tried to explain that the dragon had already eaten enough knights to wage war against all of France, but Sir Maurice wasn't to be dissuaded, and without further ado – further ado being one of his least favourite things – he took his two biggest fighting bull mastiffs by the lead, and marched off to Burley Beacon.

'Come out, come out, wherever you be, you big green slavering worm, you!' cried Sir Maurice as he approached the hill. But he didn't have to search far – the dragon was coiled around the summit of the hill just waiting for someone to come along and fill its belly.

'Haha, your time has come, dragon features!' boomed Sir Maurice, and he let go of the mastiffs' leads. The two big dogs had been straining and snarling ever since they caught scent of the dragon, and they streaked off, teeth bared and snapping, ready to tear the scaly monster apart.

The dragon opened its gigantic mouth, and the dogs were swallowed up in one big greedy bite. Well, not exactly swallowed – the dragon pushed them around in its mouth a fair bit, but decided that frankly, they tasted far too much of dog, so he spat both mutts right out, sending them limping and whining all the way home.

As if that wasn't enough, the dragon then flicked his tail in anger, and sent Sir Maurice hurtling down the hill and right into a huge expanse of holly bushes, prickly with dark green leaves and studded with poisonous red berries. His armour smashed into the trunks, and was soon coated with the very sticky sap which spills from the holly tree. He was also, of course, covered in prickly holly leaves from head to foot.

Sir Maurice heaved himself up onto his feet, and, single-minded to the last, he stampeded up the hill as fast as he possibly could, sword drawn, determined to end the dragon's reign of terror, and make a name for himself.

'Nobody chews on my dogs and lives to tell the tale! Have at ye, dragon!' the brave fool roared, and charged all the way into the dragon's yawning mouth, down his gullet, and into his enormous tummy!

The dragon looked distinctly uncomfortable. He gave a cough. All those prickly holly leaves were sticking into his insides, and he did not like the feeling one bit. Suddenly the mighty dragon began to heave, and wretch, determined to cough up the nasty prickly man who was so keen to be eaten.

He couldn't breathe! The dragon's face was turning from bright green into red, into black and – with a squealing roar, he collapsed. The Bisterne Dragon was finally dead, choked to death on the prickliest knight in England.

Sad to say, the dragon slayer followed his prey in no time at all. The daring knight quickly cut himself out of the dragon's tummy and chopped off its head, but a single scale pinged off the gigantic body, straight down Sir Maurice's throat, and he collapsed, choking, in just the same way as the dragon. And so dragon and slayer were both snuffed out at once, and nobody cheered 'HOORAY'.

Nonetheless, Sir Maurice did at least get to have grand heraldic dragon-slaying carvings all over his headstone, and had indeed made a name for himself with the lasting fame of a dragon slayer. Which is why I've just told you all about him now.

THE END

BURLEY, NEW FOREST

This tale is one of many dragon-slaying legends from this area, but there are real places which are believed to be the scene of the crime. Sadly, the Lower Bisterne Farm where the dragon's main victims lived, and the field they call 'Dragon Field', purportedly the site of the dragon's death, are private land. The same is true of Bisterne Manor House, once the home of Sir Maurice de Berkley, with its grand coat of arms depicting the dragon, and two stone mastiffs at the entrance. Some claim that the story probably involved the late Sir Maurice and a wild boar, not a dragon, but

---

58. THE BISTERNE DRAGON

although there are a few in the New Forest Wildlife Park, you needn't worry about wild boars wandering freely these days — the New Forest is all pretty woodland and furry wild ponies.

newforest-online.co.uk

59. TOM THUMB

Tattershall, Lincolnshire

I t was a proud day for the Lincolnshire village of Tattershall when Tom Thumb was born, although it was a happy event his poor parents never dared to dream about. For years Old Thomas of the Mountain and his loving wife Lily tried, but could not have children. As they wept together one night, the poor husband admitted to his love:

'For us to have a little son would be so welcome, my darling, I would not care even if he were no bigger than my thumb.'

It was a good job Lily agreed with this strange suggestion, because only three months later, she discovered that what she thought was a slightly upset tummy was actually a baby ready to be born; and without any pain or trouble, one day out popped a little child about the size of a broad bean.

This teeny-tiny baby never grew any larger than his father's thumb, but they did not care one bit. The loving couple called their magical son Tom Thumb, and always adored him every bit as much as if he had been ten feet tall.

When he was old enough to go to school, Tom was honoured by a visit from the tiny Queen of the Faeries, who kissed the young lad and presented him a new set of clothes as she sang:

'An oak leaf hat made for his crown;
A cobweb shirt by spiders spun;
With jacket wove of thistledown;
And trousers of small feathers done.

59. TOM THUMB

Plus socks, of apple-rind, within,
His shoes, both made of mouse's skin.'

When she had finished singing, Her Wee Majesty turned to Tom and said, 'Tom Thumb, you must never be ashamed of how little you are. Look at me! A few inches tall is a very handsome size indeed!' And she gave the lad a kiss and a hug, and disappeared in a glittery puff of smoke.

Tom looked a treat in his new clothes, and his parents sent him off to his lessons proudly.

But sadly Tom did not have as good a time at school as he hoped. The other boys all laughed at his size, mocked him for his squeaky shoes and silly hat, and did everything they could to give the poor little fellow a miserable time, short of actually stepping on him!

He became so angry one day that he tried to steal one bully's marbles by creeping into his felt marble bag. However, the bully caught him in the act, and shook the bag up so badly that Tom was bombarded with marbles, bruised to bits, and never went to school ever again! Poor Tom Thumb!

It seemed nobody knew what to do with a boisterous fellow as big as a thumb, and poor Tom always seemed to be getting into trouble because of his tiny stature.

One rather unpleasant day a cow gobbled him up, and he had to squelch his way out of a big smelly cowpat. He smelled very bad for weeks on end after that. Poor Tom Thumb!

It was no better than the time when Tom fell into his Mum's pudding batter and got cooked inside a plum duff! Poor Tom Thumb!

Not only that, but when a starving tinker knocked at the door, the kindly Lily gave him the pudding to eat! Tom was fast asleep inside, and was only saved from being eaten when the Tinker, while climbing over a stile, let out a loud and violent fart. Tom was immediately awoken by the noise and the smell, and cried out 'POO, WHAT'S THAT PONG?' The startled Tinker dropped the half of the pudding Tom was in and ran away, leaving Tom miles from home and covered in raisins and crumbs. Poor Tom Thumb!

Then there was the occasion when Tom had the cunning plan of driving his parents' cart by crouching in the horse's ear and whispering directions. This rather clever scheme backfired when the cart and horse were stolen by a couple of ne'er-do-wells, who thought they had found an unoccupied horse and cart just waiting to be stolen.

'Here's a bit of luck, Alf!' one crowed to the other. 'Gee up, neddy!'

Tom was incensed! Nobody was going to steal him or his horse! Thankfully, when the two thieves tried to race away across the fields, Tom had yet another smart plan – in this case, shouting 'Oi, you naughty gits, you can't nick me, I'm a talking horse!'

This terrified the ne'er-do-wells so much they ran all the way to the nearest church in panic. But Tom was still shaken up by the ordeal, and was told never to try anything like it again. Poor Tom Thumb!

It seemed no good could ever come from Tom Thumb's tiny tumbles, until one day when he had the grave misfortune of meeting a giant called Gargantua. A raven had picked the accident-prone little chap up and dropped him in a bowl of peanuts, just as the giant was about to eat a great big handful of them. Tom was so small to Gargantua, she did not notice at all when she swept him up with the nuts and shovelled the lot into her huge churning mouth! Poor Tom Thumb!

The little hero had to think quick. In a few seconds, Gargantua would swallow and he would be in worse trouble than ever! Luckily Tom had on his feather trousers, and had the brainwave of tickling the giant's tonsils, so she quickly began to cough and wretch, and was eventually sick!

Tom burst out of the giant's mouth and was swept away with the rest of the half-chewed nuts into the river which ran by Gargantua's house. A stroke of luck? No, Tom had just replaced one peril with another, as the moment he splashed into the river, he was immediately swallowed by a rainbow trout!

'Poor Tom Thumb', you would be forgiven for thinking. Surely that would be the end of his misadventures? And so it seemed to Tom, as he blacked out in the fish's stomach and appeared to be sunk for good…

And then… Tom opened his eyes… And there was daylight! And a great big hairy man wearing a golden crown, looking down at him with complete surprise! The rainbow trout had been caught that morning, taken to London and poached specially for the King's dinner!

59. TOM THUMB

Little Tom Thumb jumped out of the trout, and tumbled his way across Henry VIII's dinner table with agile somersaults that drew a delighted cheer and applause from all the dining royal family! 'Blow me,' declared King Henry, 'What a wonderful little acrobat! I shall have you as my own little jester, and I shall pay you a large gold piece per day! What is your name, tiny fellow?'

Tom bowed low. 'I am Tom Thumb of Tattershall, your Highness!' he replied with a grin.

'In that case, from this day forth, I name thee Sir Tom Thumb of Lincolnshire, my smallest Knight of all!'

And as Tom knelt, the King took a pin from his cloak, and used it as a tiny sword to ennoble the little man.

Tom Thumb lived a long and happy life, battling cockroaches in the royal kitchens, passing the salt at meals, and entertaining guests with a lute made out of a mangetout, and everyone in the Kingdom loved every inch of him!

But nobody loved him more than his proud parents, who felt he was the finest son they could ever have wished for.

THE END

TATTERHSALL, LINCOLNSHIRE

There was at least one historical Tom Thumb: the most celebrated namesake being a Victorian circus performer who became world famous for his tumbling antics. However, the oldest tales of Tom stretch back to the 16th century, and the tradition runs that the Lincolnshire village of Tattershall was the home of the real miniature hero. To this day his little grave, dated 1620, can be visited at The Holy Trinity Collegiate Church — and you may even be able to see his tiny house, high up on the roof of the nearby Lodge House, if you look hard enough!

tattershall-lakes.com

---

60. THE KING OF CATS

South Lancashire

This weird squib is known in many regions, but most often as a south Lancashire happening. Whether it occurred in Wigan or Ormskirk or some tiny village, we can only wildly surmise – but that doesn't mean it's not true!

Wherever and whenever it happened, the tale abides that one grey and cold Saturday afternoon, an old fellow was sitting by his unlit fireplace, casually eating a nice pear, when all of a sudden a caterwauling kerfuffle could be heard from somewhere up the chimney.

It wasn't Christmas, so who could it be? The old man looked up, and – WHUMPH! – the room disappeared in a shower of soot, and out popped a very black-looking cat. What colour the cat actually was is anyone's guess.

The man stared at the cat. The cat stared at the man. The man's expression would be most easily summed up as 'surprised', the cat's would perhaps be 'vaguely amused'. And then, of course, the cat spoke.

'Tell Dildrum, Doldrum's dead!' barked the cat, and disappeared back up the chimney in what must have been slightly less than one second, leaving the man alone, and goggling.

He was not alone for long, however. In less than a minute, his wife came in from the market with that night's turnips, and her own cat – a smart marmalade tom they called Prickles, who rarely left her side. 'Why is there soot all over my nice clean house?' she demanded.

'My dear,' the old man stammeringly greeted her, 'you will not

60. THE KING OF CATS

believe this when I tell you, but I promise it to be true! And I swear that I haven't touched a drop! But as I was sitting here, just now, moments ago, a black cat came zooming down the chimney in a cloud of soot, and he spoke to me!'

'You mad old badger,' his wife laughed. 'This is some sort of joke on me, isn't it?'

'I promise you!' the old man replied, 'Though I'm sure you'll never credit it, the cat looked at me and he said, "Tell Dildrum, Doldrum's dead!" I have no idea what it means, but...'

Before the old man could utter another word, the marmalade tomcat leapt up onto its hind legs and loudly shouted, 'Doldrum's dead? Then I am the King of Cats!'

And without another word to his human keepers, Dildrum dashed off up the chimney, and was never seen again.

Nobody ever believed the old couple when they tried to explain where Prickles had gone, so they soon decided not to talk too much about what happened. They also made sure to get themselves a nice non-talking dog instead.

THE END

SOUTH LANCASHIRE

Oh, if only we could tell you exactly where Dildrum, the King Of Cats, once lived! For all that is known, the very cottage where he ran up the chimney might now be a supermarket. Most people who visit Lancashire for a holiday will surely be headed to the coast, to Blackpool or somewhere similar, whereas the south is a more urban living area, to the north of Greater Manchester. A strange place indeed for feline aristocracy to wind up.

visitlancashire.com

---

61. THREE LITTLE PIGS

Shanklin, Isle of Wight

Once, and only once, there were Three Little Pigs, who all lived on the Isle of Wight. Don't bother asking where, precisely; sadly the site of their homes has not been uncovered by any archaeologists, but we do know for sure that they must have lived somewhere in the Shanklin area, as that is where this story was remembered for hundreds of years before those Three Little Pigs became world famous.

So, if you'll forgive the repetition – once, and only once, there were Three Little Pigs. These piggy triplets had been lovingly raised by their wise old Sow Mother, and she had done her very best to prepare them all for the world outside their cosy sty.

But there came a time when the sty really was far too poky for the four of them, and so the Sow Mother called her wee sons around her, and said: 'I always feared the day this moment would come, but it is time for my three darlings to make their way in the world, all on your own.'

And so she gave each of the three brothers a satchel filled with jam sandwiches and milk, and told them, 'Remember, I have always told you to use your brains, my darlings. It is a big bad world out there if you do not know what you are doing. But you will take a mother's love with you, whatever happens.'

And so they all hugged, and kissed, and said their goodbyes.

With the sun rising high up in a blue sky, the first of the Three Little

61. THREE LITTLE PIGS

Pigs set out to make a home for himself. He looked about to see what he could use to make his own shelter from the wind and worry of the world. He needed to build his own house, and what did he see all about him, but bales and bales of straw?

'I am a very clever Pig,' he chortled to himself as he whistled and wove a wonderful cosy house of straw. It had a thick thatched roof, and raffia carpets, and once he'd brought in some apples and a chair or two, he felt gloriously comfortable.

But then that night, there came a tapping at the door. Well, it was more of a rustling, as the door was also made of straw. Out of the darkness of the forest sauntered the Big Bad Wolf!

This was at a time when wolves were still roaming the forests of Britain, and the Isle of Wight was no exception. This wily wolf was the main big bad thing that Old Mother Sow had most urgently warned the Three Little Pigs about – he was indeed big, and he was terribly bad, and he liked nothing more than the savoury taste of a nice fat juicy porker slipping down into his cavernous belly.

The Three Little Pigs would repeat to themselves, 'Who's afraid of the Big Bad Wolf? Not me!' to help them get to sleep at night... But in truth, they all were very afraid.

That night, the Big Bad Wolf gave a cough, and cried out, 'Good evening, little Pig?'

The first Pig sat bolt upright in his cosy straw bed, and hiccupped: 'Who... Who is it?'

'Little Pig, little Pig, let me come in!'

'No no, by the hairs on my chinny-chin-chin!'

'Then I'll huff and I'll puff and I'll blow your house in!'

Well this was such an unneighbourly suggestion, it was all the biggest Pig needed to be certain that this was the Big Bad Wolf at his door!

But it was too late to do anything about it now. The Big Bad Wolf took a great run up, inflated his lungs fit to burst – 'HUUUP! PHOOOOOO!' – and he simply blew that house of straw right away!

The poor Pig sat quaking in the ruins of his house. The Big Bad Wolf advanced on him.

The rest... is bacon.

But what of the second Pig? Well this Pig fancied himself the most intelligent of the lot; he knew that straw made for very poor housing material, and he decided he would have to go the extra mile...

As the sun blazed down high in the blue sky, this Pig went into the woods and came out with bundles of twigs, which he happily entwined, whistling as he did so, until a whole new home stood before him, a wickerwork masterpiece! 'I am a clever Pig!' he said, as he brought in some pears and his favourite blanket, and soon felt extremely cosy in his little house of twigs.

But then that night came the tapping at the door. Which was actually more of a rattling, the door being entirely made of twigs.

'Who... who is it?' squeaked the second Pig.

'Little Pig, little Pig, let me come in!'

'No no, by the hairs on my chinny-chin-chin!'

'Then I'll huff and I'll puff and I'll blow your house in!'

And once again, before the poor Pig could even cry out for assistance, the Big Bad Wolf took the deepest breath ever – 'HUUUP-PHOOOOOO!' and he blew that house of twigs right away!

Let's draw a veil over what happened to the poor second Pig next. The Big Bad Wolf licked his slavering lips, and moved in.

The rest... is sausages.

So there was only one little Pig left. This one knew that life without his old Sow Mother was not going to be easy. 'I am not the cleverest of pigs,' he said to himself, 'but because of that I must always make a special effort to do my best!'

And so the third Pig sat down, and had a long, hard think, as the blazing sun began to slip down to the horizon. There was plenty of straw, he saw, but that was no real use. Maybe he could go to the wood and fetch some timber of some kind? But carpentry was not his strength, he felt. What else could he do?

Then he finally had his brainwave. 'Mud!' he chortled. 'Glorious mud! There's acres of it around, glooping and thick. If I can take some of that, and heat it in a fire, it will bake into hard bricks, and I can build myself the strongest house of all!'

This obviously took some time, so he baked and built every day, whistling a merry tune as he worked away, and hid himself in the forest roots at night, where nobody could get at him.

Eventually, this third Pig could stand back and admire his own pretty brick house, with a roof of wood and slate all safely glued together with more thick muddy clay mixed with sand from the beach. He even had a chimney on the top, and soon it was puffing away nicely as he put a pot on the fire and made himself a piping hot vegetable stew to celebrate.

But then came that tapping on the door. A proper RAP-RAP-RAP at the knocker. The third Pig squinted through a small hole he had put into the door to protect himself from strange visitors, and he saw right away who it was! The Big Bad Wolf, his tummy bloated with his last two rich dinners, drool still sagging from his jaws as he looked forward to yet another porky treat!

'Little Pig, little Pig, let me come in!'

'No no, by the hairs on my chinny-chin-chin!'

'Then I'll huff, and I'll puff, and I'll blow your house in!'

And he really tried. The Big Bad Wolf took the biggest run up, filled his lungs with all the breath he could, and he blew and he blew and he blew until he was bright purple in the face! 'HUUUUUP – PHOOOOOOOOOOOOOARRRRGGGGGHHHH!!!'

He panted. He gagged. He groaned. The house of brick still stood strong.

'What do you want, Wolf?' piped up the Pig, 'I am not afraid of you!'

'Why… Why should you be afraid?' panted the exhausted Wolf. 'I was only going to, um, to invite you to a day out at Shanklin Fair! We could go on the merry-go-round maybe? I'm just a neighbour welcoming you into the neighbourhood, what a pretty house, well done! Let's both go to the fair!'

'If I see you near Shanklin Fair,' replied the brave Pig, 'I will get into a butter churn and I will roll down the hill at top speed, and I will knock you flat as a pancake, you big bad bleeder! Get you gone, and leave poor Pigs to live in peace!'

'Curses!' cried the Big Bad Wolf, 'Nobody talks to the Big Bad Wolf like that, you future supper, you! If I can't blow your house in, I'll just have to find another way! Just you wait, Piggy!'

The Pig waited. Then he heard a noise up above, on his roof. The Big Bad Wolf was clambering over the tiles of the house of brick, and creeping towards the chimney. He was going to squeeze down into the house, and have that Pig in his belly whether he liked it or not!

But the Pig was much more cunning than The Big Bad Wolf. When he heard those claws clattering on his roof, and guessed what the Big Bad Wolf was up to, he quickly built up the fire that was still crackling away in the grate, moved his red hot pot of bubbling boiling stew into the right spot, and gave it a stir…

The Big Bad Wolf was certainly big, and without question he was bad, but he was not at all clever. He never stood a chance once he had jumped down that chimney, and into the hot stew. He howled, and he steamed, but soon he simmered, and never troubled another poor innocent pig ever again.

The rest... is happy. The third Pig was warm and cosy in his house for a long lifetime, and he dined that very evening on piping hot wolf stew. Wolf stew is of course disgusting, but he didn't mind, because he was a Pig.

THE END

SHANKLIN, ISLE OF WIGHT

One of our most internationally famous fairytales is also one of our most undervalued, because hardly anyone realises it's a British tale! The story can be traced no further back than Victorian English folktale collections, and the very earliest retelling features Shanklin Fair, in one of the prettiest towns on the sunny Isle of Wight — which you'll find just below the New Forest, bang in the centre of the south coast! You'll have problems trying to find even the foundations of the third Pig's strong house of brick, but you don't need any extra reason to take the ferry to Shanklin: it's an idyllic seaside spot for pig and person alike.

visitisleofwight.co.uk

62. BEWARE THE CAT!

West London

Q uite a few centuries ago, in a place called Aldersgate, near the London court of the boy King Edward, lived a man called Master Streamer, who wanted to speak with cats.

Master Streamer was a very strange man. As you may have guessed. Lots of people talk to their cats – 'does puss-puss wanna dish o' milky?' and suchlike – but for Gregory Streamer, the charming meows the cats replied to their carers was not enough – he wanted to know what really made them tick. One particular gang of cats gathered up on his roof most nights, and often he could swear that the meows that kept him awake through the night almost made sense to him – if only he could translate them!

The way that Master Streamer decided to learn the cat language, however, was not the most pleasant tale to relate, and if you happen to be enjoying a meal as the story unfolds, perhaps it would be best to save it for later.

Master Streamer owned a huge, ancient, and totally daft book of obscure wisdom, for which 'How To Speak Cat' wasn't even the strangest entry. According to the ravings of the ancients, it was possible to understand cat-talk, but only if you sat in front of the fire on Hallowe'en night, and ate an entire cat, giblets and all, while wearing the poor animal's skin. 'Cat-talk is incredibly subtle', the book read, 'but this method will make your hearing as sensitive as the beast's, and suddenly all will become clear.'

302

It brings me no pleasure to tell you that Master Streamer did just what the book said, hunting for his poor unfortunate dinner – a big tufty marmalade moggy – amid the leafy roots of St. John's Wood, which in those days stretched all the way up to Islington. That October 31st, having spent much time turning the poor dead cat into supper, Streamer sat in front of a crackling fire with a marmalade fur draped over his head, and ate an atrocious meal of feline consommé, cat burgers, kitty fries, moggy rissoles, and even a pussycat flan for afters... and he quickly felt rather ill.

Besides the strange man's complaint that his nose began to run 'with more gloopy fluids than it was thought any man could contain', which he assumed came from clearing the brain, there was one marked effect of this foul supper. Whether the bogey-ridden snooper had fooled himself into believing it or not, suddenly Streamer insisted that he could distinctly hear almost any noise being made within a hundred-mile radius, from the clatter of carts in Clerkenwell to the coughing of gnats in Shepherds Bush. Was this the super-hearing that would allow him to pry into the private affairs of the cats on his roof?

Streamer climbed out of the window and edged his way along the roof to where he could see the familiar huddle of cats – shabby tabbies, glossy Persians, kittens and moggies, amassed and mewing for all their worth. But as he concentrated, the human interloper fancied he could actually make out meanings to each meow...

'Pray silence for his worshipfulness, the Lord Grimalkin!' a snooty Siamese bellowed, and high up on an old kipper barrel arose a fine grey cat of undeniably noble bearing.

'Brothers and sisters,' Grimalkin began, 'we are hereby congregated to debate the vile slaughter of our Good King, Doldrum! Who is to stand trial for this most heartless deed? Bring forth the chief witness, Tiddles the Fourth!'

A tiny tufty white kitten was marched into the throng and leapt up onto a bucket to deliver her testimony. 'I swear that all I shall say will be the truth, and nothing else but it! So anyway...' she squeaked, rapidly continuing before the whiskery judge could get a word in edgeways, sideways, or any other ways: 'So, there I was, minding my own business, making a mouse wish he'd never been born, when what do I hear but a screech? I have been brave from my earliest kitlinghood, so I of course bounded off to investigate and it turned out to be Balgury and Balgeary having a scrap as per usual, so anyway,

62. BEWARE THE CAT!

I gave them a wide berth and set off to find somewhere to do a nice relaxing poo and then…'

With wide-eyed astonishment Master Streamer listened to the white kitten as the little witness bored the entire Cat Courtroom to tears with the details of her day. To the nosy Streamer every detail was fascinating, his ears tingling with concentration, until the irritated Lord Grimalkin stopped the witness with a swipe of his paw, and said, 'Do you all smell that? I can smell King Doldrum right here, among us.'

Streamer belched, uncontrollably. He then became aware that every cat present had turned around, and every pair of green eyes was blazing sheer hatred his way.

'Oh, I, er, I wasn't listening, honestly!' Streamer began.

'THAT'S THE MAN!' Tiddles the Fourth screeched. 'He's the one who killed the King out in the woods, and he's still wearing his skin on his head!'

The cats began to advance on the terrified eccentric, and then suddenly – 'BING BONG BUNG BONG BANG BING BONG!!!' – the bells of the nearby church of St. Botolph's chimed the hour, and to Master Streamer, it was as if every mighty clang of the bell let off a bomb in his frazzled brain. POP! went his eardrums, and he screamed for all he was worth.

In the confusion, Lord Grimalkin bellowed – ''Tis not just an eavesdropper, but the killer of the King! Get him, gang!' And the cats all sprang together, attacking Master Streamer from every angle, digging their claws in wherever they could. With a yelp which needed no translation, Streamer fell off the roof, covered in cats, and plopped into the compost heap.

Master Streamer barely managed to escape with his life, and he never heard another meow out of any cat again. In fact, all he could ever hear from that day forward was the ringing of the bells of St. Botolph's.

THE END

WEST LONDON

The sites mentioned in the original text of this story — thought by many to be the first English novel, certainly the first horror novel — are still

---

famous to this day, albeit not necessarily specific tourism sites. St. John's Wood is no longer an actual wood where you could hunt feral cats, and it's questionable which St. Botolph's church it would have been which deafened Streamer — the most likely site, in Aldgate, now boasts an 18th-century church which replaced the long-demolished building of Streamer's day. You can pop round the corner to the Gherkin if you like.

visitlondon.com

63. THE GREAT GORMULA

Tobermory, Isle of Mull

Scotland has more than its reasonable share of witches – but when you consider that most 'witches' were just women of past centuries who refused to behave exactly as the menfolk told them to, that isn't necessarily a bad thing. Okay, so some dabblers in witchcraft were known to curdle milk, suckle moggies and curse babies, but most were just expressing themselves, and where's the harm in a pleasant jaunt on a broom now and then?

Folk in those days liked to blame witches for almost anything that went wrong in their lives, from blighted cattle to stepping in dog mess, so if you were a witch, it wasn't wise to go around broadcasting the fact to everyone. The Great Gormula wasn't one to hide herself under a bushel, though. She was a noblewoman of the Western Highlands four centuries ago, and many people suspected that she was what they called 'really weird' – otherwise known as the Doideag: the greatest witch in Britain. Gormula made it her business to get involved in Highland matters, settling disputes over borders – not with her wand, but with her brains – and zooming around merrily on her broom.

Although she seemed not to give a flying fig for the scowls and screams of those who ran from her as she passed, she did have feelings, and sometimes the yells of 'Thou art the Devil, begone, foul Doideag!' could ruin her day.

'Why can't you people judge others on their actions, and not on whether they have warty noses and fly around on brooms?' complained Gormula, but nobody listened. She did try and change people's minds about witches now and then, and approached her neighbours with nice cakes she'd baked, but they would sooner gobble an icing-topped toad than eat a slice of cake baked by a nasty WITCH. And so she went her own way, and was only really friends with other witches.

That was until the island of Britain came under attack from the Spanish Armada in 1588, with England's Queen Elizabeth fending off Catholic attacks from the continent. Famously, Sir Francis Drake and his chums helped to dash the invading fleet of ships sent by King Philip of Spain – having made sure to finish his game of bowls first. But with the Armada in disarray, one ship – the *Florida* – sailed away as fast as it could, and ended up in the bay of Tobermory, off the Hebridean Isle of Mull.

The people of Tobermory were terrified! They weren't prepared to fight off platoons of bloodthirsty Spaniards! But thankfully, as they stood on the shore waving spades and such at the invading ship, they could hear a familiar cackle and a 'voom' sound, and The Great Gormula was seen streaking towards the ship on her broom! When news of the Spanish Armada's invasion had reached Gormula, she'd called on a couple of witchy friends from the isles of Islay and Tiree, and now all three of them were zooming at unimagined speeds towards the *Florida*, all firing curses from their wands and laughing fit to burst! Gormula shrieked with pleasure – 'Now THIS is what I call fun! Tee-hee-hee!'

With imperviousness spells cast on themselves, all three witches slammed into the ship's hull, passing right through the splintering wood, and criss-crossing so many times, within a minute, the proud Spanish galleon was nothing but a sieve sinking beneath the waves. 'BOOM!' went the cannon as the ship went down, its gold bullion and invading army lost forever to the briny deep – otherwise known as Davy Jones' Locker. (Who was Davy Jones? Davy Jones was a villainous sea imp, a kind of naval gremlin, and has nothing to do with this story.)

For the first time ever, Gormula and her friends knew what it was to be cheered by a crowd, so grateful were the folk of Tobermory for being saved from the Spanish invasion. They waved their wands in victory, and zoomed off for a slap-up fish supper.

Admittedly, one grumpy note came from the Duke of Argyll, who whined, 'Millions of pounds of gold is now at the bottom of the sea,

63. THE GREAT GORMULA

and as laird, I have the right to it all' – but his descendants are still trying to find it to this day.

If he had any sense, he would have asked The Great Gormula to nip down and get the goodies for them right away… but it pains me to say that she did not live very long after her great triumph, as poor Gormula drowned trying to catch a salmon with her bare hands.

This wasn't the most respectable end for such a skilled magician, but we all have our off-days, and despite it all, The Great Gormula is still remembered as the most wonderful witch in Scotland's vast history of witchcraft.

THE END

TOBERMORY, ISLE OF MULL

The Isle of Mull is one of the largest landmasses in the Hebrides, and the brightly coloured coastal settlement of Tobermory is world famous as the setting for the BBC series *Balamory!* There's not much here to mark the achievement of The Great Gormula, but that's not surprising as the historical inspiration for the witch probably wasn't born by the time of the Spanish Armada. Gormshùil Mhòr na Maighe of the Clan MacKinnon was a powerful noble from Lochaber in the West Highlands, a political mover in the early 17th century who was considered 'uncanny' in her wisdom, but who drowned in shallow water on the way to plead for her son's life, at the bridge of Allt a' Bhradain, a mile from the village of Gairlochy. As it happens, a Spanish galleon did sink in Tobermory bay, however, and untold fortunes of gold are said to be somewhere deep under the sea here — the Duke of Argyll's descendants are still after it.

tobermory.co.uk

---

64. THE KELPIE OF
LOCH GARVE

Loch Garve, Highlands

I t's a strange thought, that deep in the deepest lochs and lakes of
Britain, there is a species of water horse that can communicate
with us humans, and live for thousands of years. A very strange
thought indeed, that. But do go with it.

There are plenty of tales of these mysterious, majestic creatures
and their like whisking poor unsuspecting humans away to their
underwater grottoes, and their victims are never seen again. But
happily, the water horse in this story was a very different sort of beast.
He was a kelpie by the name of Each Uisge, which if pronounced
correctly should sound like a daddy longlegs has just flown into your
throat, so pronounce it however you like.

Each and his lovely wife Every lived in a gloomy little cave down
at the very bottom of Loch Garve, up in a chilly corner of Ross-shire.
Each was very comfy and contented with his lot, but his wife was less
happy.

'Why does it always have to be so WET down here?' Every would
regularly groan. 'And cold! So very cooold!'

'Well, we are in a bubble in a cave at the bottom of a deep, watery
loch, my love!' Each replied, but it made him unhappy to see his
beloved one shivering all the time, and so he hatched a clever plan.

The next morning, Each the Kelpie popped out of his cosy little
bubble, and swam his way up, up, up to the surface of the loch,
whereupon he roared out onto dry land in the shape of a tall, fine

64. THE KELPIE OF LOCH GARVE

coal-black stallion. Kelpies often clip-clop onto the land in the guise of normal horses, sometimes to collect apples and pears, or perhaps just to sing to small children to confuse them for the rest of their lives. This kelpie was not the kind to kidnap people and whisk them underwater to a soggy fate, but this day, Each was planning to do just that.

He galloped to the nearest village, until he found a large brick house with 'Master Builder' written across the front porch. When he knew he had the right place, he tapped on the front door with a fore-hoof.

The builder inside, Billy McCavity, knew as soon as he opened the door that this was no normal black stallion, but a kelpie. And he instantly knew, as every human does when a kelpie comes knocking at the front door, that he had no choice but to climb up onto the beast's back and ride with him wherever he would go.

Without a word of explanation or goodbye to his family, McCavity did just that, and after a fast gallop which almost blew his wig off, builder and kelpie dived down into the dank depths of Loch Garve.

But do not fret, as I already said, Each was no normal kelpie, and he did not want McCavity to drown! He turned to face his human captive, and snorted an almighty bubble out of one nostril, which closed around McCavity's head and stayed there, allowing him to keep breathing no matter how deep they dived.

Eventually they arrived at the Kelpies' chilly bubble of a cave, and Each and Every explained the problem. 'Now I never went to school, obviously,' Each said, 'but what I was thinking might solve the problem would be a nice warm fire.'

'Ooh yes please! With an ornamental mantelpiece and a special thing for toasting marshmallows on it! And lots of lovely heated water at last!' Every added, with the biggest smile she had smiled for many a year.

McCavity tugged at his beard. 'Ask anyone in the whole of Scotland if not further afield, from yon to yonder, who the finest master builder in the land is, and they're liable to shout "BILLY McCAVITY!" Which, let me tell you, is very embarrassing as I'm an awfully shy and modest man most of the time. It just happens to be true. I boast that I can build anything, and so far I have never let anyone down. But can ye really have a fireplace deep underwater?'

'Oh please try, Mr. McCavity,' cried Every. 'It would just be so perfect.'

'Yes, and we promise, if you manage it,' said Each, 'that you and your family will never want for fish ever again. I will deliver you all the loch can supply, fresh every morning.'

Well, that did it for Billy McCavity. 'I do like my kippers of a morning,' he replied. 'Ach, I'll give it a go, eh?'

And so, with crafty precision, that is what he did. McCavity spent the whole day gathering rocks and mixing cement and measuring, and before the sun was ready to set, a fine tall chimney curled up from the Kelpies' little cave all the way to the top of the loch, with special pipes criss-crossing it which would guarantee constant hot water. Once Each and Every had brought down plenty of firewood (kept dry in nostril bubbles from their own noses) they soon had a lovely warm fire going.

'Such bliss, this place has never felt so cosy!' Every beamed.

'We will be as good as our word, Billy!' Each smiled, and took the tired builder on his back once again. With a wave to the warm and happy Every, up they swam, and galloped all the way back to McCavity's home, where it was just about time for tea.

None of McCavity's family believed his story when he told them. But they all had to admit that the kippers they had for tea that night were the best they had ever tasted.

And from that day forth, any time the iciness of winter set the surface of Loch Garve solid and snowbound, you should see that there is always one patch which never ices over. This is where the Kelpies' chimney still stands, and far below it, Each and Every the Kelpies are still as snug as snug can be in their warm bubble of a cave.

THE END

LOCH GARVE, HIGHLANDS

Loch Garve is near the very wee village of Garve, and you couldn't find a more perfect peaceful Highland retreat — as long as the kelpies are nice and warm, anyway. Despite being very far north, so not ideal for sun-

64. THE KELPIE OF LOCH GARVE

worshippers, Garve has a train station on the Kyle of Lochalsh line, plus a hotel, so it isn't too hard to get to, and there's somewhere to kip when you get there. Also, the site of the famous battle of Culloden is only 24 miles away, and the Highlands provide perfect walks in every direction, for those who really want to get away from it all. Try the kippers!

northhighlandsscotland.com

65. CONJURING
MINTERNE

Batcombe, Dorset

L et's not waste time debating whether or not 'magic' exists. It can almost mean whatever you want it to – once upon a time, folk who just happened to have more than the average idea of how things work, or a small amount of medical knowledge, were seen as magicians by the less brain-encumbered people in their village.

But Conjuring Minterne knew he was a magician. The aristocratic boss of a small Dorset village called Batcombe, John Minterne had a library full of impressive books, but one was particularly special, containing as it did all the secrets of his magical arts. How to turn a newt into a frog, how to summon up demons and make them do a little dance for him, love potions, hate potions, don't-mind-that-much potions, spells which turned people's hats into trifle – all of the tricks Minterne had perfected, as the great conjuror, were collected in this big creaky leather book.

One squally white day, Conjuring Minterne was immersed in his spells, trying to find a foolproof recipe for a potion which would bring beards to life and allow them to sing, when he realised he was missing a crucial ingredient – the Dorset Mushroom, a singular strain of fungus which is long extinct, but back then was available in one place, and one place only.

'To the top of Batcombe Hill!' Minterne cried, and without a moment's pause, he jumped out of the window, straight into the saddle of his fine stallion, Dobbin, and galloped away to where he knew the mushroom could be found. It did not take long for him to find what he was looking for, but then a very important thought hit him.

'Oh, my brains and britches!' he roared. 'Conjuring Minterne, you dolt, you have fled off and left your spellbook wide open for all to browse!' The book was so precious, Minterne always kept it hidden and locked away. What if one of his servants should somehow be able to read, and uncover his secrets? What if his housekeeper should find it, and clear it away into the fire? The poor servant was still in the doghouse for that time she gathered up all Minterne's precious mushrooms and cooked them into an omelette. What if a pigeon should fly in and go to the toilet all over a crucial spell, or someone else should pass by and decide to give some dangerous magic a go? Minterne would get back to a home filled with singing beards, half-frog-half-newts and dancing demons!

He had to get home in twice no time, and so he fed his horse an apple laced with his own special potion, and as he kicked his magic spurs into Dobbin's sides, horse and rider seemed to become engulfed in flames! With an almighty neigh and a roar, the steed bounded from the top of Batcombe Hill, flying high up into the air like some kind of super-frog.

This was the biggest jump any horse has ever taken, but not quite enough to get them all the way home. As the horse thundered down to the ground, his back hoof caught the pinnacle of the local church of St. Mary, and toppled the tip of the spire into the field below.

Where Dobbin and Minterne landed, in the Pitching Plot by the church, the grass was so badly scorched by Dobbin's fiery hooves, they say that it has never grown back there to this day.

With two more huge bounds, Minterne was home, and to his relief, he found that his spellbook was safe. Nevertheless, the spire of St. Mary's lay undisturbed for many years, so afraid of Minterne's magic were the locals. Eventually, when they did dare to hoist it back up into place, it was terribly crooked – and so it remains crooked, even now.

Conjuring Minterne lived long and collected many spells, but was never much of a churchgoer, so when he came to write his will, he requested that if he had to be buried in the church, he wanted to be 'half in and half out', just in case he should find some way of coming back from the dead and want to make a quick getaway – with the help of Dobbin, the greatest horse-jumper of all time.

THE END

BATCOMBE, DORSET

If you wish to visit Batcombe itself, make sure that you go to the right one — there's a slightly larger village of the same name not far away in Somerset. In West Dorset, you will know the right Batcombe, because there are memorials to a number of Minternes (including two Johns!) in the church, St. Mary's — which, of course, has a crooked spire. You can also climb not just Batcombe Hill (though there are no mushrooms there any more) but also nearby Gore Hill, with its mysterious 'cross in hand' stone which was mentioned by Thomas Hardy in *Tess of the D'Urbervilles* — as was Conjuring Minterne himself.

visit-dorset.com

66. THE APPLE
TREE MAN

Cider Country

This old yarn is actually claimed by two fertile counties in southern Britain, on opposite sides of England. Somerset in the west, with its apples, its cider and scrumpy, has close ties to The Apple Tree Man, but that county is already so overstocked with stories you can hardly blame the eastern county of Kent for having a special place in their hearts for him as well. Kent is, after all, known as The Garden of England, bursting with orchards, bringing us apples, pears, cherries, damsons, plums, and all kinds of tasty goodness. Apples do, however, mean something special in Somerset...

Wherever the tale's roots are embedded, whether it happened in the east or the west, it concerns two brothers who sadly did not get on at all well. Unusually, in that place and in those times, it was the youngest son who inherited everything on the death of a parent. When one rich old farmer popped his clogs, leaving everything to his younger son Ned, the lad in question was suitably grateful, and generous to everyone but his older brother, Ted. To that poor sap, he rented the crumbliest old cottage on the family's acres, with an old ox called Jock that was preparing to breathe its last, and a donkey called Dunk who was no further from the grave than the ox.

Nevertheless, this philosophical older brother counted his blessings, and did what he could to toughen up the beasts, taking good care of them, and allowing them to graze in the shade of the old apple trees which stood near his cottage. Soon Jock and Dunk were looking better than ever, and the trees were also bursting into life again, ripening with juicy fat fruit on every bough.

But all this hard work didn't help when Ned came round wanting his rent for the crumbly old cottage. When Ted tried to explain how hard times were, the younger brother growled and sighed and whistled through his teeth, but made sure that every penny came his way eventually.

One day, Ned came by the old crumbly cottage and offered Ted an astonishingly silly deal. 'Now look here, Ted,' he began, 'it'll be Christmas Eve tomorrow, and as you and I know well, that's the time when animals do talk.'

'Do they?' asked his perplexed brother.

'They do, you knows they do. So Dad always told me, anyway. The thing is, there's always been talk of old, old treasure here on this land, and Dad said that if anyone knows where it is, it's that geriatric donkey, Dunk. So when the midnight chimes are nearly here on the morrow, I'll be by to hear all about it from the donkey's own lips, and don't you be earwiggin', mind, blast yer! Just wake me up in time, leave me in the cattle shed, and if I hears what I wants, I'll knock sixpence off yer rent.'

Ted agreed, and when Christmas Eve rolled round and the sun had long gone down, the older brother finished his usual duties by cosily bedding down Jock and Dunk in the cattle shed with an extra bale of hay, and a sprig of holly to chew on. He took his tin mug and filled it with a glug of his best apple scrumpy cider, then he planted it in the cinders of the fire to mull. When it was warm, he headed out to the orchard to feed the delicious concoction to the roots of the apple trees.

As he poured out the warm scrumpy and the trees sucked up all the mulled goodness, Ted wassailed, which is a crusty old way of saying he sang – quietly but tunefully:

'Here's to ye, me apple tree, and many apples shall we see!
O apple tree, I wassail ye, bags full, hats full, bushels of fruit for tea!
Stand fast root, bear well top, bud and let your beauties drop.'

As Ted turned to stroll back to the cottage, he heard an unearthly and yet extremely earthy rustling gloopy sound, and span around to see

66. THE APPLE TREE MAN

the roots and branches of the biggest apple tree standing tall and proud – as a big creaky wooden man with a grinning russet face.

'Hoo hoo! Ta for the scrumpy, me old lover!' chuckled The Apple Tree Man. 'Ah, you bin very good to me, looking after me roots and that dear old donkey and the ox, and so I'm gonna do you a good turn for the friendly season an' all. Take a good look deep down in my roots, mate!'

And when Ted gazed down at the hole in the ground where the tree had been rooted, he saw a gloriously shining bucket of gold coins! The fortune of several lifetimes!

'Roman or whatever they do be, old lad, them coins now be yourn!' smiled The Apple Tree Man. 'But mind you don't tell a gaspin' soul how you come across 'em, and keep 'em stashed away for yourself – you deserves 'em. And few do.' The Apple Tree Man lifted a leafy bough and tapped the side of his nose, wisely.

Ted took up the gold, and The Apple Tree Man settled his roots back into the ground with a grateful gurgle. 'Thank you, Apple Tree Man!' said Ted, still agape at all he had witnessed.

'Ah, don't mention it, Teddy boy,' came the reply. 'But you go and wake up that little brother of yourn now; 'tis nearly witches' hour. Oh, and before I goes – Merry Christmas!'

And with that, and one final grin, The Apple Tree Man closed his eyes, and settled back down once again into just an old apple tree.

Ned hurriedly pushed Ted off to bed once he arrived at the cattle shed. He wanted to be sure that he was the only person to learn the secret of the treasure – treasure Ted had already gratefully stuffed into his sock drawer. Therefore the younger brother was all alone as the midnight chimes carried on the chill air from the nearby village church. As the last gentle bong ceased to vibrate, Ned gazed around the old shed, where the donkey and the ox were comfy in their hay.

'Hee-haw! Hahahaw! Oh aye, here he is then,' Dunk the donkey brayed, 'Here's that no-good maggot of a lad Ned, then, wanting to know all about where that treasure's been hid, then.' And he laughed – a big, noisy donkey laugh: 'Hee hee haw haw hahahahaw!'

Jock the ox joined him in a mooing guffaw, just as tickled as his friend. 'But the greedy fool's out of luck, ain't he, Dunk, because he won't ever get it, a better man already found the treasure for himself! Mooohooohoohahaha!'

'Hee-ha! Pass us some of that lovely holly, Jock.'

318

'There you go, my lover, happy Christmas!'

Nobody knows for sure how Ned reacted to watching these two animals laugh at him, but he must have passed out cold in the cattle shed, because when he came to, his hair had turned white. The best change of all, however, was that Neddy was never cruel to his brother Teddy ever again. The next day, on Christmas Day itself, the two of them sat down to a fine roast goose together, and swore to be good brothers from that day forward.

There's an old Shropshire tradition that if the sun shines through the apple trees on Christmas Day, the following year there will be a bumper crop of apples growing on every tree, and from those apples there would be pies, puddings, sauces, and of course, the very best scrumpy cider. As Ted made his way back to the crumbly cottage after dinner that December 25th – with, of course, a kind word to the wordless ox Jock and donkey Dunk as he passed – he smiled to see the warm sun shining through the apple trees, shedding light exactly where The Apple Tree Man had wished him a Merry Christmas.

THE END

CIDER COUNTRY!

This tale could be set in almost any county — Kent, Somerset, Shropshire, Herefordshire, Dorset, anywhere they take their apples seriously.
Somerset is especially famed for its ciders, but while 'The Apple Tree Man' is based in no particular area, you don't have to travel far to find acres of orchards bursting with tasty fruit.

somersetwildlife.org
kentorchards.co.uk
dorsetorchards.co.uk
ciderroute.co.uk

---

67. THE KINTRAW DOONIES

Kilmartin, Argyll

There are so many tales of fairies in Britain, north, east, west and south, it's little wonder that many places have their own distinct kinds of magical people. The Doonies, or Dunnies, of Scotland, for instance, are said to resemble either wizened little old folk, or ponies – some lead lost humans safely home, whereas others have a more vicious attitude towards the invaders who took over their lands thousands of years ago...

This emotional old saga tells of a farmer and his family in the wild and windy wastes of Kintraw, in the western county of Argyllshire – and the story begins as sadly as it ends. The farmer's wife, you see, had given birth to three healthy children, two girls and a boy called Hetty, Betty and Archie – but when they were all only very small, she suddenly disappeared, on the darkest, stormiest night imaginable.

The local minister, Father Jock Martin, was a loud and angry man, well known for his long and fire-and-brimstone-filled sermons, and he commanded respect for many miles around. It did not take Father Jock long to decide for all that the farmer's wife was gone forever, perhaps washed out to sea by the floods of rainwater, and that everyone should thank the Lord that they'd been spared the same fate. The farmer's heart was smashed to smithereens by this, and his children cried enough tears to flood the farm afresh, but eventually they all realised that there was nothing for it but to build a life without their mother.

Every Sunday the farmer would obediently troop off to church and leave the children home alone – Hetty was only ten years old, but she had grown into such a sensible lassie that it was agreed she could easily be left in charge for an hour or two.

One Sunday, the farmer returned to find the children smiling like he had not seen them smile in so long – since the loss of his wife, indeed.

'Why smile ye so, children?' the glum farmer asked, 'and on the Lord's day, too?'

'Why, Father, ye'll not believe it!' chirruped Hetty, 'but Mother has been here to see us after all! She brushed our hair, and kissed us each three times, but she said she had to go away again before you came home.'

The farmer's face flashed bright red. 'Believe it? Of course I don't believe it, my girl, don't you dare talk of your mother like that, the poor woman's dead and gone and that has to be the end of it! Do ye see? TELL ME YE SEE!'

The children were afraid to hear their father shout like this, but despite his protestations, they all seemed so certain of what had happened, even the farmer began to have his doubts. He could see that the children were on the verge of tears when he was so harsh with them, and so he relented, and said: 'I will leave you here again when next I go to church, and you must ask this woman who says she is your mother where she has been and why she left us as she did. There's something more than fishy about this, my darlings.'

The next week, once their father was once again at church, a pale figure appeared at the door, and let herself in with her own key. It was indeed the children's mother, thin and pale as she now was, and though their hearts leapt to have her back among them, young Archie remembered his father's request.

As Mother combed his curls, a tear fell down her white face. He gazed up at her, and asked, 'Mother, why did you leave us? Where did you go, and how have you come back?'

'Oh my darling Archie,' she replied, 'Hetty, Betty. I could never walk out on any of you, I love you with all my heart. But I got lost, and suddenly this little old man and little old lady with a little old pony came by, and promised to take me to safety. They called themselves The Good People, but I know now they are the Doonies, and they live under yon green hill. They took me in through a secret door, and now I have to look after them as best I can forever – they

321

only allow me one hour's freedom every Sunday to come and see you. And now I can hear them calling once again.' She kissed each child three times. 'I am sorry, my darlings, you know you have my love, forever and a week, but I must...'

And she didn't even finish her sentence, but was suddenly gone.

The children told their father what had been said, when he returned from that Sunday's church service, and the look on the farmer's face was a picture never to be forgotten. He wanted to believe them, and in his heart he tried, but he could not believe in something as silly as the Doonies!

And so the farmer did what he always did in these situations, and ran straight to Father Jock to ask the minister's advice. At the very mention of 'Doonies', the old purple-faced, white-whiskered zealot flew into a rage. 'Your children are lying little fools!' he thundered. 'It is a disgrace to our Lord Jesus that anyone should be talking of such pagan nonsense in this modern day and age! And in fact, I shall give a sermon on this very subject next Sunday – bring the children, and let them hear what foolishness it is that they speak.'

So that was what happened. There were no children at home the following Sunday to meet Mother, if she had shown up. Instead the poor confused little ones sat in the church pews and heard Father Jock shouting and spitting from the pulpit at the blasphemy of even daring to mention the name of 'these so-called "faeries", "sprites", "little people" and godforsaken "Doonies" in these days of Our Lord, where we know such things to be the superstition of STUPID CHILDREN! Those who believe this NONSENSE and call it the truth will be going directly to the everlasting fires of HELL! HELL, where DEMONS poke you eternally in the BEHIND with their jagged PITCHFORKS, and SATAN HIMSELF glories in your never-ending PAIN!'

The children wept and wailed at this horrifying tirade, but their father insisted that there could never be any arguing with Father Jock. And eventually, they had to admit that he seemed to be right.

They returned to an empty cottage. None of them ever saw their poor pale mother again.

However, there was a macabre twist to this story just a few weeks later. A hill walker visiting the area stumbled upon a cold, stiff body, stretched out on the very green hill said to be the home of the Doonies. The startled rambler turned this body over, and saw a face wide-eyed in astonishment, and bleached of all colour – usually it was an unhealthy shade of purple. Father Jock appeared to have been trampled by a pony, but each hoof mark was scorched into his skin like it had been made with a red hot poker...

'You do not speak against the Doonies,' Hetty, Betty and Archie would one day tell their own children. 'Because they will be hiding somewhere, and they will hear you, and they are easily offended.' When they said this, each of them held their own children tighter, and kissed them three times each, and thought of their long-lost mother.

But Mother was never truly lost. Having waited too long for her children that one Sunday, she was barred from returning to the Doonies' hill; instead she became a Caoineag (pronounced 'Koony-Ag'). A Caoineag is a kind of Scottish banshee, a spirit with no home to go to, who wanders abroad, never at rest. But as far as she travelled and as long as her shade persisted, the poor pale Mother always kept a special eye on those three children, who she loved so much.

THE END

KILMARTIN, ARGYLL

The exact hill where the Doonies dwelt is not known for sure, but it is a fascinating experience to explore the area of western Scotland where it's said to be — the hills of Gorlach are thought of as the most likely place. These hills are a couple of miles north of the village of Kilmartin, near the western coast, and there are also some exciting standing stones to be found here, including a grand cairn known as The Danish King's Grave. But that name denotes another story entirely...

exploreargyll.co.uk

68. THE MERMAID
OF ZENNOR

Zennor, Cornwall

N o wonder the people of Britain have always been a maritime bunch – no matter where you are on the island, you're never more than seventy miles away from the rolling blue-grey waves of the sea, be it the Atlantic ocean, the freezing North Sea, the choppy English Channel or the murky Irish Sea. Year after year, century after century, the people of the coast have had salt air in their lungs and lived and died by their relationship with the ocean, fishing for food and exploring the planet.

Some people say, then, that the very idea of a mermaid, or merperson – folk who look very like you and me at first, but are all scales, fins and fishy bits from the belly button down – must be the product of the busy imagination of fishers, explorers and paddlers. Perhaps sailors, far from home and yearning for the comforts of their faraway lovers, imagined that they saw the flick of a tail or heard the siren song of a mermaid, and that is how the legend of the merfolk came to take hold all over the world.

But that doesn't quite explain the story of the Mermaid of Zennor, who seems to have been seen by the whole population of the small Cornish seaside village, not that many centuries ago.

One of Zennor's proudest sons was a young man called Matthew Trewella. He was tall, and handsome, and charming – and above all, had the sweetest singing voice of anyone in the parish. Every Sunday

324

he was chosen to lead the singing in the church, St. Senara's, and his soft, low voice never failed to bring tears of pleasure to the locals.

Unseen to most of the congregation, however, Matthew had one particular fan who always hobbled in wrapped in a cloak which entirely hid their identity. This stranger sat far at the back of the church, just to hear Matthew singing, but they were always gone by the time the folk filed out for their Sunday dinners. This went on for many months, and of all the people of Zennor, it was Matthew alone who spied the stranger in the shadows. As he sang, he could not look away from the twinkling green eyes of whoever it was, and he was sure he could see silvery tears falling from them as his voice carried over on the musty morning air.

One torrentially rainy Sunday morning, Matthew began singing a particularly sweet old folk tune, and after only one verse, another voice joined his. Everyone in the church was simply electrified by the sound, and were glued to the pews as the two voices harmonised. It was impossible to tell which of the two sounded more beautiful – Matthew's low lilting voice, or this stranger's high, fluting, achingly sad sound. Everyone bathed in the sublime music that filled the dusty church.

Once the song was sung, Matthew could take no more, and when he saw this mysterious figure get up to hurry out to the graveyard, he ran down the aisle in chase, and out into the driving rain. Some other parishioners tried to catch up with him as he closely pursued the clearly startled stranger along the path to the edge of a high cliff overlooking the churning waves of the sea.

The stranger looked behind to see if they had made their escape, and only when they stumbled did the cloak fall enough for Matthew to see the face. That face decided Matthew's fate, if the heart-tugging singing had not already wound its spell. The reddest rounded lips, the most welcoming deep green eyes, and long blonde hair which dripped with sea water. And, as the cloak fell to the floor, so did the figure, and below her belly button, all was silver and green scales, flailing on the grass. The Mermaid looked to Matthew with a pleading fire in her eyes.

Not a word was spoken between them. As the puffing villagers drew near, all they saw was Matthew Trewella picking up this bundle of blonde hair and scales – and leaping off the cliff, and down deep into the ocean. He was never seen again.

68. THE MERMAID OF ZENNOR

For many weeks the people of Zennor watched the sea with desperate hope for signs of the beloved singer, but eventually they had to admit that what was lost would stay lost. Weeks became months became years, and no Matthew.

And then one day, when the story of Matthew Trewella seemed to be nothing but that alone to all but the oldest residents of Zennor, a stranger hobbled into the village, and ordered a large rum at the inn. He was clearly a sailor in some distress.

'Blasted barnacles, I'll go to Davey Jones' locker, pieces of eight and shiver me timbers,' he began, and went on with another five minutes' worth of shiveringly spat maritime swearwords.

'What be the problem then, old salt?' asked the barmaid.

'I just avoided a watery end, my girl, let me tell ye!' he replied. 'I just cast anchor off Pendover Cove to do a bit of shopping, and, believe me, boys and ladies, never has a vessel been so buffeted and a-shooken!'

'Choppy day, be it?' asked the barmaid.

'Blast yer eyes, woman, it's the gentlest millpond Monday as ever a sailor slept through! There be barely a ripple of a wave. But still the ship did list and wobble till I thought my ship's biscuits were on their way back up! And then I heard it. This voice, tinkling and magical like you never heard before.'

'Cor! What were it saying?'

'This tinkling, musical voice said, "OI YOU, SHIFT YOUR BLASTED ANCHOR OFF OF MY FRONT DOOR! I AM PRINCESS MERVEREN, DAUGHTER OF LLYR AND I CANNOT GET HOME TO MY HUSBAND MATTHEW AND OUR FISHY CHILDREN!"'

'She sounds a bit annoyed.'

'I reckon she was, mate. 'Twas a mermaid, I swear to Neptune, and not a drop of grog had I gulped beforehand. As I weighed anchor, I saw this blonde fishy figure flapping near the shore, combing her hair like she owned the place, preening herself in a looking glass no less, before she gave me a wink that went right down to the bottom of me boots, and she dove deep down below.'

Of course, everyone believed him. And they drank a warm toast to Matthew's safe survival, and to Princess Merveren – singers of the most beautiful musical duet Zennor had ever heard.

THE END

ZENNOR, CORNWALL

A crucial Cornish destination for any lover of stories, Zennor is a small
village oh-so-very-nearly at the tip of the country, right down in
Cornwall, not far from Penzance. If you visit St. Senara's Church, you will
find the Mermaid of Zennor herself, carved into a pew, holding a mirror
and admiring her long hair. And do keep a lookout if you're near the
beach and hear any particularly wonderful singing...

cornwalls.co.uk

69. THE TIDDY MUN

The Ancholme Valley, Lincolnshire

Sometimes, when you walk along the road, it can be tempting to try and avoid the cracks in the paving. Whether you do this or not, you should always be aware of the ground beneath your feet, because you never know where it's been. Maybe once upon a time your house was at the bottom of a lake, or in the middle of a forest. Just as British settlers learned how to cut down trees, they also re-routed rivers and drained lakes, moulding the landscape into shapes which better suited the cities and industry of the folk.

This is probably more true the further east you travel, as the fenlands of Lincolnshire and beyond have been pushed and pulled about by town planners more than any other natural land. 'Damp' would be the best way to describe the Anglian countryside in its natural state, with soggy fens once stretching miles further all around than you'll find nowadays. The very geography of east England used to be quite different.

During the time of Charles I, Dutch builders were invited across to this island to reclaim all the precious land possible. In the east, they drained fens and dug canals and did all they could to dry out the land and use it to build, and grow crops. Many villagers of the Ancholme valley were stunned to see their familiar watering holes disappearing day by day. The area was proud of its sogginess – grey, dribbling, limpid and chilly were those fens, and so it always had been, as far as most of the folk were concerned. But here they were, all washed up as the ground cracked and dried around them.

This would have been bad enough, but with the water went lots of other things – mainly peace of mind. Ask anyone on the planet what Britain is known for, and it's likely to be rain – we have as many names for droplets falling from clouds as the Inuit have for snow! But even in soggy Britain, sometimes the rain can disappear, and that caused problems in the Ancholme valley. With hot sun burning down, the crops refused to spring up in spring, cats and dogs croaked in the streets and folk wandered the dry highways crying 'Cursed is this land!' to anyone who wasn't already shouting it themselves.

It was only then that the oldest fen-woman of them all, an ancient lady from the town of Brigg, known to all as Great-Great-Grandma Frank, arose in the town square and told the gathered crowd about the Tiddy Mun.

'Before the Dutch came,' she said, 'we had the Normans, and before them the Saxons, and before them the Romans, but before them…' (At this stage Great-Great-Grandma Frank had to pause a few moments to regain her thread) '… everyone was friends with the Tiddy Mun. Out there in the grimy greyness of the fenland fug, little men and ladies in wispy grey clothes could be glimpsed, creatures of the water who happily shared their watery homes with us and let us be. They had tiny green bodies, humungous feet and broad mushroom-lid hats which flopped over their eyes and left them staggering around in the drizzle, hardly able to see a thing.'

'I never seen one!' chirped up one tiny rebel.

'Not these days, no, love. Nor even when I was your age!' Frank returned, 'But you could hear them, as they made a sound just like the peewit!' The peewit was a marsh-dwelling bird otherwise known as the lapwing. 'And when you heard the "peewit!" sound,' Frank went on, 'you knew that a happy Tiddy Mun was near! Either that,' Frank admitted, 'or perhaps it was an actual bird, it was hard to be sure.' Great-Great-Grandma Frank swore blind that she had heard one when she was very small, and she could tell the difference if nobody else could.

The old woman's point was that the villagers used to highly respect the Tiddy Mun, and would pay homage to their King every once in a while with a special tribute, often in the form of swords thrown into the watery depths, or jewels cast away with a sad plop. Great-Great-Grandma Frank could just about remember some of the old traditions, which perhaps everyone in Brigg should try now, she suggested, if they wanted their fortunes to return to the good.

This caused a kerfuffle among many of the villagers, who complained that the idea was childish, idiotic and 'Ungodly'! But as the days passed and the sun grew hotter, and famine was foreseen, soon everyone agreed that any solution, no matter how desperate, was worth a go.

One warm and sticky twilight, on the first appearance of the first new moon of the summer, all the villagers gathered in the last even vaguely soggy area of the old fens, just where the river Ancholme diverged, and each of them was equipped with a full bucket of muddy water.

There in the misty grey light, they groaned, as one:

'Tiddy Mun without a name, the weather's thruff! Here's water for thee, take thy spell undone!'

Nobody really knew what they meant by 'thruff' – some said it meant 'rough' and some said 'through', and Frank couldn't remember. Some people complained that the incantation didn't even rhyme. And they felt very silly up to their knees in silt, slopping buckets of water around.

But then, nobody was complaining about it being nonsense when the clouds rumbled and broke open over the astonished villagers, and the Tiddy Mun curse was declared officially over.

Nobody really thought that it was down to the Tiddy Mun, of course; after all, this was 1626, and nobody believed such silly things in those modern times. But the Tiddy Mun never cared about whether anyone believed in them or not. As the waters rose once again, they just happily went about their business with only the occasional piercing 'peewit!' sound to give them away.

Find a soggy bit of Lincolnshire on a particularly misty day even today, and you may still be lucky enough to hear that magical sound – if you bring the Tiddy Mun a watery gift, that is. They prefer the non-fizzy kind.

THE END

THE ANCHOLME VALLEY

The Ancholme valley was where the Tiddy Mun tale was first captured in the telling, but as our story says, it's a great deal drier there than once it was. Those who remain keen to try and track down Tiddy Mun could try plotting a course for the northern market town of Brigg, though. That's where the river Ancholme branches into two — there's the original route, and also the man-made tributary that caused all the trouble in the first place.

visitlincolnshire.com

70. THE PIPER OF DICKMONTLAW

Angus

Scotland is famed for the bagpipes – tartan contraptions that make squealing and heart-tugging noises which delight and torture people the world over. It's also a country filled with tales of folk getting lost in caves. There's one story about a robber who hid out in a cave near a waterfall called Reekie Linn, until he was visited by one of Britain's plentiful big black ghost dogs – this particular dark hound introduced himself as the Devil, and the robber was so terrified he ran out and all the way to the nearest prison cell, rather than stay hidden away.

On the other hand, this story is a little sadder. It seems that one night, somewhere on the Angus coast about halfway down the right-hand side of Scotland, a merry piper called Tammy Tyrie and his wife Flora – plus their wee dog, Lassie – were on their way home from a wedding.

There had been plentiful supplies of wine, ale and good strong Scotch whisky shared at this wedding, and both husband and wife were only just managing to hold each other up as they staggered home, singing old songs as loud as they liked. The dog had drunk nothing but buttermilk, but tragically, she didn't know the way home anyway.

The three of them were still far from home when they somehow tumbled into a forbidden cave which was hidden among the crags of the coast in this area. Locally, the cave was said to be filled with demons and witches! Some even insisted that it was the home of

Sawney Bean, a terrifying old cannibal who used to hide in caves on the west coast of Scotland and lure people into his home for dinner.

Once you're lost in a network of caves, it's hard to know where you might end up. We can only imagine the arguments poor Tammy and Flora had once they realised their mistake. They wandered here, they wandered there, but as it was so dark, they could have wandered anywhere.

The next morning, a couple of shepherds near the cairn at Dickmontlaw, miles from the coast, heard a terrible noise. At first they thought it was their plumbing playing up, or perhaps a fly had taken up residence in their earholes. It was a muffled but very annoying whine, and once the two of them sat down and listened hard, they could tell it was coming from under the ground.

'Do ye hear that, Hamish?' asked the one.

'Aye, that I do, Dougal!' replied the other.

'You know what that is? That's the pipes!'

'There's no pipes running under this cairn, Hamish. That's not nature's way!'

'Ach, not water pipes, Dougal! Someone is playing the bagpipes under the ground!'

'How queer! And not only that – whisht!'

'Ye wished what?'

'No no, I said "whisht"! It means, shut up and listen!'

And then they could hear it – a dolorous singing which accompanied the wailing of the pipes:

'Lone, lost and weary, plays Tammy Tyrie,
Beneath the barns of Dickmontlaw...!'

Poor Flora Tyrie – for it was she – went on in this way for many an hour, as the pipes wailed and folk gathered to tearfully listen – but nobody knew how to help. Some tried to dig, but even ten feet down, there was no way through. Eventually, the music and the singing just... stopped. And nobody saw the piper or his wife ever again.

But what of poor Lassie? Well, at least she had a happy ending – after a day or two, the poor dog pelted back out of the cave they had originally tumbled into. She was starving, confused and trembling with fear, but at least she was alive.

Lassie needed a new home, and luckily for her she was soon

70. THE PIPER OF DICKMONTLAW

discovered by those two shepherds of Dickmontlaw, Hamish and Dougal. They took great care of her, and she was good company out in the fields…

But they soon learned not to stay out after dark, when poor Lassie would howl for all she was worth, and the muffled sound of ghostly bagpipes drifted up from somewhere forbidden, deep underground.

THE END

ANGUS, HIGHLANDS

This tale is something of a mixture of a few similar stories in Scottish folklore; while the coasts and border of Scotland are rich with tales, the sparsely populated highlands of Scotland have far fewer stories to share with us, and so this is three tales in one — the story of Sawney Bean has its roots in Edinburgh and Bennane Head on the west coast, the waterfall of Reekie Linn is in the north-west of the county of Angus, and there on the coast, north of Dundee, is the cave that the piper's family fell into, a couple of kilometres away from Dickmontlaw itself. You can visit any of these places, but they will also know all about them at the Highland Folklore Museum many miles further north, in the central village of Newtonmore. Pay a visit in the summer months, and see how many stories they know!

highlifehighland.com

---

71. THE SHILLINGTON GOBLINS

Shillington, Bedfordshire

You might look forward to Christmas or Easter every year, or even the summer solstice every 21 June, but there was a time, just a few hundred years ago, when the good people of Britain had a whole host of different feast days to look forward to all year round, especially at the turning of the seasons. Meat and drink would be shared, songs would be sung and games would be played as the hardships of life were tucked away for the occasion, and everyone mucked in to share their happiness and gratitude for what they all had, together.

This had been the case for thousands of years – the reasons for having parties may have changed, as different beliefs came and went, but the people always had their fun, when the day's work was done.

That was until, on a cold day in the middle of the 1600s, things changed. A politician called Oliver Cromwell defeated King Charles I in the English Civil War, and chopped the King's head clean off. And from that day forward, a bunch of religious crazies called the Puritans were in charge of the country. These Puritans believed in simplicity and humility, and – worst of all – in never having a good time, because they were certain they would be rewarded for their glum, sad lives after they were dead.

This meant that there would be no more cakes and ale at times of traditional merriment. Songs would have to make do with only one or two notes, and giggling on a Sunday was punishable with violence. From coast to coast, Britain was now told to behave itself, and the people could forget about Easter, and Midsummer, and, yes – even Christmas!

But they couldn't stop absolutely everyone having fun, as one little boy and girl discovered one Midsummer Eve in the village of Shillington, to the north of the smoky old city of London.

This little pair – let's call them Sue and Jeff – lived by the village church, which was of course run by Puritans. This one June evening, they had said their prayers, as they were ordered to by the Puritan elders, and gone to bed… but they felt like they'd only been dozing for a few minutes when they were awoken by the distant sound of extraordinary singing and merriment in the field just outside their cottage! Making extra certain not to disturb their parents as they snored loudly away, the two little adventurers crept to the back door and out into the moonlit field.

Forming a raucous circle right there in front of a wide-eyed Sue and Jeff was a whole bunch of – well, what would you call them? In years to come they became labelled as 'goblins', but the strange Odds and Ends in that circle could not all be summed up by that one name. Some of the happy creatures were ten feet tall, covered in hair and horns and bright green. Others were tiny little people with beards and polka-dot faces wearing golden armour. Then there were the upside-down things with faces like tigers and tails like monkeys. And not to mention the orange-striped weirdoes – now they really were strange!

Whatever these creatures were, they were merry, and they were kind, and they quickly welcomed the young lass and lad in to their party. The whole gaggle of oddities danced around so happily, they sang and laughed and they blithely shared leafy flagons filled from a gigantic punchbowl full of a sparkling brew that seemed to change colour with every dip of the ladle.

Young Sue and Jeff couldn't remember a great deal about that Midsummer party, except that they had the best time ever. And they certainly always remembered one song that all the goblins took great pleasure in singing out loud, lustily and merrily:

'Summer is a-comin' in! Time to laugh, and leap, and sing!

What we call joy, they call a sin! You can't do down a goblin!
They will try and stop our cheer! But we will jump, and jape, and jeer!
Every turn of every year! You can't do down a goblin!
Keep your silly human rules! We will dance, and drink, and drool!
Enjoy your life, or you're a fool! You can't do down a goblin!'

The next morning, as the sun rose, there was not a single sign of the goblins' larksome party in the field, just two very happy little children in the dawn dew, who swore to each other that they would never tell anyone else about what they saw, and what fun they had.

For more than ten long years, the Puritans held down the happiness of the people of Shillington and elsewhere, but every turning of the year, whether it was in the middle of summer or the depths of winter, the goblins held their jolly party right there in the field; and every year, the growing Sue and Jeff were invited to join in the dance.

At long last, however, the Puritans fell out of power, and the jolly King Charles II restored the monarchy to the throne of England, bringing back all the old traditions, the parties, and of course, Christmas, and Sue and Jeff became musicians for every royal festivity. From the moment the new Charles parked his bottom on the throne, there was no more need for the goblins to keep their vigil.

However, when they returned home to Shillington at each turn of the season to play their music, Sue and Jeff could not help noticing that when the folk of the village were enjoying themselves, singing and dancing as they always used to, a small circle of mushrooms – a kind of fungus-henge, if you will – grew right there in the field where the goblins had held their parties.

They both knew it was a kind of promise, that if ever the people of Britain were going to be banned from having parties and enjoying themselves ever again, the goblins would be right there, ready to keep up the old traditions. And to have a bit of a knees-up.

THE END

SHILLINGTON, BEDS

As the Home Counties continue to be gobbled up by the endlessly

---

71. THE SHILLINGTON GOBLINS

expanding metropolis of London, pretty corners such as Shillington should be especially prized. Sadly, visitors will not be able to find the henge of mushrooms where the goblins played, as the reputed site — where New Walk and Hillfoot Road meet, by Shillington Church — has now been built over. One final note of interest is that the famous singer Vivian Stanshall was evacuated to the village as a baby, and he claimed to have witnessed the infamous crash of one of the first German planes of WWII to be shot down on British soil. But he never mentioned any goblins.

shillington.org.uk

72. THE BROWNIE
OF BODESBECK

Dumfries and Galloway

Trying to identify all the loopy flavours of ancient tiny peoples lurking in Britain's green and pleasant land can get very confusing. What's really the difference between a hobgoblin and a pixie, for instance? Nobody has managed to run tests on them in a lab and lived to tell the tale. We can never be entirely sure which of the myriad species of little people have even clung on into the third millennium.

There are some pretty clear rules, however. A brownie could be called a faerie, but it is by no means an elf. Elves by their very nature tend to be quite large and attractive beings, more in line with humans, though completely contemptuous of our inability to fly or perform magic. Brownies, on the other hand, are small, squat, hairy, and not in the least bit attractive to any but the most bizarre human beings. They are cousins of the goblins and hobgoblins, who tend to dress themselves in little brown hooded gowns and stick to the shadows – and a great many of them live in Scotland.

Perhaps 'lived' may be a better word to use. You just can't get the supernatural staff these days. But even just a hundred years ago, there were few homesteads in Scotland which were not glad of their very own live-in brownie. Brownies were good-luck mascots of the households they served – and maybe they still are, on the quiet.

You couldn't ring a bell and have one make you a cup of tea, of course; almost nobody ever actually saw any more of a brownie than a fleeting glimpse of its back heels, or a rapidly withdrawing hand. Having a chat with one was most unlikely. Brownies dwelt in the murkiest corners of houses and barns, and would rarely move a muscle until darkness had fallen.

Leithin Hall, in the southern Scottish county of Dumfriesshire, near the hills of Moffat, was a fine old house, centuries old, and grand, the air nimbly and sweetly meeting the senses. They had a fine Brownie, who had been part of the household for over three hundred years, busying himself throughout the night sweeping the stables, blacking the grate, and all the other chores which thankfully few of us ever have to do any more. The Brownie wanted no thanks, just the roof above his head and a handful of the horse's oats every now and then, when he felt like a treat.

For years, all was happy and spick and span at Leithin Hall. But one day, when the old Laird of Leithin passed away, a new family moved in. The new Laird had been sent to posh school down in England, among the Anglo Saxons (who the Scottish call 'sassenachs'), and he arrived with a very English accent, and very new ideas for how the Hall would be run.

The whole house was redecorated from ceiling to carpets, and all the servants dressed up in a special plaid design which had been created for the Laird down in London. None of the servants liked the new costumes – or livery, as it was called – but they did like their jobs, so they just said 'thank you very much, sir,' and wore what they were told.

But when the Laird heard about the one extra unpaid servant living at Leithin Hall, he was outraged. 'I won't have some stumpy little hairy geezer hiding in my rafters, spoiling the look of the place! I don't care how long he's lived in the Hall, if he works for me he'll do what I say!'

And so, the Laird engineered a face-to-face meeting with the Brownie. This was not easy, and required many hours crouched up in the rafters. But after all, the Laird was the new master of Leithin Hall, and the Brownie knew it was traditional to greet each new master.

And so, in the murky dusk, the wee fellow stepped out of the shadows, and bowed low to the Laird.

'Greetings to the new Laird of Leithin Hall!' he cried. 'Don't you worry about me, sir, I'll just carry on with my work as ever I did, and long life to ye!'

'Oh good God, you really are a hideous little brown perisher, aren't you?' the Laird rudely replied. 'But well, I suppose there are traditions to uphold and all that, so if you're determined to stay, small Brownie, you may as well. But look here, you wee tyke, I can't have you hanging around the place in a filthy old brown sack like that. So, as a special gift from me and my family, here's a lovely costume for you made of the finest tartan cloth, oh, and a golden guinea for all your good work over the years.'

That did it. Brownies, you see, can never accept any payment for their work – it goes beyond a rule or even a curse, it is just how they function. They are shy, retiring and humble creatures who only ask to do a good night's work and hide away. To offer them payment, let alone a hideous costume with a pompom hat thrown in for good measure, was the wickedest, cruellest thing you could ever do to a brownie.

The Brownie held the garish criss-crossed costume. He saw the golden guinea glint in the failing light. And he let out a wail the like of which the Laird had never heard before, and would never again forget. The Brownie sagged, and sobbed, and his nose gushed with the snot of sadness.

'Three hundred years!' he wailed. 'Three hundred years have I served yon family, but as of this day I have no home here.'

And to the Laird's astonishment, the small hairy servant jumped down from the rafters and slunk out of the hall, never looking back, only crying and yelling at the top of his voice: 'Ca' cuttie ca'! A' the luck o' Leithin Ha' gangs with me to Bodesbeck Ha''

The Laird, being English-educated, didn't get this, but the terrified servants translated: 'My good Laird, he said something like, in your English tongue, "Poor little one! All the luck of Leithin Hall goes with me to Bodesbeck." Sir, we're done for! We'll be lost without yon Brownie!'

And sadly, they were right. You'll find little trace of Leithin Hall around the hills of Moffat today – but Bodesbeck Hall, the neighbouring estate where the Brownie fled, is at least remembered, and fared well for many generations more, no doubt thanks to the quiet, modest service of that sad wee Brownie.

Of course, although the name of Bodesbeck survives, there's no hall any more. The last of the Bodesbecks was a very religious woman who refused to live in the same house as a magical creature, and so

72. THE BROWNIE OF BODESBECK

she deliberately fed the poor Brownie on porridge with honey, which was too sweet and tasty for him. And so, at last, he was homeless once again, and the Bodesbeck fortunes crashed.

There's no record of where the Brownie went from there, but let's hope he found somewhere warm, where they really understand a good brownie's needs, and he's still out there doing a good night's work to this day.

THE END

DUMFRIES & GALLOWAY

All of the characteristics of brownies match legendary goblins all over Europe, and brownies themselves have been considered part of families in England and Wales as well as Scotland. But if there is any one place that could be deemed brownie central, it's the Moffat Hills in southern Scotland, where folklorist James Hogg decided to set his novel *The Brownie of Bodsbeck*. Intrepid extreme sportspersons can get their thrills from exploring the snowy hills — while anyone else can just enjoy the scenery, and keep an eye out for little hairy brown folk doing some dusting.

visitmoffat.co.uk

---

73. TAM O' SHANTER

Carrick, Ayrshire

Tam o' Shanter was a brawny Scottish farmer whose smallholding filled a few acres of Carrick, in south-west Scotland. He was a regular face among the markets of Ayr, wearing his gaily coloured bonnet with a red pompom on top, and leading his fine nag, Meg, as he dropped off grain to the brewers. Many a brewer would stand him a drink when he visited, for Tam had the gift of the gab and many friends who loved to hear his stories and songs.

There was one person who didn't enjoy his stories so much, and that was his wife Kate, who had to hear them every time he came back home late after drinking rather a lot of drinks – past Alloway kirkyard, and over the bridge which crossed the river Doon – while she had been waiting with a piping hot haggis for his tea. Tam was one of those fellows who was claimed to be scared of nothing, but he sometimes made an exception for his wife.

'Tam o' Shanter, ye good for nothin' puddin' of a husband!' Kate would roar, after suffering another of his tall excuses for coming home in a very wobbly state. 'You've been supping at the bar all the live-long evening, leaving me here like a prune! A prune, I tell ye! Well, let me tell you something, ya big baboon…' And so she did, at length, until finally the two of them dropped off to sleep, and awoke the next day to do it all over again.

Tam did try his best – he didn't want to upset Kate, and have his ear

73. TAM O' SHANTER

gnawed off with rebukes for hours on end. He resolved to try and get home early from market, but the lads did insist on his having a wee dram with them, or maybe three, and every market day seemed to be the same... Until one very memorable night – October 31st, otherwise known as Samhain, or Hallowe'en.

As ever, the evening had worn on considerably by the time Tam lifted his pompom hat and declared, 'That's me away up the road, boys!' It wasn't, of course, not for a while at least, as he staggered around the inn and all his pals shouted for him to have just one more dram. But eventually, he managed to find the door, clambered onto Meg's saddle, then turned the right way round, and headed off up the road with the cheers of 'the lads' sending him on his way.

Now, Meg was no old nag, and when Tam said 'gee up!' she was away like a thoroughbred. Soon they were passing the old church at Alloway, but it was already dark as could be – what people in this area called 'the wizard hour', lost somewhere between day and night.

And so it was the sudden blaze of flaming light from the kirkyard which caused Tam and Meg to bridle as one. He gently calmed her nerves, dismounted, and quietly led her to the old rusty gate, to peep through into the yard where all the graves stuck out at any angle, nature reclaiming the land in every mouldy corner.

Tam's mouth gaped open in amused surprise at what he saw: a circle of seven old ladies in their nighties, all jiggling around an infernal fire, dancing away for all they were worth. There, on a high sepulchre, stood their old blackguard master, ten feet tall including his horrific horns, brawny and bristling with flame. This demon played the bagpipes with awful brio, and every blast from his pipes caused the weird old women to caper higher and higher.

Tam thought he had never seen anything so entertaining in all his life! He recognised most of the dancing ladies as local grandmothers who kept themselves to themselves, but here they were all prancing around like spring chicks! Bedazzled by the sight and the music, he began to clap his hands and cheer, and when one old lady executed a particularly impressive leap, he yelled: 'Well leapt, Nannie with the cutty sark!'

'Cutty' meant short, and 'sark' was the nightshirt which was leaving nothing to the imagination. But it doesn't matter what the words meant, as the cry acted like a bomb thrown into the hellish dance party. All the witches – for witches they undoubtedly were – turned towards Tam and Meg and hissed, while their dark master did nothing but point, and boom:

'GRAB THE INTERLOPER!'

Tam may have been a few sheets to the wind, but he knew it was time to leave – and fast. With an agility he would have been incapable of ten minutes earlier, he jumped into Meg's saddle, and they hared off towards the Brig o' Doon, as much like a flash as Meg could possibly manage.

'WE'LL TAKE YE, TAM O' SHANTER! PREPARE YER BOTTY FOR HELL!' shrieked the old women, who were possessed with an unearthly speed, and seemed to fly along the ground. One or two of them actually were flying, and had mounted brooms or gateposts, streaking through the moonlit sky towards their prey, howling in anger and positively puking oaths at poor Tam. 'AND YE, MEG! WE'LL BOIL THE BOTH OF YE IN THE POT AND WEAR YOUR SKIN FOR OUR SAMHAIN DANCES!' And they all cackled with glee.

Of course, everyone – including Tam – knew that such creatures of the night were utterly incapable of crossing flowing water, so all he needed to do was cross that bridge and he was home and safe! Meg's hooves thundered on the dusty highway as she galloped and galloped to safety, the wicked sisters closing in on them with every hoof's fall, closer, nearer, their wands spewing out curses left, right, and centre, and their vicious claws poised to rake into Tam's skin... 'THIS IS YOUR LAST HALLOWE'EN, TAM O'SHANTER!' they screeched.

Meg reached the bridge and jumped... and they landed on the other side, safe! Clattering over the brow, racing at full pelt, and the evil monsters would just have to go home and wash their nightshirts!

'Haha! It's home and dry we are, Meg,' yelled Tam, 'and yon crones can whisht and wail away! Haha!'

With a wailing chorus of cries, the witches reached the bridge one second behind Tam and Meg, Nannie's twisted clawed fingers reaching out to catch her prey – but all this witch could get hold of was poor Meg's fine tail, the only thing poking out from that side of the Doon. The pained horse whinnied with fright as her tail frazzled away at the touch, and Tam's pompom hat plopped into the river with all the commotion.

But Tam and Meg were at least safe, and dodged the last few wicked spells the witches tried to send their way, before the crones limped dejectedly back to the ruined kirk, their party frankly ruined.

Meg's tail never would grow back, and the sight of the singed stump would always remind Tam that he had to get home before

73. TAM O' SHANTER

dark from then on, no matter what. Well, partly the singed stump, but mainly the reaction Kate gave him when he got home that night, and tried to tell her exactly how he had lost his hat, and why he was so late. That terrified him more than any witch or demon ever could.

THE END

CARRICK, AYRSHIRE

As with 'The Marriage of Robin Redbreast', Ayrshire is Burns country, and you will never be short of places to visit linked to Scotland's favourite bard. The tale of Tam o' Shanter is said by general agreement to have been written by Burns with inspiration from the Carrick village of Kirkoswald, where Rab was schooled, and where Dougie Graham, the 'real Tam' was said to drink, and kept a smuggling boat called *Tam o' Shanter*. Further east along the coast is the Ayr suburb of Alloway, where Burns was born, and you'll find the ruined Alloway Kirk as scary a place to wander today as in Tam's time — and of course between Kirkoswald and Alloway is the famed Brig o' Doon. How fast do you think you could get from Alloway to Kirkoswald — with a witch on your tail?

carrickayrshire.com

burnsmuseum.org.uk

---

74. BLACK SHUCK

Bungay, Suffolk

The counties of this fair and shadowy land are, of course, positively stuffed with tales about enormous ghostly black dogs – there's probably at least one within reasonable distance of where you are now. These homicidal curs are said to be gigantic, with slavering jaws, razor claws and eyes like saucers – never plates, only saucers! Some ghost dogs dramatically howl on the moors, some viciously attack churches during thunderstorms, and at least one was revealed by Sherlock Holmes to be just a big pooch covered in fluorescent paint. But if there is one sepulchral hound to whisper of with wobbly awe, it has to be Black Shuck.

Black Shuck has long been said to haunt the counties of Norfolk and Suffolk, both highway and byway, and they do say that terror grips the heart of anyone who crosses the colossal canine's path. The size of a shire horse, this dark demon mutt has teeth like red-hot daggers, and yes, eyes like saucers which glow yellow in the dark that always enshrouds it.

Worst of all, in the summer of 1577, Shuck was said to have rampaged into two churches in the Suffolk towns of Blythburgh and Bungay during a horrific thunderstorm, and savaged a whole pew of choirboys in a vicious spree of fire-spreading, blood-spurting violence. On reflection, few deny that it was the electrical storm that did all the damage to the church with bolts of lightning, but the dog was so feared in those areas, all the blame was laid on that dark muzzle. The folk of Bungay even marked the mindless violence by adding a black dog to their coat of arms. As the centuries went by, many continued to walk the streets of Bungay very cautiously, forever fearing a run-in with the hideous Black Shuck.

74. BLACK SHUCK

Sofia had been brought up on these dark tales like any Bungay native, but there was no corner of her mind where Shuck's existence seemed at all likely. She was far from unimaginative, but when Sofia found herself walking the streets alone, it wasn't thoughts of phantom dogs which were likely to prickle her skin with alertness – there were enough solid threats out there.

Never let it be said, of course, that the streets of Bungay were ever more treacherous than those of any other town or city in Britain or elsewhere – it's a pretty place with a fine history. Nevertheless, when Sofia left work one autumn evening, and saw how dark it had become and how suddenly, the shadowy streets took on a very different atmosphere. She had to take the quickest route back to her home, she was hungry and it was long past teatime, but she knew she'd have to hurry through poorly lit alleyways, places where any kind of danger could be loitering in the shadows – not ghosts, but people, the kind who find strength in shadows. She had to speed up.

When Sofia turned into the darkest alleyway, one she knew well in daylight and dark, she suddenly found herself slowing to a halt. The dark here was somehow not right, not normal – was it real, or was her mind creating it? – and there somewhere amidst the blackness, the yellow eyes. Big as saucers they were, and a gentle gruff slow panting could be heard on the evening air. The eyes seemed to get closer to where Sofia had frozen mid-step, but although her own eyes grew wider with every passing millisecond, she never felt any real gut-sinking sting of fear.

The towering indistinct hulking figure of a giant dog, for such she knew it was, seemed to settle before her, and eye her keenly. Then, it turned, and padded on a few paces, before turning round as if to encourage Sofia to walk with it.

Very slowly, she obeyed, inching herself almost blindly through that murky long alleyway, with its many doorways and hiding places. As they proceeded, the dog's growl seemed to rise with caution and threat, but Sofia never felt it was she who was being threatened by Black Shuck, but that the great dog sensed another somewhere in the darkness, and bid them keep away. Then a bark rang out like cannon-fire – deep, loud and unlike any dog Sofia had ever heard. There was a distant squeal, and Sofia swore that a dishevelled figure pelted from a doorway up ahead and out of sight, leaving Sofia and this growling presence alone again in the dark.

Sofia kept close to the walking black hole next to her, and as they neared home, brief glimpses of Black Shuck began to reveal themselves by what light the moon could shed – the high muscled hips rolled with each step, the long torso with its bony ribs steamed in the darkness, and a shining nose led the way. She was tempted to put a hand out to run her fingers through the dog's shaggy hair. Its presence was anything but cold; she felt great warmth emanating from the padfoot as it panted by her side.

But then she was home, before she knew it. The streetlights just ahead were outside her house – and Black Shuck, it was clear, would go no further. In the last pool of impenetrable darkness, the dog stopped, and its yellow eyes blinked, clearly sending Sofia on her way.

But she could not help herself. She put out a hand to just below the yellow eyes, and patted the enormous muzzle of Black Shuck, the terror dog of Bungay.

'Good girl!' she said, and raced off home to bed.

THE END

BUNGAY, SUFFOLK

In 2014, Leiston Abbey in Suffolk claimed to have found the remains of an enormous dog which could well have been Shuck. This is just one site connected to the hound, and the counties of Norfolk and Suffolk are rightly proud of their Black Shuck legends, particularly near the coast. However, the two towns of Blythburgh and Bungay in particular warn all tourists of the dangers of walking abroad in the dark, and to listen out for spectral howling. The former's Holy Trinity Church even displays the scorch marks of the devil dog's claws on its door, and Bungay has commemorated the hell hound with its football team, the Black Dogs! Visitors can spot many allusions to their big black famous resident, as they explore the town's castle and ancient streets — try and keep to the well-lit ones.

lovebungay.co.uk

---

75. LUKKI-MINNIE

Fair Isle

Good stories travel. A little tot in the quietest corners of Central Africa can be entranced by a story from the furthest tip of Scandinavia, and vice versa. One person tells one gang, who each then tell their friends, some of whom write it down, and there you are – the story belongs to everyone.

So it shouldn't be too much of a stretch to note that the tales of Molly Whuppie, that hero of the Western Isles of Scotland, are still popular up in the Northern Isles of Scotland.

One little lad called Wullie who lived on Fair Isle, a tiny chunk of land halfway between Orkney and Shetland off the north east-coast of Britain, was a particularly big fan of Molly Whuppie. He thought she was the smartest, bravest warrior of them all, and he liked to roam the crags looking for bogles to burst, just like Molly used to.

'Ach, there's no such thing as bogles!' his mother would chastise him, 'Just you look where you're going, Wullie, or you'll be in the soup!'

But one day he was getting under her feet, cooped up indoors on a lovely afternoon, so she sent the lad out for a walk and any adventure he liked, with a tasty bannock of his own for when he got hungry.

The wide open Shetland sky blazed blue above little Wullie as he rolled his bannock up bens and down glens, until he reached the lower slopes of Malcolm's Head, in the south-west of the island. He had seen nary a bogle, nor a brownie, nor a brag, nor a boggart. But he wasn't all that downhearted, and he whistled a merry tune as he raced his rolling lunch home down the slopes.

Wullie was rather a good whistler, and the ancient melody he whistled on that windswept crag rang far around the fields on that sunny warm day. He felt like he hadn't a care in the world. And he didn't have, for at least a few minutes. Then a big one came along.

Wullie's bannock bounced along ahead of him... and then what looked a little like a brush of purple heather erupted in one lightning fast move. Two spindly arms shot out, grabbed hold of the bannock, and pulled it back into a hole in the ground! Wullie, perplexed, drew closer but had no time to investigate this mystery before the heathery bush erupted once again, and he was enclosed in a sharp and strong grip. Less than half another second later, he disappeared underground too – 'PLOP!'

There was another 'PLOP', and the purple sprouting disappeared from above ground too, revealing the tiny hole that led to the stinking lair of Lukki-Minnie.

Lukki-Minnie was a trow – a particularly troublesome kind of troll, who had been regularly cursed by the folk of the Shetland Isles for many a year, but nobody who had seen her had lived to tell the tale. She was rather green and stumpy, prickling with sharp hairs and jagged claws, dressed very badly in rags of bloody leather, and with a forest of bright mauve hair sticking right up out of her greasy old head, making her look a little like a four-foot-tall thistle. And SPIKY, she was!

Wullie was absolutely terrified, but he cried out nothing but 'Where am I?'

'Why, you're in Lukki-Minnie's den, my laddio,' grinned the warty trow, revealing a hundred razor-sharp dirty teeth. 'And what a fine whistler you be! Us trow cannot whistle, you see, because of having so many – TEETH!' And she gave Wullie a horrifying wink. He shook like a frightened leaf having its worst nightmare.

From the light of a miserable looking peat fire, on which bubbled an enormous pot full of glooping dark red soup, Wullie could make out a few things about this not-so-cosy den. There were heaps of bones and skulls, the stench of mulled muck and somewhere, in the corner, a belching and sniggering creature of some sort. It couldn't be a dog or a cat or a badger or anything of the sort, but it was half Lukki-Minnie's size, and seemed to be her pet.

'This is my bogey, Barry,' the hideous trow purred, giving the smelly bogey a stroke, and allowing him to swallow Wullie's bannock in one big greedy gulp. Barry then belched contentedly and lay in her arms, picking away at his big hairy ears, and eating whatever he found in them. And then belching again. 'He likes your whistling too, young human. And so, this will now be your home, until your last breath – which will, I assure you, be soon, and it will be a whistle. And you'd better make it a tuneful whistle! We want to be able to have a nice tune, whenever we give you a prod.'

'But that wouldn't really be ideal for me,' Wullie replied. You may be thinking 'Wow, where did the quivering puddle of fear we previously thought of as Wullie get the gumption to sound so cool when talking to a hideous trow?' Well, you see, Wullie had, of course, been thinking about brave old Molly Whuppie, and all the times he had heard about her way of dealing with bogles, and he swore he would not let his hero Molly down. 'It's a little bit poky and smelly down here, and I'd like to go home if that's okay with you.'

'No it is NOT okay, you pinky little runt!' snarled Lukki-Minnie, tracing her jagged foot-long fingernails threateningly along poor Wullie's cheek.

'But what about when I feel hungry?'

'Oh don't worry, I'm going to fatten you up, my laddio,' Lukki-Minnie hissed. 'And there's plenty to eat down here! For a start, you're going to eat anything that comes out of Barry's ears.'

'Ugh, I'm not doing that!' Wullie yelped.

'Shut your face! You'll hurt Barry's feelings. No, your ear gunk is delicious, my preciousss,' she murmured to her stinky familiar. 'And if that's not good enough for you, I am churning my own special butter over here to feed you.'

There in the corner was a fetid butter churn, dribbling over with dirty white grease.

'Where did you get the milk?' Wullie asked with a grimace.

'Why, from myself, of course, I just told you! Yum yum yum, you'll enjoy that. And then when you're nice and fat for me, I'll cook you up in the pot as you whistle away, and have dinner with entertainment! Won't that be nice?'

Wullie's brain was whirring, escape plans forming in his head. He tried to speak, but couldn't. Or even nod. He gave Lukki-Minnie two unconvincing thumbs up.

'But first, I need to collect a few more things to go with my whistle soup – some chives and tatties and suchlike. So it's into the sack with you, my laddio, and don't you make a peep until I get back!'

And before he could react, Lukki-Minnie scooped little Wullie up in her jagged talons, and thrust him into a sack she secured with chains and hung up from the roof of her cave.

All was total blackness. Wullie waited until he was certain that Lukki-Minnie had really left her cave, and carefully took out of his pocket a small pencil he used to scribble down his own story ideas. As quickly and carefully as he could, Wullie pushed the sharp pencil through the sacking and worked his way neatly out of one corner of the dirty old sack – neatly, because he had an idea which he remembered had once been very useful for Molly Whuppie in one of her face-offs with a bogle of some description.

Barry the bogey was belching in his sleep until Wullie caught his attention with a little whistle. 'Would you like to know how to whistle, Barry?' Wullie asked. 'It's very simple, you just put your lips together, and blow!'

Bogeys have very big blubbery lips, but Barry quickly understood and gave it a go. After a few disgusting bile-and spit-spewing attempts, suddenly the little bogey managed a definite, if slightly soggy, whistling noise! And he belched with pride.

'Good lad, Barry, and now – into the sack with you!' said Wullie, and lowered the empty sack over the bogey's head, throwing in a few plates and dishes he found, tying up the corner as best he could, and then hanging the bulging bag back up on the chain where he had been hanging. Barry didn't seem to mind so much, and was still whistling away inside as best he could.

This had all happened quickly, and in no time Wullie heard the cackling of Lukki-Minnie on her way back to the cave. He was frozen to the spot in the gloomy corner, and had no time to think of a hiding place. Fortunately, he never had to, as Lukki-Minnie swooped back down to the den with a 'PLOP-PLOP', and saw the bulging sack exactly where she had left it, whistling away.

'Aye, that's the idea, laddio!' she cackled. 'Just you keep on whistling away, while I tenderise the meat for the whistling soup!' And without any time lost, she picked up a sturdy stick from by the fire, and began whacking the sack for all she was worth!

The plates and dishes began to crack, and the crazy trow just cackled. 'Haha, I can hear your bones breaking now, whistling boy!' Poor Barry began to howl with torment at this sudden treatment. 'Haha, and I can hear you yowling too, you should be whistling!' And then the sack belched. 'Hang on!' cried Lukki-Minnie, 'I know that belch! Where's my baby Barry?'

Lukki Minnie was evil, and squat, and smelly, but she was anything but stupid. And she had heard the tales of Molly Whuppie herself! Nasty little ginger tramp, she thought her. Not fair to bogles.

She span round, and fixed Wullie with a horrifying glare just as he managed to scramble his way up to the hole. But she was too late. In half a tick he was back out in the welcome fresh evening air, which he hastily gulped down as if it was medicine after so long in the pong-filled cave.

Wullie had no chance to rest. Lukki-Minnie was soaring out after him in less than a whisker of time, with her scaly grasping fingernails splayed out in attack, and a scowl of pure hatred carved into her nasty face. All Wullie could do was run and run and hope he came across a bridge of a hair's breadth like good old Molly Whuppie, because he couldn't be the best whistler and the best runner in the world all at once!

'I'm a-gonna get you good, whistling boy, come to Lukki-Minnie!' she screamed as she pelted towards him, licking her lips.

In the gloom of twilight, Wullie pelted homewards as fast as his legs could possibly speed, until he came to a burn which gushed forth at the bottom of Malcolm's Head, and he leapt for all he was worth to the other side.

Lukki-Minnie was hot on his heels, and leapt only one second later… But the thing about trows, as everyone knows, is they have the shortest, hairiest little legs of all the troll family. She only got halfway across the burn before splashing right into the rushing waters, and was swept downstream towards the sea.

Wullie didn't care where she went. All he had in his mind was 'HOME!' And home he went, running inside and slamming the door behind him. When he had finally got his breath back, his mother asked him where he had been and why he was so out of breath. But she would never have believed him.

'Oh, nowhere,' Wullie said. And he gave a little whistle.

THE END

FAIR ISLE

Fair Isle is going to be quite a challenge for anyone to get to — it's only reachable via Shetland, the busier northern island, and Shetland itself is a long, long journey away, where the Scottish Isles almost blend into

Scandinavia. The Orkneys are just a tiny bit closer, and Lukki-Minnie is still remembered in that fascinating, ancient place. The bay of Hesti Geo sometimes collects a scummy sea of foam at certain times of the year, and locals have been heard to comment, 'Lukki-Minnie's been churning her butter, I see!'

fairisle.org.uk

76. THE LOCH NESS MONSTER

Loch Ness, Highlands

Everyone on Earth – or certainly, everyone who doesn't live in a hole in the earth – has heard of the Loch Ness Monster. Nessie! The last of the dinosaurs, still living its mysterious life up in the mists of a Scottish lake. And yet, of all the monsters that have plagued the British Isles over the centuries, Nessie is one of the newest.

Besides the odd scrap of gossip and rumour – far-fetched stories of St. Columba battling the beast in 565 AD and so on – nobody had really paid any attention to stories of a monster in Loch Ness until the year 1933, when a couple of day-trippers from London raised the alarm: they SWORE they had seen a long-necked serpentine beast clumsily crossing the road right in front of their car, before it disappeared under the water!

Before the year was out, another visitor called Hugh Gray showed the world that he had taken a photograph of this Loch Ness monster rising from the waves. The picture he showed everyone was very bad quality, and could just as well have been a big twig, or perhaps a snorkelling elephant.

Nevertheless, from that day onwards, Loch Ness was famous, and all any tourist wanted to do was get a look at this voracious monster, who they said would gobble up any human being for breakfast without even burping. Its teeth were said to be jagged and merciless, and it had a taste for the blood of man, woman and child. This was the new legend, at least.

Not that most people really believed any of this, of course. One particularly cynical 12-year-old girl lived locally, and her name was Lulu. She regularly walked alongside the loch, and had no time for the rigmarole of photographers and hopeful anglers who swamped the shore, hoping to catch a glimpse of the monster.

Lulu was always more concerned about the bullies at school who had marked her out as a weirdo because she was ginger-haired and covered in freckles, didn't like P.E. lessons, and lived in an old cottage with her grannie and around a dozen cats. She tried her best to fit in, pretending to care about boys and hairstyles and hockey, but this just made her all the more unhappy. One gaggle of girls from the year above always seemed to hang out at the school gates picking on anyone they liked – or rather, didn't like – and Lulu was regular prey for them.

'Here comes the girl who stinks of haggis!' they would laugh, and Lulu would lower her head, grow red in the face, and storm off, glad at least to escape being tripped or generally roughed up. She didn't smell of haggis even slightly, she knew that. They were just being mean. Why didn't they like her?

Lulu had taken to staying on at school a little longer to do her homework, knowing that the bullies didn't like hanging around for too long, and so by the time she reached the path alongside Loch Ness it was dusk, and the tourists had also packed up and gone home.

Very very quietly, a sob escaped from a large clump of bushes by the loch, and found its way into Lulu's ears. Where was that snuffling coming from?

'Hellooo there?' Lulu asked, as the bushes began to rustle.

'No, you never heard me, nor saw me!' a husky voice replied from the foliage, and with an explosion of leaves and branches, a long shiny neck sprang out of hiding, and at the top of it, a very sad little face. 'And no, I never just burst out of the bushes and oh goodness me...'

The poor leathery animal was easily fifteen feet high, dripping wet, and, Lulu had to admit, totally real. But for some reason Lulu wasn't in the least bit afraid, and instantly felt concern for the poor sobbing creature.

'So it is you after all, then?' she wondered. 'The Loch Ness Monster is real?'

'Is that what they're calling me?' squealed the poor animal with a hurt look. 'I knew, somehow I could just tell that I had been seen

357

by you little thingummies – call me paranoid but I can sense it. But I don't see what I've done that's so bad that I should be called a MONSTER!'

'They say you chew people up and drag them under the water!' Lulu explained, gently.

'Why should I want to eat you, or anyone at all like you?' replied the animal, astonished. 'Do you think you're especially delicious or something?'

Lulu admitted that no, she didn't know anyone who looked or smelled particularly good to eat. 'And I don't smell of haggis!' she added.

'What? Well, of course you don't, my dear, what an absurd idea. Well, this just about takes the shortbread, but I'm going to have to move. I can't think of anything worse than having all you terrible flashy-box-clicking, noisy-fast-machine-driving pink perishers hanging around my lovely loch all the time, snooping on what I'm up to. Luckily I have a secret cranny that leads to the North Sea, and there's plenty of room for privacy up there. I'll come back home when the fuss has died down.'

'But why are you telling me all this?' Lulu asked.

'I like your face. Nice little brown dots all over it. Something comforting about that. But above all, before I go, I just wanted to tell one of you lot once and for all that I AM NOT A MONSTER. I am just, well, myself, I suppose, and I do no harm to anyone. As for eating you interlopers, I wish it to be known that I am a pescatarian!'

'What does that mean?' puzzled Lulu.

'Fish, dear! I eat nothing but fish! Sometimes a little krill, or some seaweed if I happen to be entertaining guests, but never, ever, stringy nasty pink two-legged types like you. So there you are. My advice to you, young dotty one, is to tell everyone to mind their own business! They must have very empty lives to want to snoop into other people's business like this. Life is for living, not for snooping! Now I shall go and live my life, and leave you to live yours. I hope you enjoy it. Au revoir!'

And with that unexpected display of bilinguality, the enormous non-monster jumped up in the air, and with an almighty 'SPLA-LOOSH', dived deep, deep down beneath the waves of Loch Ness.

Lulu never saw Nessie again, nor did she expect to. Of course, she risked even greater bullying than ever by telling everyone that Loch

Ness was home to a creature, but not a monster, and that it only ate fish. But she never forgot the lesson she learned that dusk, and never once cared for what small-minded people thought about her.

Lulu lived her life, and made a success of herself as one of the world's leading palaeontologists, which is how she came to theorise that the animal she spoke to was an evolution of the Plesiosaur, which had somehow managed to survive in isolation for millions of years. She often thought about her pescatarian friend, but never tried to intrude on her private life from that day to this.

THE END

LOCH NESS, HIGHLANDS

Don't let Nessie's dislike of tourists put you off — we already know that the Loch Ness Monster is no longer found at this address! However, and despite decades of debunking the myths, it's still well worth a visit to the loch itself to discover the history of the mythical creature and gaze out over the waves yourself, with just that one tiny speck of hope in your heart that something monstrous may be out there...

lochness.com

77. THE WILD HUNT

St. Germans, Cornwall

These infamous 'big black ghost dogs' who plague the shadows of Britain – Black Shuck, Black Vaughan, Dusky Gertie, Padfoot and all – have a great deal in common. Not least is the fact that they are all part of the same monstrous pack of hounds – the howling leaders of The Wild Hunt. The Wild Hunt has been going on for longer than numbers existed to count the years, and it is impossible to pin the hunt down to any one region of Britain, or indeed Europe. One shadowy dusk you may be unlucky enough to look up to the sky and see a host of dark figures, racing across the moon on the backs of skeletal horses, with the baying black hounds scampering ahead of them. We wouldn't recommend you put any money on seeing this, but if you do, don't fret – they are probably not hunting you. What they are hunting, nobody knows, and it will never be found.

Legend whispers that a whole host of the most infamous names in folklore ride with the hunt: Wild Edric and Hereward the Wake – mighty Saxons who tried to take on the Norman invaders a thousand years ago, poor old Herne the Hunter of course, Conjuring Minterne, Sigurd the Mighty, revolting old Tegid Foel and Ceridwen the witch, gods like Nuada and Hecate, Odin and Satan, Morgan le Fay, even the great King Arthur himself – all are said to be fated to chase their impossible prey unto the crack of doom.

There is some justice in the rumour that The Wild Hunt is made up of those people who spent their lives riding around in red jackets blowing horns and tearing apart foxes, stags and other innocent animals for sport. Whether they 'ran to hound' or lurked in the bushes with their guns cocked, waiting to squeeze a trigger and end another animal's life (with little need to eat the meat or wear the fur to survive), each and every hunter was fated to feel a cold and heavy hand on their shoulder when they breathed their last, and they were doomed to ride on the shadows of the night forever more, never finding home ever again.

One of the worst of these huntin', shootin', fishin' types was a drunken Cornish clergyman named Dando. This man of the cloth made his parishioners' lives miserable with his growly, dribbly sermons, while eating and drinking them all out of house and home at every opportunity. His nose was red and blotchy due to a lifetime of heavy boozing – his only other pleasure in life being the killing of animals, whether it was squishing a bug on his knee or cutting the throat of a noble stag and wiping the blood on his ugly old face.

One grey Boxing Day, Dando had spent the whole afternoon and evening riding around with his hounds, killing foxes, badgers, and at least one unfortunate peasant who had accidentally got in the way of a partridge. He throttled his poor steaming horse to a halt, called the hounds to heel, and announced something he considered extremely important:

'I say, my hip flask is absolutely empty!' he slurred, holding his small silver bottle of brandy upside down. 'Not just that one, but ALL my booze has gone! Who drank it? Oh yes, it was me, but nevertheless, this is an OUTRAGE! Who sent me out on my horse with only TEN bottles of brandy to drink?' He belched, and hiccupped, and thundered: 'WHERE IS MY SERVANT? I'd ride to HELL for a drink of vintage port right now.'

At these words, out of the mist appeared a hooded and mysterious figure, bearing a shining golden goblet.

'Is that you, Urswick?'

'Indeed it is,' came the reply. 'Here is a drink for you, sire, you'll find it the richest that ever you drank.'

'About time too,' spat the ungrateful hunter, snatching up the goblet and knocking back the whole lot, bar one ruby-red drop which hung from his lower lip as he swallowed the brew. 'Ooh,' he said. 'Gosh. That one has quite a kick. Warm feelings. I must have more.'

'But I have no more drink with me, sire,' replied the servant.

77. THE WILD HUNT

'I MUST HAVE MORE!' Dando boomed. 'I WILL RIDE TO HELL FOR MORE OF THAT FINE VINTAGE!'

'Then be my guest!' laughed the servant, throwing back his hood to reveal long sharp horns, jagged fangs and eyes of blazing fire. 'Come, Dando!' cried the Devil himself, 'Now you are with the Wild Hunt, and will never see home, nor drink booze, nor kill any beast, ever again!'

And before the drunken hunter knew what was happening, his horse had flown up into the darkening winter sky, following behind the laughing Devil and those haunted hounds, to begin his endless quest among the other doomed killers who make up The Wild Hunt.

THE END

ST GERMANS, CORNWALL

Surely not another legend based in Cornwall? Well, The Wild Hunt itself obviously has no real foot nor hoof based in any area of Great Britain — but there really was a horrible clergyman called Dando, and he lived in the small east Kernow fishing village of St. Germans. Few folk even bother remembering him these days, and there's been no sight of The Wild Hunt for generations — but St. Germans is still a pretty base from which to explore both Devon and Cornwall...

cornwalls.co.uk

LOCATIONS INDEX

Acknowledgements

B rother Bernard and Jem Roberts would like to thank everyone who made this insanely overdue 21st-century treasury of tales a reality, particularly publishers John Mitchinson and Xander Cansell and editors Kwaku Osei-Afrifa and Annabel Wright of Unbound, the real Sister Sal Kate Harbour plus Olly and Jack, Darrell Jones for his wonderful design suggestions, Paula Clarke Bain, Professor Carolyne Larrington, Dee Chainey and everyone at Folklore Thursday, our wonderful famous patrons (Cerys Matthews, Neils Innes and Gaiman, Sir Tony Robinson, David Lloyd, Francis Pryor, Alex Collier, David Ziggy Greene, Andy Fanton, Davey Jones, Shappi Khorsandi, Greg Jenner, Hugh Fraser, Dirk Maggs, John Jencks and of course, Brian Blessed), everyone at the Rondo Theatre, The Bell Inn, Bath, The Blue Boar, Ludlow, Frome College, The Merlin Theatre and the many venues which have invited us to tell our tales over the years (get in touch if you'd like a show!), Anita Bigsby, Adam Tutt and Stanton Stevens of the Ludlow fringe and Castle Bookshop, Nick Steel of the Bath Comedy Festival and Marick Baxter of the Bath Folk Festival, Peter J. Allen and everyone at Godchecker, and especially the tales' many many test audiences, particularly nephews Nathaniel, Bennett, Sam, Lucas and Harvey.

But perhaps most thanks of all should go to two comedy heroes – Rik Mayall, for whom every single one of these tales was written, to perform in his irreplaceable style, and of course Terry Jones, who gave us belief in *Tales of Britain* back when every agent and publisher was massively missing the point. They, along with Tony Robinson, Anthony Minghella and Anthony Horowitz, are the true inspirations for this book's existence.

If there are any tourism inaccuracies throughout, or you're outraged that your favourite tale isn't included, we sincerely hope to rectify this in future editions and volumes, because there is no plan ever to stop collecting these bizarre, hilarious, fascinating and frustrating folktales: write to bernard@talesofbritain.com, and we can continue to build the ultimate treasury, together.

TALESOFBRITAIN.COM

Patrons

Matthew Alford
Kate Anderson
Craig Arnush
Hatty Ashton
Emma L. T. Bailey
Martin Bain
Will Barber
Ian Beswick
Carmina Biryana
Theodore & Pandora Biswas
Martin Blacher
Carolyn Black
Holly Blades
Neil Blumfield
Jana Boardman
Gilly Bolton
Daisy Boop-Greenwood
Paula Brown
Dominic Brunt
Anthony Burdge & Jessica Burke
Kevin Byworth
Dee Dee Chainey
John Clark
Tracy Clow
Alex Collier
Melusine Colwell
Lesley Cookman
Jo Cosgriff
Sam Cottle
Christina Dale

Sue Daniels
Caitlin Davies
Rosemary Dun
Hugh Fraser
Susan Fuller
Alex Fury
Elly-Mae Gadsby
Liz Galvin
Andrea Garratt
Lynn Genevieve
BG Geri
Jay Glen
Martin Goodson
Darren Gravett
Stewart Hamilton
Matthew Hanson
Jamie Harding
Luke Harmer
Simon Harper
E O Higgins
Bronwen Hobbs
Amy Hodges
Terry Hoke
Crystal Hollis
Samuel J. Hooper
Rob Jenkins
Trish Johns
Kitty Johnson
Dorothy Jones
Jennie Jones
Tim Lund Jorgensen
Martin Kelly
Pauline Kenna
Nick Kent
Dan Kieran
Joanne Kilgour
Helen Lacey
Caroline Lee
Lia Leendertz
Simon Legg
Chris Limb

David Lloyd
Polly Logan-Banks
Caroline Lord
Anna Lyaruu
Deian Lye-Vella
Vicki M Burkhardt
Pamela Marchant
Jessica Martin
Charlotte Martyn
Anita Matthews
Jim McCauley
Katie McNab
Annalisa McNamara
David Merrick
John Mitchinson
Karen Mosley
Uisdean Murray
Carlo Navato
Jonathan Norton
Liz Norton
Ruth O'Leary
Alan Outten
Simon Patrick
Neil Philip
Debbie Phillips
Sian Powell
Sarah Prosser
Nicky Quint
Rainy101
Victoria Randall
Pam Richards
Tim Roberts
Nigel Roberts
Anthea Robertson
Lucy Ryder
Andy Sampson
Sam Semple
Romy Shiner
Maaike Siegerist
Matt Smith
Ben Southwood

Jenny Sparks
Gregory Spicer
Nick Steel
Daylan Stephens
Ellie Symonds
Sam Taylor
Chocolate Teapot
Lois Temel
Ruth Temple
Ben Thomas
Heather Tweed
Louise Van Geffen
Mo Warden
Richard Whitaker
Jonny Wilkes
Jenny Williams
Zoë-Elise Williamson
Derek Wilson
Matthew Wood
Wendalynn Wordsmith
David Wrennall
Ryan Yard